AN INTRODUCTION TO
THE STATISTICAL THEORY OF CLASSICAL
SIMPLE DENSE FLUIDS

AN INTRODUCTION TO

The Statistical Theory of Classical Simple Dense Fluids

BY

G. H. A. COLE

Professor of Theoretical Physics
University of Hull

PERGAMON PRESS
OXFORD · LONDON · EDINBURGH · NEW YORK
TORONTO · SYDNEY · PARIS · BRAUNSCHWEIG

Pergamon Press Ltd., Headington Hill Hall, Oxford
4 & 5 Fitzroy Square, London W.1
Pergamon Press (Scotland) Ltd., 2 & 3 Teviot Place, Edinburgh 1
Pergamon Press Inc., 44–01 21st Street, Long Island City, New York 11101
Pergamon of Canada, Ltd., 6 Adelaide Street East, Toronto, Ontario
Pergamon Press (Aust.) Pty. Ltd., 20–22 Margaret Street, Sydney, N.S.W.
Pergamon Press S.A.R.L., 24 rue des Écoles, Paris 5e
Vieweg & Sohn GmbH, Burgplatz 1, Braunschweig

First edition 1967

Library of Congress Catalog Card No. 67 – 22833

1490/67

CONTENTS

PREFACE

THE statistical theory of matter is designed to relate the observed macroscopic properties of matter in bulk to certain collective properties of all the constituent molecules taken as a unit. The origins of the modern theory can be traced back rather more than a hundred years. During this period, the theory of matter in equilibrium has achieved a remarkable formal completeness for both classical and quantal systems. But the wide generality of the theory is associated with extreme mathematical difficulties in the calculation of thermodynamic properties. Until recently these properties could be derived with precision only for the cases of a dilute gas and of a crystalline solid, these being the two limiting cases of the density range available to gross matter. Mathematical problems had precluded the quantitative study of dense gases and liquids, called collectively dense fluids. In contrast to conditions of equilibrium, no theory of comparable generality has yet been devised for matter not in equilibrium, although certain theories of restricted scope are now well established and other general approaches are being actively explored. Of particular importance are the theories of dilute gases and of crystalline solids, based on molecular models characteristic of these two states of matter. Only relatively recently have quantitative studies of dense fluids proved feasible. These studies have developed from the recognition of the importance of reduced distribution functions describing the relative distribution of small groupings of particles in space. The exact form of these functions is determined by the nature of the interaction force between the molecules, and describes the details of the particle spatial correlation effects. For equilibrium conditions, the mathematical apparatus according to which the reduced distribution functions are to be deduced is already available. The practical problems are primarily those of mathematics and not of physics. For non-equilibrium, on the other hand, the mathematical apparatus is still incomplete and problems of physics are still to be encountered in the study of dense gases and liquids. Although still undoubtedly only in its early stages of development, the modern statistical theory of dense fluids is already an important branch of statistical physics. It contains much of interest to a wide audience, including physicists, chemists and engineers.

The literature of the subject is now both wide and varied, involving the full range of approaches from the firmly empirical to the extremely formal. The study still remains a specialist field having its own formalisms that may be unfamiliar, in spite of its obvious general technological importance. It is difficult for those unacquainted with the field readily to find out the present achievements and the future prospects of the theory, and to attempt a safe application of the arguments in specific cases. The present book is an attempt to provide for the non-specialist a short readable introductory report of certain aspects of the study of dense fluids, based on the analysis of the correlation effects between representative small groupings of molecules. The attempt is made to use only simple mathematics, and those branches of the subject which are at present primarily of mathematical interest are firmly excluded. This restriction particularly affects the theory of fluid nonequilibria, where much of the recent work, although of very great importance for the future development of the theory, is not in a form to interest the non-specialist directly in all its many ramifications. We are primarily concerned with liquids in the pages to follow, and our arguments will have liquid densities particularly in mind. However, the theory of the correlation between small groupings of particles is also applicable to gases and it will be of interest to consider restricted application to gas densities where this gives additional insight into physical aspects of the theory. For this reason we use the words "dense fluids" in the title rather than the single word "liquids". In order to contain the book to a moderate size it is necessary to make a careful selection of the material to be included and the arguments to follow are restricted in several ways.

To begin with, we shall suppose that the de Broglie wave length of each molecule is small when compared with the average distance between the molecules. Thus we consider only classical fluids, obeying classical mechanics and classical statistics. While excluding the highly interesting liquid Helium II from consideration, this restriction is an obvious one to make. Quantum properties are shown markedly only by helium, and to a lesser extent by hydrogen and possibly Neon in their lower temperature fluid ranges, but by essentially no other fluid of the horde that remain. The essential properties of fluids, whether in equilibrium or non-equilibrium, are shown fully by a classical dynamical system of particles. In particular, the physical principles of irreversibility appear independent of whether application is made to a classical or a quantum system. Although the mathematical analysis used in quantum theory is different from that used in the corresponding classical theory, the underlying physics is apparently the same. Within the classical theory, the constituent molecules of the fluid are supposed spherical, at least to some reasonable approximation. This means that monatomic fluids play an essential role in our investigation and Argon can be considered typical. We consider insulating fluids only, the fluid being supposed to have no electrical properties. Further, we consider only single component fluids, problems of solutions and of kinetics being ignored. We do not consider phase changes nor are surface effects considered. One important omission in the text is that of any critical discussion of the approach of molecular dynamics or of the Monte Carlo method using electronic computer techniques. These methods seem likely to play an increasingly important role in the future study of dense fluids, and even now can provide "experimental data" to act as a standard of comparison for testing alternative calculations. The omission of this work is due entirely to the fact that the author has no personal experience of it. Appropriate references to the work are given in the Appendices.

The time is not ripe for a mature text-book on the statistical theory of fluids, and the present book is to be regarded as an extended report on work still in progress. As a general rule we have supposed the reader to have some knowledge of statistical mechanics without being proficient in using it. Wherever possible we have used the canonical ensemble rather than the grand canonical form, as still being the more usually familiar. Although we are concerned with a simplified account of the study of correlations in dense fluids it is necessary to set our arguments within the framework of the wider literature. This is done here by dividing the book into two parts of different character. Each part is equally important for our purposes and must be read in conjunction with the other. The main text, where the arguments are developed, is supported by an extensive set of Appendices containing references to the general literature, and many comments on the main text. In this way the particular path chosen for our main discussion is related to alternative work which either extends, parallels or supplements it. In this way it is hoped that a consistent study of the statistical theory of dense fluids can be made which is compact and simple and which is also set into the framework of the general literature. The references to the literature are broadly representative up to about the beginning of 1965, although it has been possible to include some later references. It is hoped that the more significant papers are listed although the wide extent of the literature precludes the possibility that the list will be complete. Many of the books and papers quoted will themselves provide further references. In this way the reader who wishes to pursue the arguments further will not be lacking in references. As an aid in making an overall assessment of the statistical theory, the main features of the equilibrium and non-equilibrium theories are set out schematically in the two charts that follow this preface.

There remains the pleasant duty of acknowledging help from several people. My greatest debt is to Professor Eisenschitz, not only for reading parts of the manuscript, but also for having introduced me some years ago to this fascinating subject. The present book owes much of its existence to the friendship and stimulation that he has given me over many years. Dr. Killingbeck of the University of Hull read the manuscript and made a number of helpful comments, and also read the proofs. Mr. A. Moreton kindly allowed me to use hitherto unpublished data for the construction of graphs 29 to 34; I offer him my best thanks. I also thank my wife and Miss Linda Barclay for invaluable help in preparing the manuscript for the Press.

G.H.A.C.
1966.

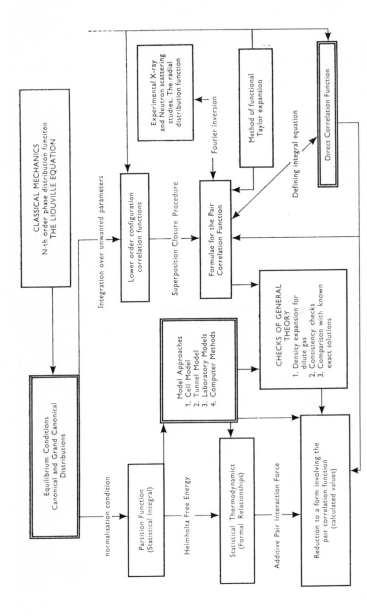

CHART 1. Diagramatic Representation of the relation between various aspects of the theory of liquids in equilibrium. (The boxes contain links in the chain of formulae, while the words not in boxes refer to specific mathematical procedures and approximations. The double boxes refer to places where the chain of argument can start.)

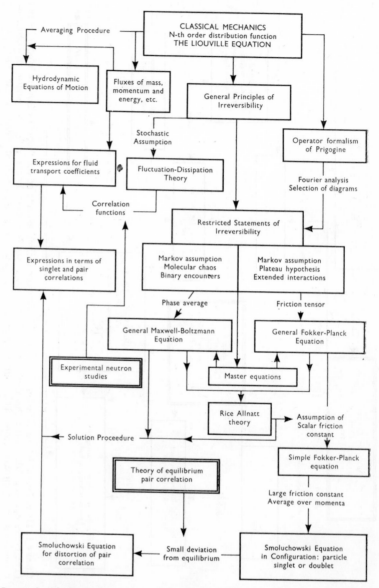

CHART 2. Diagramatic representation of the relation between various aspects of the theory of liquids not in equilibrium.

CHAPTER 1

EMPIRICAL CONSIDERATIONS

1.1. INTRODUCTION

THE aim of statistical mechanics at the present time is the exploration and explanation of the dependence of the gross properties of matter in bulk, whether in equilibrium or non-equilibrium, on the properties of the atoms and molecules of which all matter is composed. Macroscopic matter can exist in three stable forms, or phases, i.e. solid, liquid, and gas. In the present report we are concerned with the methods of statistical mechanics in their application to liquids and dense gases, collectively called dense fluids. Although our main concern is with liquid densities it will be found necessary to make restricted reference to gases at lower densities. We are concerned, then, with attempting to construct a quantitative interpretation of the gross properties of dense fluids (the macroscopic properties familiar in the laboratory and outside such as the equilibrium equation of state, or the transport coefficients like viscosity or thermal conductivity) in terms of the molecular (microscopic) properties, and particularly the interaction force between the molecules, using the minimum of *ad hoc* assumptions.

For this purpose, we can suppose that all the necessary macroscopic and microscopic fluid properties are known to sufficient accuracy. The various necessary macroscopic properties can be determined experimentally under appropriate conditions. Once the link between the macroscopic and microscopic worlds is properly established this link itself becomes available as a method of exploring the microscopic features and also can be expected to suggest further experiments of value in connection with the exploration.

In developing a statistical theory of matter it is necessary to represent the real world by a model, constructed so as to account only for those features of actual matter that are found relevant from the theory. More precisely, macroscopic matter of interest to us is represented by a collection of N particles contained in a volume V. The particles will not be all the same in general but will fall into one or other of several classes of particle representing the presence in the real sample of matter of more than one chemical component. Also, in the general case the particles must be assigned certain internal degrees of freedom, such as those associated with vibration, although in the simpler cases that will concern us here such internal degrees of freedom can be neglected as inoperative. Each of the N particles of the model is to be in continual motion at non-relativistic speed, and in continual interaction with the other particles through the interparticle force. The strength of this interaction depends upon the geometrical arrangement. Because in real matter the number of molecules contained in even a small macroscopic volume is astronomically large ($\sim 10^{20} - 10^{23}$ in 1 cm^3), the theory will almost always be concerned with the asymptotic limiting conditions $N \to \infty$ and $V \to \infty$ but such that $N/V = n$ is a finite constant. This means that while both the number of particles and the containing volume are each to be indefinitely large, the average number of particles per unit volume is to be constant and finite. It can be noticed in this connection that the product of the mass of each molecule m, and the mean number density n can be interpreted as the mean density of matter determined experimentally. In this way, the measured densities of solids and liquids are to be interpreted as implying that the molecules for these two phases of matter are always close together while the lower density range available to gases implies instead that the molecules are generally well separated in these circumstances.

The two limiting cases of the model are immediately recognised, viz. where the particles are as tightly packed as possible (high density limit) and where the particles are all indefinitely far from each other (low density limit), and these limiting cases are open to ready macroscopic interpretation. The physical interpretation of the low density limit of indefinite dilution in terms of a microscopic dilute gas is obvious. The high density limit can be interpreted generally in terms of condensed solid matter but the distinction between crystalline and amorphous structure cannot be drawn immediately in quantitative terms. The place of liquids in the scheme also requires further discussion.

The strength and nature of the interparticle force depends upon the separation distance. At small separation distances it must be strongly repulsive in character to maintain the ultimate impenetrability of matter. At larger distances, it must be attractive to account for the cohesive features observed in macroscopic condensed matter, such as the appearance of a free surface in solids, for example, which is generally stable against varying density conditions outside. In these general terms two separate contributions to the total particle energy (i.e. kinetic energy of particle motion and potential energy of particle interaction) can be recognised;

they are in uneven competition in the two limits of density. In the low density limit, where the particles are widely separated essentially always, the average potential energy of particle interaction is negligibly small: the low density limit is then characterised by the features of the particle kinetic energy. In the high density limit, on the other hand, the particle kinetic energy is less effective than the energy of particle interaction and this latter energy critically controls the general particle trajectory. In the intermediate cases one energy does not swamp the other so completely, and a balance between the effects of the particle kinetic and potential energies must be envisaged.

The theoretical treatment of the general case where the effects of the kinetic and potential energies are comparable in determining the trajectories of the particles is highly complicated and is yet still very far from its final presentation. The limiting cases have advanced further: it is always more easy to assess the effect of two contributions when one overwhelms the other than when it does not. While the solid and gaseous states of matter are to be associated with the limiting cases presented by the model, it is the liquid state that is associated with the general model situation. In treating liquids we are faced with this general problem of accounting for the comparable effects of the kinetic and potential energies. It is this fact that gives the theory of liquids both its difficulties and fascination, and which has caused the development of the theory to lag seriously behind the corresponding theories for solids and gases. While mathematical perturbation techniques are directly applicable to the study of solids (to account for the small relative effects of kinetic energy on the effects of the potential energy) and to the study of dilute gases (to account for the small effects on the particle kinetic energy due to the potential energy) these techniques are not directly applicable to the study of dense fluids. For the effects of one energy cannot be said then directly to perturb the effects of the other in a simple way.

Although severe mathematical difficulties stand in the way of any easy construction of a general statistical theory of liquids, significant progress has been made recently in the development of such a theory. The central problems are now at least becoming clear and numerical predictions can be made which, while being far from satisfactorily accurate in many cases, are definitely better than mere orders of magnitude. The theory has moved on a fairly wide front beyond the level of empirical dimensional argument. But fundamental problems still remain, not least of which is quantitive understanding of the passage from one phase of matter to the other, i.e. an understanding in numerical terms of the processes of melting and vaporisation. We shall not, however, be concerned in any way with problems of phase change.

Within a single phase, the form of the theory at the present time depends upon whether conditions are those of thermodynamic equilibrium or not. For all matter in equilibrium the general physics of the theory has led to the concepts of the grand canonical and canonical ensembles. Application of these arguments to specific calculations for liquids is restricted by purely mathematical problems, but of the severest kind. The theory proceeds through the use of approximations, introduced largely for reasons of mathematical expediency, designed to circumvent in as harmless a way as possible the restricting mathematical difficulties. Physical arguments are of the greatest importance in assessing the status and value of these approximations.

For matter not in equilibrium, problems of mathematics certainly exist but there are also still more essential problems of physics to be dealt with. The theory of non-equilibrium of comparable scope to that already existing for equilibrium is still awaited, although important general progress would seem to have been made in recent years. This work will be considered later.

In the development of a new theory it is important to begin with the simplest general case. Only when there is proper agreement between theory and experiment in this case is it possible to generalise to more complicated general situations on the one hand, and to detailed study of specialised situations on the other. The statistical theory of liquids is still in the stage of the development of the simplest general case and only this case will be considered in this report. The simplest general statistical model of matter is that where all the particles are identical (i.e. there is only a single chemical component) and further where all have complete spherical symmetry with no internal degrees of freedom. This is the model that will concern us in almost all that follows. Fortunately, this simple case has direct experimental interest because it seems to be appropriate for the description of the simpler features of the noble elements, of which argon is typical. Much of the comparison between predictions of the present theory and experimental data has involved argon in one or more of its phases. The essential problems for dense fluids are present under both classical and quantum conditions, but the overwhelming number of fluids of practical interest are fully described in classical terms. Consequently, all our arguments will be restricted to the realm of classical physics (but see Appendix 3.12).

1.2. PHYSICAL CHARACTERISTICS OF FLUIDS

For the purposes of the statistical theory of matter in its present stage of development, it is necessary to enunciate clearly the characteristic features of each of the three phases of matter in molecular terms. For our present purposes we wish to use the characteristic features of dense fluids for the construction of a theory of dense fluids.

The three phases of matter can be conveniently distinguished macroscopically in terms of the properties of density, cohesion, compressibility, and rigidity. The solid and gaseous states can be firmly separated in these terms, but the liquid state appears in a sense to lie midway between these two.

Both a solid and a liquid below the critical point are able to form a free surface although for a liquid the surface is more open to external influences through the vapour pressure. The density of a liquid is only slightly below that of the corresponding solid; there is usually only about a 5 per cent expansion on fusion although there are cases where the volume change is much greater than this. Both a solid and liquid have a unique volume for given external conditions of temperature and pressure. In this respect, solids and liquids are quite unlike a gas which does not form a free surface and which does not have a volume independent of the size of the containing vessel — a gas fills any volume into which it is sealed. These properties are closely linked with that of compressibility. Both a solid and a liquid have a small compressibility, but a dilute gas in contrast is highly compressible although the gaseous compressibility does decrease as the density approaches that of condensed matter. For temperatures below the critical temperature, compression of a gas always ultimately causes it to condense to the liquid phase. Above the critical temperature this is not so and a gas of density comparable with that of a liquid does not now form a free surface. We conclude that liquids at temperatures below the critical temperature bear a certain resemblance to solids.

But there is no more than a certain resemblance as an appeal to rigidity data shows. Solids are rigid in that they can remain in equilibrium under the action of shear forces (that are not too high to surpass the yield conditions). For simple elastic solids this equilibrium can be described by using the linear (Hooke) relation between applied stress and strain. Liquids and gases in common cannot normally withstand shear however small, and flow under its action. This common property of flow is sufficiently important to allow liquids and gases to be designated collectively as fluids. The continual breakdown of the fluid under shear can be specified by using a relation between applied stress and resultant rate of strain. For the simple cases envisaged here a linear relation can be stated between stress and rate of strain (Stokes' law), and such fluids are said to be Newtonian. Many fluids of practical interest are non-Newtonian in this sense but will not be considered here.[1]

The essentially isothermal interphase regions of fusion and vaporisation can be described thermodynamically by the Clausius–Clapeyron equation which relates the volume change ΔV of unit mass due to phase change, at temperature T and pressure p, to the latent heat (of fusion or of vaporisation) L per unit mass. Explicitly

$$\frac{\mathrm{d}p}{\mathrm{d}T} = \frac{L}{T\Delta V}.$$

For fusion, $\Delta V = V$ (liquid) $- V$ (solid); for vaporisation, $\Delta V = V$ (vapour)$- V$(liquid). For vaporisation ΔV is positive always, so that increasing pressure is always associated with increasing temperature of vaporisation and vice versa. For fusion, ΔV is positive for most substances but there are notable exceptions such as water, bismuth, germanium, and tin. The regions of phase change are interesting in that during fusion the material suffers a drastic loss of rigidity even though its free surface remains and its density is usually not drastically affected; during vaporisation its free surface is lost and the density becomes dependent upon the applied pressure.

These various features can be understood easily in qualitative terms from elementary arguments, and particularly from considerations of the dependence of density on the temperature. Increasing the temperature of macroscopic matter can be expressed alternatively as an increase in the total energy of the constituent molecules. For the simpler molecules such as will concern us here, temperature change does not involve actual molecular change and in particular the interaction potential between molecules remains unaffected. Consequently, temperature change must act microscopically in changing the relative molecular space configurations and the molecular trajectories. Apparently, the three stable phases of matter are to be distinguished in terms of the arrangement of molecules in space.

If the molecular mass is known, a knowledge of the density allows a molecular separation distance to be calculated that is to be associated with the actual average separation distance. The small increase in the volume of a solid on melting but the large discrepancy between corresponding solid and gas volumes (under normal standard conditions of pressure and temperature) is evidence that the molecular separation is only a little greater in a liquid than in a solid (by a factor of about 1·2) whereas it is much greater (by a factor of perhaps as much as 10) in a gas. Since there is but little space between the molecules in a crystal solid (there is always some unoccupied space between spherical particles even when they are touching), we can conclude as a preliminary assessment of the characteristics of the physical state for the three main phases of matter the following: for a crystalline solid the constituent molecules are highly ordered in space (in accordance with particle packing problems) and the interparticle force has a critical effect in determining the properties of the molecular assemblage; for a gas the molecules are essentially disordered, following trajectories that are independent almost all the time; and for a liquid the molecules are not as close together as in a solid so that the effect of the kinetic energy of the molecules is sufficient to overcome the strong ordering effects of the potential energy, even though the molecules remain always close together. The ordering of molecules in space in a liquid is therefore of only local extent, or short-range: the long-range ordering of the corresponding crystal is destroyed by the increased molecular movement.

This very broad preliminary microscopic distinction between the three phases of matter is very idealised and is open to many objections. To begin with, it is not quantitative and does not answer such questions as why the liquid state exists at all. Again, the solid has been treated as a crystal and having only a single phase. While most substances have only one liquid phase (although there are exceptions like helium that have two phases, and certain complicated substances can form liquid crystals), it is usual for more than one crystal phase to occur in practice for one substance. And more than one crystal phase can coexist with the single liquid phase. But in spite of this, the preliminary discussion given above is still useful for simple substances which we are concerned with here.

In terms of our theoretical model the ideal crystal is conceived as the high density limit where the particles are all confined by strong interaction forces to mean equilibrium positions set on a lattice structure: the total lattice arrangement is to be constructed by the continual repetition of a basic unit (the unit cell) over large microscopic distances. Particle kinetic energy is accounted for in terms of particle vibrations about the equilibrium lattice position; although harmonic vibrations are the most elementary motion, the ideal model can be relaxed to portray special measured properties of crystals by allowing also for the effect of anharmonic vibrations. The low density limit of the model readily portrays the disordered conditions of a gas. As distinct from the high density limit, the particle kinetic energy now determines the particle trajectories: the effect of the potential energy of interaction is accounted for by the direct perturbing effect of the infrequent collisions between particles.

On this model the liquid is to be regarded as a collection of particles which are always sufficiently close to each other to be constantly in the force field of neighbours but where the strength of the kinetic energy precludes the stability of any lattice structure.

Two things must be noticed before we attempt to make a more quantitative specification of liquid structure. We have considered crystals above, but amorphous solids also exist. These show no recognisable crystal structure and usually no definite fusion point. As the temperature of an amorphous solid is slowly and continually increased the solid gradually softens until it becomes a liquid. An amorphous solid is clearly very akin to a liquid. Indeed it is often useful to regard an amorphous solid (like pitch or glass) for many purposes as a complex liquid with abnormally high shear viscosity. Such a fluid will flow under the action of a force however small if it is applied for a sufficient length of time. But the viscosity coefficient is extraordinarily high in value; e.g. for a normal liquid it will have a value of a few thousandths of a poise, but glass can be assigned a shear viscosity of some 10^{10} poise. The ratio of anomalous to normal viscosity is thus of the order of about 10^{13}! In such cases, the problem of melting for crystalline solids is replaced by the problem of explaining so dramatic a change in the shear viscosity within a relatively small range of temperature change about some specific temperature.

The presence or absence of rigidity has been used as one method of recognising the distinction between a solid and a fluid. One way of deciding whether a given substance is rigid or not is to subject it to shear; if it withstands shear for the time of the observation then it is rigid. By making the time of application of a force suitably small on the time scale of molecular movement in the liquid, it might be expected, because of the inertia of molecules, that a liquid could manifest under these extreme conditions features more characteristic of a solid. This is, in fact, observed in experiments such as those involving ultrasonic energy propagation. Alternatively, currently in geophysics the mantle of the earth is accepted as being solid for the frequencies associated with the propagation of seismic waves even though over many millions of years it may possibly undergo convective translation like a heated viscous liquid.

There is, then, a characteristic time τ involved in the comparison between the liquid and solid phases of matter, the so-called relaxation time. Some physical interpretation of τ will be attempted later, but for the moment it is sufficient to realise that in a general way it can be expected that matter will behave like an elastic solid for time variations significantly less than τ but will behave like a liquid for time variations involving a time significantly greater than τ. For our everyday experience the division between solids and liquids is to some measure a matter of the comparison between the characteristic time scale of naturally occurring forces and τ. For normal liquids of low viscosity $\tau \sim 10^{-11}$ sec; for quasi-liquids like glass τ may be of the order of days.

1.3. MEASURED MOLECULAR SPATIAL DISTRIBUTION

The distinction between the three main phases of matter is to be made in terms of the distribution of the constituent molecules in space. The molecular spatial distribution must be described precisely for the purposes

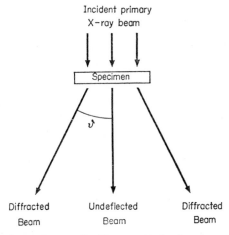

FIG. 1. Experimental set-up for X-ray scattering in schematic form.

of constructing a statistical theory of matter, and the distribution must be amenable to direct experimental measurement. Two experimental methods are available for this purpose, one involving the study of the passage of a coherent beam of X-rays through a specimen of matter, while the other involves a collimated beam of neutrons. The X-ray studies of fluids (and particularly liquids) has been of decisive importance in the construction of a statistical theory, and the method has become classic since its introduction nearly 40 years ago.[2] The neutron studies are of more recent origin and are still under development.[3] The X-rays, or alternatively neutrons, will be scattered in their passage through a fluid specimen in a way dictated by the spatial distribution of fluid particles. The two methods give rather different information about the structure of matter; for the passage

of X-rays through the specimen the constituent molecules are effectively
at rest while the neutrons have essentially the same thermal speed as the
molecules.

The general principle of the X-ray method is shown schematically in
Fig. 1.

(a) *Various Diffraction Patterns*

Experimentally determined X-ray patterns for gases, liquids, amorphous
solids, and crystalline solids show characteristic diffraction patterns. In
particular, that for a liquid is quite different from those of a crystalline
solid or a gas. The recognition of this situation (long ago now) was the
essential first step towards a recognition of the difference between dense
and dilute fluids. In this way the previous attempts to treat a liquid by
means of simple extensions of the arguments contrived originally for gases
by van der Waals were shown basically inadequate.

The X-ray intensity curves for a crystalline solid and for a gas are quite
distinctive; in the former case, the pattern is a system of symmetrically
placed points of high intensity, while in the latter case it is a system of
rings scattering at small angles and centred on the undeflected beam. The
diffraction patterns for an amorphous solid, or very fine powder of crystallites, are again quite distinct from those for a crystalline solid or a gas.
A ring pattern is now evident resulting from large-angle scattering and
consisting of a number of fairly sharp rings, usually most intense towards
the centre.

For a liquid the diffraction pattern[4] also consists of a ring pattern about
the undeflected beam as axis and so is similar to the pattern of an amorphous solid. There is one principal ring, usually rather diffuse and for this
reason often called a halo, possibly surrounded by one or more secondary
rings, both more diffuse and less intense than the primary ring. The radius
of the primary ring has been used to determine the molecular radius and
the value derived in this way is in good agreement with alternative derivations.

The incident X-ray beam excites the molecules of the specimen to become Huygens sources; the X-ray beam that emerges from the specimen is
then the resultant of the excited emissions of each of the molecules. The
emergent beam in this way contains two distinct types of information: the
exact form of the radiation that each particle is induced to emit by the
primary beam depends upon the structural details of the particle; and the
exact nature of the resultant of the superposition of the induced radiation

from each particle depends upon the relative spatial distribution of the particles. For our present purposes, we are concerned only with the latter details which are found theoretically to concern the larger-angle scattered pattern. The molecular structural details are assumed known and form part of the microscopic information about which the statistical theory is concerned.

The diffraction pattern for a crystalline solid is fully explained in terms of the extensive repetition of a basic geometrical arrangement of a small number of molecules. This basic arrangement, the unit cell, is repeated many times without fault so that a crystalline solid shows extreme molecular ordering over large regions, and ideally throughout the whole volume. This is the interpretation of the extensive diffraction pattern associated with crystalline solids. Each crystal molecule is to be regarded as being at the centre of long-range ordering which can be taken as the characteristic feature of the crystalline solid phase. On the other hand, the absence of large-angle scattering for a dilute gas is in accord with random molecular movement, in this case virtually without spatial ordering. A fine powder of crystallites has molecular ordering of a restricted kind only: each crystallite is composed of molecules in highly ordered spatial array independent of that of the other crystallites, but the volume of each crystallite is small and its orientation is random. The random distribution of crystal patterns gives the observed resultant ring pattern. The similarity of the diffraction pattern for an amorphous solid and a fine powder of crystallites shows that the former structure is ordered in a real sense even though the ordering is not that of a crystal. Neither is it that for a fluid, for it is a structure that can sustain shear (providing that it is not too great) that is involved, and a liquid cannot sustain shear except instantaneously.

But the similarity between the X-ray patterns for a crystal powder and a liquid, together with the fact that in a certain sense a liquid is midway between the corresponding solid and gas, is significant in suggesting that in a liquid the molecular spatial order is also restricted. A liquid has, however, a macroscopic structural coherence which a crystal powder has not, so that the liquid molecular ordering can only be superficially similar to that of a crystal powder; and an amorphous solid is not a fluid liquid so its spatial ordering must also differ in critical detail from that of a normal liquid. It is, however, suggestive to interpret the X-ray diffraction patterns for a liquid in terms of a localised, or short-range, order characteristic of a liquid and quite unlike that of a solid. It is this short-range spatial ordering that is at present regarded as characteristic of the liquid state (see Table 1).

TABLE 1.

General features of X-ray diffraction patterns for crystalline solid, crystal powder, liquid, and gas, based on experimental information

Substance	Scattering form	Molecular ordering in space
gas	very small angle rings only	no ordering
liquid	one sharp ring; possibly one or more secondary rings	short-ranged
solid crystal	highly ordered point pattern	long-ranged
crystal powder	diffuse ring system	mixed crystallite; random orientation

Intermediate states of matter are interpreted on this classification as impure forms of one or other of these idealised main states of matter.

The intermediate character of the macroscopic behaviour of liquids is also now intelligible. Those macroscopic liquid properties depending explicitly on the details of the intermolecular force and which have a direct counterpart in the solid state can be expected to be little affected by the small increase of free volume on melting: on the other hand, those properties not explicitly controlled by the intermolecular force are unlikely to be grossly changed on evaporation.

More quantitative information about the structure of liquids and dense gases can be found by considering the details of the theory of X-ray diffraction.

1.4. SCATTERING BY A CONTINUOUS MEDIUM

By considering the interaction between an incident plane electromagnetic wave and the constituent particles of the specimen, a formula can be derived relating the intensity of radiation scattered through angle ϑ and the spatial distribution of the particles themselves. The special value of X-radiation lies in the fact that the wavelength of this radiation is of the same order of magnitude as the mean distance between the molecules in condensed matter. But optical wavelengths are also of value under special conditions, such as those at the critical point.

Let I be the scattered intensity due to the total specimen and let λ be the wavelength of the incident radiation. If r_{lj} is the magnitude of the separation between particles l and j, and s is defined by

$$s = \frac{4\pi}{\lambda} \sin \vartheta \qquad (1.1)$$

for total scattering through the angle ϑ, then for N scattering molecules

$$I(\vartheta) = I_0 \left[1 + \sum_{l,j=1}^{N}{}' \frac{\sin (sr_{lj})}{sr_{lj}} \right], \tag{1.2}$$

an expression often called the Debye[2] equation. Here I_0 is a constant fully determined by the experimental set-up and $\sum'$ stands for the total summation excluding the contribution $l = j$ referring to the effect of any molecule on itself.

The formula (1.2) is seen to contain two distinct terms. The first term I_0 is the total contribution arising from the collection of N isolated molecules. It is characteristic of the given collection of molecules and does not depend upon the relative spatial arrangement of the particles. It would be the complete observed scattering if there were no intereference between the scattered intensities of one molecule and another at large distances. The second term describes the effect on the scattered wave of one molecule due to the scattered wave of a neighbour at a distance r_{ij} away; the second term is in consequence a function of the relative molecular spatial arrangement. This term is a fluctuating function of the separation distance and its exact form depends upon the physical phase of the specimen. It is this fluctuating function that must be investigated in detail if an attempt is to be made to account for the observed differences in the experimentally determined diffraction patterns.

The way in which the second term in (1.2) is to be developed depends upon the physical system involved. Properly, it must involve a summation because it is concerned with the superposition of discrete molecular contributions. But if the scattering material is such that its microscopic structure is usefully described by a continuous distribution of particles then this second term can be rearranged into a mathematically simpler form where an integration procedure replaces the summation. It is necessary to account explicitly for the discrete structure in treating a crystalline solid, and the total intensity pattern can be understood in terms of the various possible symmetry arrangements of molecules in this case. For fluids (liquids and gases) the molecular spatial arrangement is not known and the continuum representation is unavoidable, at least in our present analyses. The representation of fluid structure by a continuous distribution of particles is apparently satisfactory for many purposes, and the recognition of the value of this approximation has allowed the description of fluid structure to proceed in the absence of more detailed knowledge.

Consider any particle within the main fluid volume as origin and consider the number of particles per unit of volume that are to be found at any distance r from the origin particle. Let this number density be denoted by $\varrho(r)$. We make the simplification that ϱ is to be a function of r alone, and that any angular dependence actually present is to be averaged away. This is to be achieved as follows.

Construct about the origin molecule a thin spherical shell of radius r and of thickness dr, comparable to a molecular diameter. Then the volume of this shell is $4\pi r^2\, dr$: let the shell contain dn particles. The number of particles contained per unit volume of the shell is then

$$\varrho(r) = \frac{dn}{4\pi r^2\, dr},$$

i.e.

$$dn = 4\pi r^2\, \varrho(r)\, dr. \tag{1.3}$$

By its definition $\varrho(r)$ is independent of the angular molecular arrangement, since it is an average quantity over the total volume of the shell. Expressed alternatively, suppose the space surrounding the origin particle is fully broken up into a succession of spherical shells, each of volume equal to that of any other. Then variations in ϱ as function of r are a measure of the difference in the number of particles contained within different shells. By allowing dr to assume infinitesimal values, $\varrho(r)$ can then be assigned a continuous form: the qualitative nature of ϱ as function of r will be considered in a moment.

With $\varrho(r)$ introduced according to (1.3) the following replacement can be made:

$$\sum_{l,j=1}^{N}{}' \frac{\sin (sr_{lj})}{sr_{lj}} = \int_{0}^{R_1} 4\pi\varrho(r)r^2\, \frac{\sin (sr)}{sr}\, dr, \tag{1.4}$$

where the integration limit, R_1, is a length larger than that characterising the specimen. The insertion of (1.4) into (1.2) gives

$$I = I_0 \left[1 + \int_{0}^{R_1} 4\pi\varrho(r)r^2\, \frac{\sin (sr)}{sr}\, dr \right]. \tag{1.5}$$

It is this expression that is used to derive from experiment information about the fluid molecular spatial distribution necessary for the statistical mechanical theory of simple fluids.

1.5. THE RADIAL DISTRIBUTION FUNCTION

The function $\varrho(r)$ is defined by (1.3) in relatively local terms. The distinction between a definite fluid spatial structure and essentially no structure can be conveniently portrayed by comparing $\varrho(r)$ locally with the mean number density $n = N/V$. The ratio $\varrho(r)/n$, being the local fluid number density in terms of the mean fluid number density, is called the radial distribution function and is denoted by $g^{(2)}(r)$. Thus,

$$\varrho(r) = ng^{(2)}(r). \tag{1.6}$$

The superscript in $g^{(2)}$ serves to indicate that two particles are involved: this notation also fits that to be used later in the theoretical description of fluid spatial ordering.

From (1.3) it follows that the average number of particles in the thin spherical shell of radius r and thickness dr can be written in terms of the radial distribution[8]

$$dn = 4\pi nr^2 g^{(2)}(r)\,dr. \tag{1.7}$$

In terms of the total number of particles N and the total volume V this can be rearranged further:

$$\frac{dn}{N} = \frac{4\pi r^2\,dr}{V} g^{(2)}(r). \tag{1.8}$$

It is clear that $g^{(2)}$ is dimensionless as defined here.

According to the preliminary discussion of section 1.3, the molecular spatial ordering in a liquid can be described as local or short-range, while in a dilute gas the ordering is virtually absent. Consequently, for a fluid we have the condition for large separation distance,

$$\operatorname*{Lt}_{r \to R_2} g^{(2)}(r) = 1, \tag{1.9}$$

where R_2 is some suitably large distance, relative to the molecular separation. The alternative limit of vanishing separation distance can also be specified: because the molecules are impenetrable, one cannot penetrate another entirely, so that

$$g^{(2)} = 0 \quad \text{for} \quad r = 0. \tag{1.10}$$

The local deviation from a statistically uniform distribution is represented by $\varrho(r) - n$: denoting this by $nh(r)$ then

$$h(r) = g^{(2)}(r) - 1. \tag{1.11}$$

When r becomes sufficiently large, $h(r) \to 0$. Thus $h(r)$ reflects the range of the short-range order for the fluid. The deviation of $h(r)$ from zero is a measure of the correlation between the molecules, since $g^{(2)}(r) = 1$ only when the molecules are sufficiently far apart. For this reason $h(r)$ is often called the total correlation function.

The interesting result of X-ray scattering experiment is the scattered intensity as function of the difference between the actual spatial ordering and the uniform ordering. For a fluid, characterised by short-range order and adequately described by the approximation of continuous spatial molecular distribution, the previous scattering intensity formula (1.5) is rearranged to the form

$$I(s) = I_0\left[1 + 4\pi n \int_0^\infty h(r)r^2 \frac{\sin(sr)}{sr}\,dr\right]. \tag{1.12}$$

Because of the short-range nature of $h(r)$, the upper limit of integration can be taken formally to the mathematically convenient limit of becoming indefinitely large.

The function $(I(s)/I_0)$ is experimentally determined: the total correlation function $h(r)$ is to be determined by Fourier inversion[5] of (1.12). Formally it follows that

$$nrh(r) = \frac{1}{2\pi^2}\int_0^\infty\left[\frac{I(s)}{I_0} - 1\right]s\sin sr\,ds, \tag{1.13}$$

which yields $h(r)$ from measured data (see Fig. 2).

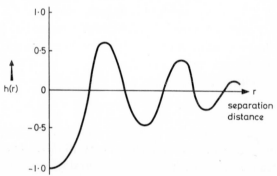

Fig. 2. General features of measured total correlation function h(r) as function of the separation distance, in schematic form.

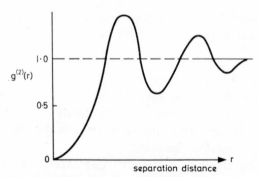

Fig. 3. General features of measured radial distribution as function of the separation distance, in schematic form.

The inversion expression (1.13) has limited quantitative value because of the peculiarities of the Fourier inversion procedure.[6] The details of the extremes of the angular range are important; thus large-angle scattering is associated with small separation distances and small-angle scattering is concerned in the theory with large separation distances. Experimentally, these ranges are difficult to explore quantitatively so that experimentally determined information about the radial distribution can be expected to have ill-defined, though admittedly small, spurious details hidden in it (see Fig. 3).

The arguments here have involved X-ray scattering, but important information can also follow from a study of optical scattering. This must, however, involve small-angle scattering:[7] (1.13) then applies but only in the limit $s \to 0$.

1.6. THE MEAN POTENTIAL

In applying the radial distribution function for the description of the microscopic fluid structure it is necessary to make clear its relation to the molecular trajectories. It has become customary for this purpose to treat the radial distribution for an equilibrium fluid as a thermodynamic potential by writing it in terms of a function of the separation distance, written $\Phi(r)$, having the dimension of energy and called the mean potential. Thus define $\Phi(r)$ according to

$$g^{(2)}(r) = \exp\left\{-\frac{\Phi(r)}{kT}\right\},$$

where k is the Boltzmann constant and T is the absolute fluid temperature. Written alternatively, Φ is defined by

$$\Phi(r) = -kT \ln g^{(2)}(r). \tag{1.14}$$

It is now asserted that the mean relative force acting on each member of a pair of molecules, $\langle \mathbf{F} \rangle$, and under the action of which the actual molecular movement proceeds, is derived from Φ by simple differentiation according to

$$\langle \mathbf{F} \rangle = -\frac{\partial}{\partial \mathbf{r}} \Phi. \tag{1.15}$$

The expressions (1.14) and (1.15) relate the radial distribution to the mean force acting on a liquid particle, and the actual movement of liquid particles is expressed in terms of the dynamics of neighbouring particles together with the interparticle force law through the radial distribution.

Although the mean force has been introduced for equilibrium conditions it is further asserted that it also controls the motion of the molecules of liquids not in equilibrium. This assumption allows for the calculation of non-uniform properties using only the laws of particle dynamics and the actual intermolecular potential. Naturally the pair distribution to be used now is that appropriate to the particular non-uniformities imposed on the fluid.

The form of a typical mean potential curve is shown in Fig. 4. At zero separation distance, the mean potential has a very large, though possibly finite, first maximum. In the immediate neighbourhood of the origin, Φ

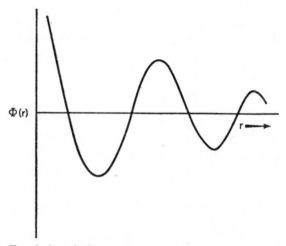

FIG. 4. A typical mean potential curve for a liquid.

is likely to be largely indistinguishable from the potential of the actual particle interaction. The mean potential shows a first minimum corresponding to the principle diffuse ring of the X-ray diffraction pattern. Secondary maxima and minima occur at larger distances corresponding to the weaker rings of the X-ray intensity pattern. These features show decreasing amplitude with distance, and ultimately disappear, the mean potential approaching zero at large distances. It is usually unnecessary in calculations to consider details of Φ beyond the second maximum.

1.7. MOLECULAR MOTION IN LIQUIDS

Each molecule in a liquid is permanently in the force field of neighbours and both the kinetic and potential energy contributions are important in determining the molecular trajectory. More precisely, the motion of each molecule is a combination of vibration about an instantaneous centre of force and a complex translation of the centre. This model, which reflects the intermediate position of a liquid between a crystalline solid and a dilute gas, has been evolved slowly, principally from the arguments of Prins, Peterson, Bernal, and Frenkel. This vibration–translation model is akin to a crystal in that there are vibrations about an equilibrium position, but for a liquid the equilibrium position migrates relatively quickly. The model is also akin to a gas, even though the direct concept of mean free path finds no place in the description of dense matter, in that the liquid molecules have a definite freedom of movement, albeit limited, which changes abruptly from time to time.

Two distinct microscopic time scales can be recognised, one associated with the potential energy, τ_v, and the other associated with the kinetic energy, τ_d. The physical premises of the liquid model require the assertion that $\tau_d \gg \tau_v$. The time τ_v is to be identified as the mean time for one vibration of each molecule about its equilibrium position, while the time τ_d is to be identified as the mean time taken by a representative liquid molecule to move a distance of the order of a molecular diameter. The condition is thus postulated in which a molecule performs a large number of irregular vibrations as it diffuses irregularly through the main macroscopic body of the fluid. The average vibration frequency (i.e. $1/\tau_v$) for a liquid molecule can be expected to be only slightly different from that of the crystal near the melting point. At the same time the migration time τ_d for a liquid molecule will be substantially smaller than that for a crystal, as is witnessed by the fluidity of the former phase. For more complex molecules, which are not spherical or which also may perform internal vibrations, the migration will involve, in addition, abrupt changes of orientation or internal vibration.

The molecular diffusion in a liquid is to be visualised as occurring abruptly so that a typical molecule vibrates about an equilibrium position for a time large compared to the time during which the molecule jumps from one equilibrium position to another. Consequently, τ_d can be interpreted as essentially the duration of an equilibrium position. Movement from one equilibrium position to another involves the rearrangement of neighbouring molecules against the attraction of the interparticle forces. Molecular diffusion must involve, therefore, the surmounting of a force barrier: conservative conditions are assumed so that the movement from one equilibrium centre to another involves the surmounting of a potential barrier w. The time τ_d is thus the time taken for a representative molecule to acquire, through continuous interaction with neighbours, sufficient kinetic energy to overcome the potential energy which on the average restrains it to a specific region of space. In terms of the time for one oscillation as a standard, the time between migrations in a liquid can be expected to have the general form[9]

$$\frac{\tau_d}{\tau_v} \sim \exp\left\{\frac{w}{kT}\right\}. \tag{1.16}$$

Now τ_d refers to molecular diffusion and is associated with self-diffusion in the liquid. If a is the average intermolecular distance then the ratio a^2/τ_d, having the dimensions of (length)^2 divided by (time), can be interpreted as proportional to the self-diffusion coefficient: explicitly

$$\frac{a^2}{\tau_d} \sim 6D \tag{1.17}$$

where D is the usual diffusion coefficient. For simple fluids, experiment provides the values $D \sim 10^{-5}$ cm^2 sec^{-1}, and $a \sim 5$ Å, so that the relation (1.17) leads to the estimate for the time $\tau_d \sim 10^{-11}$ sec. It was this value that was denoted by τ in section 1.2. Combining (1.17) and (1.16) we obtain

$$D \sim \frac{a^2}{6\tau_v} \exp\left\{-\frac{w}{kT}\right\}. \tag{1.18}$$

The ratio a^2/τ_v can be expected to be temperature-dependent, but the controlling temperature-dependence can be expected to arise from the exponential term. Consequently we have the approximate formula:

$$w = -kT \ln D + \text{constant}.$$

The precise macroscopic manifestation of the fluid depends upon the circumstances. The conditions envisaged above refer particularly to equilibrium conditions. There, the average kinetic and potential energies balance and the thermodynamic circumstances will later be described in these terms. For non-equilibrium this balance is not operative; macroscopic flows result due to the action of applied forces, from which transport coefficients, such as viscosity and thermal conductivity, can be defined and calculated in molecular terms.

The time τ_d depends upon the temperature according to (1.16); τ_v can be expected to be rather insensitive to change of temperature. Apparently, the higher the temperature the smaller τ_d; the higher the temperature, the more rapid is the migration process. Self-diffusion is found in a solid but to a far lesser degree than in a liquid. The value of τ_d determines, at least semi-quantitatively, whether a physical system is a solid or a liquid. If the characteristic time for an externally applied disturbance is large in comparison with τ_d then the collection of molecules behave as a fluid; if the characteristic time is small in comparison with τ_d the molecules behave collectively like a solid. Self-diffusion is still evident, but molecular migration plays then a relatively minor role.

CHAPTER 2

MICROSCOPIC REPRESENTATION

THE semi-quantitative arguments set down so far are to be used in the construction of a theory of dense classical fluids. The basic model is that of N identical particles in constant mutual interaction and contained in the volume V. The relation between the macro- and micro-scales for real matter are such that in the model it will be necessary most often to consider the limit $N \to \infty$ and $V \to \infty$, but in such a way that $N/V = n$ remains finite and constant.

For the application of a statistical theory of matter to real problems, it is necessary to specify carefully the trajectories of the constituent particles, and to state clearly the rules by which a knowledge of the trajectories is to yield information about those macroscopic properties of matter that can be measured experimentally. This theory is to be of sufficient generality to apply to the three phases of matter; but in this report we are concerned primarily with the application of the theory to the description of dense fluids. It will be found convenient to sketch the general theory first in this chapter, and then later to make specific application to fluids. Application to fluids will involve the use of mathematical approximations selected on the basis of the evidence of Chapter 1.

2.1. THE INTERPARTICLE FORCE

The molecules of real matter are in interaction with each other even though they may not be in actual contact; this interaction-at-a-distance must be included along with any direct contact interaction in defining the interparticle force field.[1] It is a sufficient approximation for present purposes to assume the interaction between particles to be an instantaneous process because relativistic speeds will not be encountered. Consequently, the potential energy is not explicitly dependent upon the particle speeds.

The general features of the force field are easily deduced. The identity of individual molecules is preserved only if the tendency of any molecules to merge together is prohibited by the action of a very strong intermolecular repulsion when the separation distances become small (such as when

21

the separate electron clouds overlap). On the other hand, the existence of gross matter in condensed forms implies the existence of cohesive effects that must be associated with intermolecular attractive forces at separation distances of a few molecular diameters. The study of intermoleculer forces has a firm theoretical basis, but it has not so far yielded many formulae of general validity that are at the same time mathematically simple. Consequently, for theoretical discussions of the structure of matter it is still necessary to employ idealised approximate force formulae designed to imitate the more accurate expressions sufficiently for particular restricted purposes.

It is assumed that the interparticle force to be used in the theoretical microscopic representation of real matter can be equated to the negative gradient of a single potential function. Explicitly, the total potential energy for the system of N particles located at the vector positions $(\mathbf{r}_1, \mathbf{r}_2, \mathbf{r}_3, \ldots \mathbf{r}_N)$ will be written $\Psi(\mathbf{r}_1, \mathbf{r}_2, \mathbf{r}_3, \ldots \mathbf{r}_N)$. If the interaction between any two particles is not directly influenced by the presence of a third particle, the total potential Ψ can be replaced by the sum of the separate pair interactions. For this case[2],

$$\Psi(\mathbf{r}_1, \mathbf{r}_2, \mathbf{r}_3, \ldots \mathbf{r}_N) = \sum_{1 \leq i < j \leq N} \psi\,(\mathbf{r}_i, \mathbf{r}_j), \qquad (2.1)$$

where ψ is the interaction potential for the representative pair of particles i and j: ψ is usually called the pair potential. The summation in (2.1) is to include all the contributions from the $\dfrac{N(N-1)}{2}$ pairs of particles that can be constructed from the N particles of the system.

The simplest case is that applying to spherical particles where the interparticle force is central. In this case the potential depends only upon the distance between the particles: for the pair of particles i and j the separation distance is $r_{ij} = |\mathbf{r}_i - \mathbf{r}_j|$ and we have

$$\psi(\mathbf{r}_i, \mathbf{r}_j) = \psi(r_{ij}). \qquad (2.2)$$

This situation will be of particular interest in the theory now to be developed.

It should be remembered that the assumption of the additivity of interparticle potentials (2.1) is not generally rigorously correct[2] but for simple systems any necessary correcting terms make only a minor contribution to calculated quantities and can be neglected.

The interparticle force is to be derived from ψ by differentiation. For the case (2.2) the interparticle force F is given by

$$F(r) = -\frac{\partial \psi(r)}{\partial r}, \quad \text{i.e.} \quad \psi(r) = \int_r^\infty F(r)\,\mathrm{d}r. \qquad (2.3)$$

For non-spherical particles there is a contribution to the force which arises from the particle relative orientation.

When the expression (2.1) is valid, interest is centred upon the specification of the pair function ψ, and the case (2.2) is of especial importance. As a function of the distance from the centre of the particle, ψ is large and positive at small distances with a negative gradient corresponding to a strong repulsive force. At a distance of a few angstroms the potential becomes negative and soon shows a zero gradient. It is this minimum value that is located at a distance from the centre of the particle which is associated with the particle diameter of the simple kinetic theory of gases. At distances beyond this minimum the potential remains negative but approaching zero, and with its gradient always remaining positive. In the absence of charges or dipoles, i.e. for particle spherical symmetry, ψ is essentially vanishing at a distance of three or four particle diameters.

It is not easy to translate this qualitative data into a quantitative form for specific cases, especially if the form is to have some mathematical simplicity. The most generally useful simple formula is that suggested by Mie[3] and is the simple sum of a repulsive term proportional to r^{-m} and an attractive term proportional to r^{-n}. Quantum mechanical calculations lead to the value $n = 6$ for the principal attractive van der Waals potential contribution for a non-polar spherical particle. For the repulsion, it is found empirically that $m \sim 12$ corresponds reasonably well with the actual molecular repulsion for rare gas atoms. There results the expression first proposed by Lennard-Jones:

$$\psi(r) = 4\varepsilon \left[\left(\frac{\sigma}{r} \right)^{12} - \left(\frac{\sigma}{r} \right)^{6} \right], \tag{2.4}$$

where σ determines the spatial extent of the force and ε determines its strength. For rare gas atoms σ is of the order 3 Å while ε is of the order 10^{-14} ergs: actual values of σ and ε are collected in Table 2. The expression

TABLE 2.   Data for the force potential
expression (2.4) for the rare gas atoms.

Substance	$\varepsilon \times 10^{-14}$ erg	$\sigma \times 10^{-8}$ cm
He	0·141	2·56
Ne	0·490	2·76
Ar	1·653	3·41
Kr	2·290	3·66
Xe	3·030	3·95

(2.4) is plotted schematically in Fig. 5. Comparing expression (2.4) and the details of Fig. 5, it is found that the distance OA is to be identified with the distance σ while ε is to be identified with the depth BC.

Modifications of (2.4) are also sometimes used, in which the repulsive term is left arbitrary:

$$\psi(r) = A\left[\left(\frac{\sigma}{r}\right)^{m} - \left(\frac{\sigma}{r}\right)^{6}\right]. \tag{2.5}$$

The form of (2.5) is the same as that of (2.4): σ is still the particle size and A is still associated with the depth of the potential at its minimum value. A and ε are in fact related by

$$A = \varepsilon \left(\frac{m}{6}\right)^{6/m-6} \frac{m}{m-6}. \tag{2.6}$$

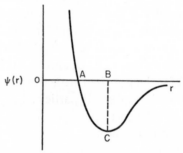

Fig. 5. General form of the interparticle force potential for simple spherical particles.

Many alternative values of m have been suggested for special problems:[4] these usually lie in the range 10–15, although $m = 28$ has been used in connection with polar molecules.

Expressions for ψ other than (2.4) or (2.5) are also useful.[5] A specification of ψ alternative to (2.4) has been constructed by Guggenheim and McGlashan,[6] which can be expected to be an improvement on the Lennard-Jones form but which is also not too difficult to use. The application of this expression will be considered in a later chapter.

Expressions for ψ which are mathematically simpler than those considered so far are often useful in spite of their unrealistic overall form. They are useful in qualitative calculations because of the important mathematical simplifications that they introduce into the theory. There are five expressions of particular importance:

(i) the hard-sphere which treats the particle as if it were a billiard ball, completely impenetrable and with no attraction;

(ii) the square-mound, which has a finite height to the repulsive potential, and has no attraction;

(iii) the power-law repulsion, where the repulsive effect is relaxed considerably, but where again there is no attraction;

(iv) the square-well potential which involves both repulsion and attraction but represented formally;

(v) the Sutherland potential where the repulsion is that for a hard-sphere but where the attraction is according to the r^{-6} law.

The mathematical expressions for these several potentials are set down in Appendix 2.7 together with other expressions that are also important for calculations. These several potential forms will be referred to again later when numerical data are studied.

2.2. CLASSICAL PARTICLE TRAJECTORIES

The formulae of particle mechanics yield the details of the particle trajectories performed under the action of the interparticle force within the main body of the system of particles. Only classical mechanics will be considered in this report, and we collect here some formulae and concepts for later reference.[8] Only spherical particles without internal degrees of freedom will be considered.

The position of the j-th particle is defined by the coordinates of its mass centre, $\mathbf{r}_j$ having components (r_{jx}, r_{jy}, r_{jz}). The particle momentum is denoted by $\mathbf{p}_j$, with components (p_{jx}, p_{jy}, p_{jz}). In specifying the total system of N particles, j is to range from 1 to N.

The total kinetic energy is given by

$$T = \sum_{j=1}^{N} T_j = \sum_{j=1}^{N} \frac{(\mathbf{p}_j \cdot \mathbf{p}_j)}{2m} , \qquad (2.7)$$

and this is not explicitly a function of position or the time. The potential energy, V, is a function of position alone. Two distinct contributions can be recognised: $\Psi(\mathbf{r}_1, \mathbf{r}_2, \ldots \mathbf{r}_N)$ being the potential of interaction between the N particles of the system; and $\mathfrak{K}$, the potential of interaction between the particles of the system and the containing boundary wall. Because all the interparticle forces are assumed short-ranged, $\mathfrak{K}$ will be effective only in the immediate vicinity of the boundary and will be inoperative within the main volume of the system of particles. Thus,

$$V = \Psi + \mathfrak{K}, \qquad (2.8a)$$

but for the main body of the system we may write

$$V = \Psi. \tag{2.8b}$$

The total energy, or Hamiltonian function $\mathcal{H}$, is

$$\mathcal{H}(\mathbf{p}^N, \mathbf{r}^N) = \sum_{j=1}^{N} \frac{(\mathbf{p}_j \cdot \mathbf{p}_j)}{2m} + V(\mathbf{r}_1, \mathbf{r}_2, \mathbf{r}_3, \ldots \mathbf{r}_N), \tag{2.9}$$

a scalar function that will play an important part in the later development of the theory.

The time rate of change of momentum and position (i.e. the velocity) of each particle is obtained from $\mathcal{H}$ by differentiation: thus we have the so-called canonical equations of motion:

$$\dot{\mathbf{p}}_j = -\frac{\partial \mathcal{H}}{\partial \mathbf{r}_j}, \quad \dot{\mathbf{r}}_j = \frac{\partial \mathcal{H}}{\partial \mathbf{p}_j}, \tag{2.10a}$$

where $j = 1, 2, 3, \ldots N$. In using these formulae Ψ is to be replaced by (2.1). The equations (2.10) can be regarded as an alternative statement of Newton's laws of motion. From Newton's second law $\dot{\mathbf{p}}_j$ is equal to the vector force acting on the particle, written $\mathbf{F}_j$, so that

$$\mathbf{F}_j = -\frac{\partial \mathcal{H}}{\partial \mathbf{r}_j}. \tag{2.10b}$$

This expression is in agreement with the previous formula (2.3).

(a) Geometrical Representation

Following the nomenclature of Gibbs, the information given by the combination of the particle positions and momenta from (2.10) is called the phase. The time evolution of the system of N particles contained in volume V is then to be represented by a specification of the phase as function of the time. Such a representation can conveniently assume a geometrical form. The geometrical plotting can refer either to each particle taken separately from the remainder, or to the total system of particles treated collectively. The most complete information is that for the phase, but it is often sufficient to treat only the less complete information given by the momentum or the position (configuration) treated separately.

The plotting of the trajectory of a single particle in three dimensional space, where the Cartesian components are used as axes, is elementary. And so is the addition of the remaining $(N-1)$ trajectories within the same 3-dimensional framework. The N configurational trajectories in 3-dimensional space can be plotted alternatively as a single trajectory in the

$3N$-dimensional space formed by taking the totality of the three coordinates of each particle as $3N$ coordinate axes.

The same constructions can be made for the momenta: thus the vector momenta of the N particles as function of time can be plotted alternatively as N points in the 3-dimensional momentum space of a single particle or as a single trajectory in the $3N$-dimensional momentum space for the system. The hypothetical nature of the momentum spaces, and of the configuration spaces for more than three dimensions, should not cause the reader undue concern: there is nothing mystical about such geometrical representations, and they should not be viewed in any way other than being a convenient and concise description of an intrinsically complicated situation.

The configuration and momentum space representations can be combined within the phase space structure by treating the components of position and of momentum collectively as relating to a set of six independent coordinate–momentum axes for each particle. The total phase of N particles at some time instant can then be represented as a distribution of a cloud of N points in a 6-dimensional hypothetical phase space. Such a space, showing the phase of each particle separately from the others, is called μ-space. The change of phase with time is then expressed geometrically by the time movement of the cloud of N points in the μ-space.

Instead of plotting N points in a 6-dimensional phase space, the same information can be conveyed by specifying one point in $6N$-dimensional phase space. This single point represents the entire system: the $6N$-dimensional space is referred to as γ-space and the single point as the γ-point. For a given system of particles, different phases are associated with different γ-points; consequently the most general time evolution of a system of particles is the representation as a cloud of points in motion in γ-space. The γ-space representation will play a central role in the arguments to follow.

2.3. THE LIOUVILLE THEOREM

The system of particles is represented by a single point in γ-space, and all possible phase developments for the physical system resulting from all possible initial phases can be represented as a cloud of points in γ-space. Because the number of particles in the system is to be very large then so also is the set of initial phases and the γ-space cloud is virtually a continuum. The time evolution is represented by the motion of the cloud and each particle moves according to the laws of mechanics. This situation will be considered again later in section 2.5 in terms of a representing ensemble of systems, but it is convenient to anticipate that work now and to consider the volume characteristics of the γ-cloud about any chosen point. The γ-cloud is to be treated as a continuum and so can be regarded as of the nature of a macroscopic fluid. There is interest in asking whether the cloud behaves as if incompressible or not. It is, in fact, very easy to deduce that the phase cloud behaves as an incompressible fluid.

The hydrodynamic condition for incompressible flow is that the divergence of the fluid velocity vanishes: for the present case this is the divergence in phase. From the definitions of phase space and the divergence operation, it follows that

$$\text{div}_{\text{pr}} \, \mathbf{v} = \sum_{j=1}^{N} \left(\frac{\partial \dot{\mathbf{r}}_j}{\partial \mathbf{r}_j} + \frac{\partial \dot{\mathbf{p}}_j}{\partial \mathbf{p}_j} \right), \tag{2.11a}$$

where $\mathbf{v}$ here is the phase velocity involving $\dot{\mathbf{r}}$ and $\dot{\mathbf{p}}$. Using equations (2.10),

$$\frac{\partial \dot{\mathbf{r}}_j}{\partial \mathbf{r}_j} + \frac{\partial \dot{\mathbf{p}}_j}{\partial \mathbf{p}_j} = \frac{\partial}{\partial \mathbf{r}_j} \left(\frac{\partial \mathcal{H}}{\partial \mathbf{p}_j} \right) + \frac{\partial}{\partial \mathbf{p}_j} \left(-\frac{\partial \mathcal{H}}{\partial \mathbf{r}_j} \right) = 0,$$

so that from (2.11),

$$\text{div}_{\text{pr}} \, \mathbf{v} = 0, \tag{2.11b}$$

which means that the phase cloud does indeed behave as an incompressible fluid. This result depends only upon the validity of the equations of motion (2.10) and is equally true whether the associated physical conditions are those of equilibrium or not.

Because the phase fluid flow is incompressible, the magnitude (though not generally also the shape) of any phase volume remains unaffected by the phase flow which describes the time evolution of the actual physical system. This result is one way of expressing Liouville's theorem. If $\mathrm{d}\gamma(N)$ is an elementary volume of phase for the total system of N particles, so that

$$\mathrm{d}\gamma(N) = \mathrm{d}\mathbf{p}_1 \, \mathrm{d}\mathbf{p}_2 \, \mathrm{d}\mathbf{p}_3 \, \ldots \, \mathrm{d}\mathbf{p}_N \, \mathrm{d}\mathbf{r}_1 \, \mathrm{d}\mathbf{r}_2 \, \mathrm{d}\mathbf{r}_3 \, \ldots \, \mathrm{d}\mathbf{r}_N, \tag{2.12a}$$

then on integration over some phase volume $\mathcal{V}$, we have

$$\gamma(N) = \int_{\mathcal{V}} \mathrm{d}\gamma(N). \tag{2.12b}$$

Liouville's theorem now takes the form:

$$\gamma(N) = \text{constant}, \tag{2.12c}$$

for all values of $\mathcal{V}$ available to the system.

2.4. THE VIRIAL THEOREM

We consider now a theorem[9] of extreme utility in kinetic theory arguments based on the laws of particle dynamics. It differs from the previous considerations in that it is in essence statistical, involving a time average over an indefinitely large time interval.

Consider a function of the phase, say $G(\mathbf{p}_1, \mathbf{p}_2, \ldots \mathbf{p}_N, \mathbf{r}_1, \mathbf{r}_2, \ldots \mathbf{r}_N)$, which is not explicitly a function of the time. It will be assumed further that G remains finite throughout the particle motions. The total time derivative of G is

$$
\begin{aligned}
\frac{dG}{dt} &= \sum_{j=1}^{N} \left(\frac{\partial G}{\partial \mathbf{p}_j} \cdot \dot{\mathbf{p}}_j \right) + \sum_{j=1}^{N} \left(\frac{\partial G}{\partial \mathbf{r}_j} \cdot \dot{\mathbf{r}}_j \right) \\
&= \sum_{j=1}^{N} \left(\frac{\partial G}{\partial \mathbf{p}_j} \cdot \mathbf{F}_j \right) + \sum_{j=1}^{N} \left(\frac{\partial G}{\partial \mathbf{r}_j} \cdot \frac{\partial \mathscr{H}}{\partial \mathbf{p}_j} \right),
\end{aligned}
\tag{2.13}
$$

the second step following from the equations (2.10).

Let us now average this expression over some time interval τ, taking the limit when τ becomes indefinitely great. More specifically the time average of function Q will be defined by

$$
\bar{Q} = \underset{\tau \to \infty}{\text{Lt}} \left\{ \frac{1}{\tau} \int_0^\tau Q \, dt \right\}.
\tag{2.14}
$$

Then, (2.13) becomes

$$
\overline{\frac{dG}{dt}} = \overline{\sum_{j=1}^{N} \left(\frac{\partial G}{\partial \mathbf{p}_j} \cdot \mathbf{F}_j \right)} + \overline{\sum_{j=1}^{N} \left(\frac{\partial G}{\partial \mathbf{r}_j} \cdot \frac{\partial \mathscr{H}}{\partial \mathbf{p}_j} \right)}.
\tag{2.15}
$$

Because G remains finite always throughout the motion the left hand side of (2.15) vanishes: using the expression (2.9) for $\mathscr{H}$ in connection with the second term remaining in (2.15) we obtain the general relation,

$$
-\overline{\sum_{j=1}^{N} \left(\frac{\partial G}{\partial \mathbf{p}_j} \cdot \mathbf{F}_j \right)} = \overline{\sum_{j=1}^{N} \left(\frac{\partial G}{\partial \mathbf{r}_j} \cdot \frac{\mathbf{p}_j}{m} \right)}.
\tag{2.16}
$$

This relation is known as the general virial theorem.

The force $\mathbf{F}_j$ does not need to be conservative or derivable from a potential function. The expression (2.16) is therefore of very wide utility: for the present purposes we are concerned with the particular situation where

$$
\mathbf{F}_j = -\frac{\partial V}{\partial \mathbf{r}_j},
\tag{2.17}
$$

and V is the potential given by (2.8a). Thus the force in (2.16) contains contributions which arise from the particle interaction as well as contributions arising from the action of external forces on each particle (e.g. due to the boundary walls).

The exact form assumed by (2.16) depends upon the exact form of G. The best known is that given by Clausius and follows by setting

$$G = \sum_{j=1}^{N} (\mathbf{p}_j \cdot \mathbf{r}_j).$$ (2.18)

The insertion of (2.18) into (2.16) gives

$$-\overline{\sum_{j=1}^{N} (\mathbf{r}_j \cdot \mathbf{F}_j)} = \overline{\sum_{j=1}^{N} \frac{p_j^2}{m}}.$$ (2.19)

The left hand side is the virial of Clausius and is the average of the product of minus a force times a distance: the right hand side is the average of twice the total particle kinetic energy. The equality of these two terms is the usual statement of the virial theorem. Other forms of the theorem are obtained by choosing G differently from (2.18), and these can have physical importance, as will be seen later. Of particular importance is the possibility of including forces arising from a boundary wall into the virial argument.

2.5. DISTRIBUTION FUNCTIONS

The geometrical representation of the time evolution of a mechanical system of N particles contained in a volume V as a cloud of particles in phase space leads at once to a general method for describing the behaviour of the system in terms of the concept of probability.[10] The introduction of probability arguments into the theory is necessary both in principle and practice. The extreme mathematical complexity of treating the astronomically large number of particles ($\sim 10^{23}$) per unit of volume ($\sim 10^{23}$ particle volumes) which are assigned to represent the real system makes the numerical computation of particle trajectories quite impossible. But even before this difficulty is faced, the exact initial phase could never be measured.

Let us denote by

$$f^{(N)}(\mathbf{p}_1, \mathbf{p}_2, \dots \mathbf{p}_N, \mathbf{r}_1, \mathbf{r}_2, \dots \mathbf{r}_N) \, d\mathbf{p}_1 \, d\mathbf{p}_2 \dots d\mathbf{p}_N \, d\mathbf{r}_1 \, d\mathbf{r}_2 \dots d\mathbf{r}_N$$ (2.20)

the probability that at some time instant t the particle 1 will have momentum $\mathbf{p}_1$, and be at the location $\mathbf{r}_1$, within the respective limits $d\mathbf{p}_1$, and $d\mathbf{r}_1$, and simultaneously particle 2 will have momentum $\mathbf{p}_2$ and be at location $\mathbf{r}_2$ within the respective limits $d\mathbf{p}_2$, and $d\mathbf{r}_2$, and so on for all the particles. The function $f^{(N)}$ is called the specific phase distribution of order N for the system (specific because specified particles have specified phase). As defined in (2.20), $f^{(N)}$ has the dimensions (momentum times length)$^{-3N}$ i.e. inverse action raised to the 3Nth power. Because (2.20) refers to a probability, then $f^{(N)}$ must satisfy the normalisation condition:

$$\int \cdots \int f^{(N)} \, d\mathbf{p}_1 \, d\mathbf{p}_2 \cdots d\mathbf{p}_N \, d\mathbf{r}_1 \, d\mathbf{r}_2 \cdots d\mathbf{r}_N = 1. \qquad (2.21)$$

The condition (2.21) merely states that the system must exist in one of the possible phases open to it, i.e. that the system cannot spontaneously disappear. The specification of $f^{(N)}$ is the most general γ-space description of the N-particle mechanical system necessary for the statistical study of the macroscopic properties of matter. The detailed specification of the distribution of particles over phase is a central problem of the theory that will concern us later. It will be found that for equilibrium conditions $f^{(N)}$ has the canonical form of Gibbs; for non-equilibrium the appropriate distribution is to be determined from equations that are still under construction.

The canonical equations of motion (2.10) are of the first order, so that a knowledge of the phase at any time t is sufficient to determine the phase at any later (or earlier) time. It is this property of the Hamilton equations (2.10) that is central to the derivation of the result (2.11b) that the γ-phase distribution behaves as an incompressible fluid. An alternative statement of this incompressibility property is that the specific probability itself remains constant along the trajectory representing the system, i.e.

$$\frac{df^{(N)}}{dt} = 0, \qquad (2.22a)$$

where d/dt is the hydrodynamic phase operator and is

$$\frac{d}{dt} = \frac{\partial}{\partial t} + \sum_{j=1}^{N} \left(\dot{\mathbf{p}}_j \cdot \frac{\partial}{\partial \mathbf{p}_j} \right) + \sum_{j=1}^{N} \left(\dot{\mathbf{r}}_j \cdot \frac{\partial}{\partial \mathbf{r}_j} \right). \qquad (2.22b)$$

Consequently (2.22) can be rewritten in the form:

$$-\frac{\partial f^{(N)}}{\partial t} = \sum_{j=1}^{N} \left(\mathbf{F}_j \cdot \frac{\partial f^{(N)}}{\partial \mathbf{p}_j} \right) + \sum_{j=1}^{N} \left(\frac{\mathbf{p}_j}{m} \cdot \frac{\partial f^{(N)}}{\partial \mathbf{r}_j} \right). \qquad (2.23)$$

This is an alternative statement of Liouville's theorem and is called the Liouville equation. It determines the time evolution of $f^{(N)}$ according to the dictates of classical particle mechanics. The Liouville equation will form the basis of the arguments to follow.

The phase distribution function $f^{(N)}$ can be given a geometrical interpretation in γ-space, first proposed by Willard Gibbs, and which has proved of extreme value in the development of the statistical theory of matter. This involves the concept of the ensemble. This is a collection of an indefinitely large number Γ of identical virtually independent copies of the original system. Every possible phase distribution of the original system is represented in the Γ systems so constructed. Thus, the full range of phases open to the actual physical system is mirrored in the ensemble of systems, each possible phase being represented by one of the Γ systems. The relative probability for the occurrence of a phase element is proportional to the number of ensemble points within the phase element. The ensemble distribution applying in practice is to be determined by comparison between theory and experiment in a way to be indicated in the next section. The whole ensemble of systems is to be used in specifying the associated macroscopic system. Gibbs first showed that the construction of such an ensemble is not possible from a knowledge of macroscopic parameters alone, and that an additional hyphothesis must be introduced into the theory at this stage. This is the hypothesis of equal *a priori* probability, according to which the ensemble phase distribution is as uniform as is compatible with the macroscopic data. Put another way, the weighting of the microscopic mechanical states is to be as low as is possible for the description of measured macroscopic states. The hypothesis of equal *a priori* probability of mechanical states cannot be substantiated by an appeal to the laws of particle dynamics: its justification can best be based on the successful comparison between theory and experiment.

The ratio of the number of ensemble particles in the elementary non-vanishing phase volume ($\delta\mathbf{p}_1$, $\delta\mathbf{p}_2$, ..., $\delta\mathbf{p}_N$, $\delta\mathbf{r}_1$, $\delta\mathbf{r}_2$, ..., $\delta\mathbf{r}_N$), written simply $\delta\mathbf{p}^N \delta\mathbf{r}^N$, to the total number of ensemble particles Γ is the probability that a system of the ensemble chosen at random will be found in the phase element $\delta\mathbf{p}^N \delta\mathbf{r}^N$ about $\mathbf{p}^N\mathbf{r}^N$. Provided that Γ is sufficiently large, this probability is essentially a continuous function of the phase and will be assumed to approach a definite value as the magnitude of the phase element approaches zero. It is this limiting value of the probability that is to be identified with the distribution $f^{(N)}$ defined in (2.20). This distribution is said to be fine-grained because it is associated with a phase volume element that becomes indefinitely small; in classical mechanics there is no intrinsic limit to the fineness of the phase specification. In this respect, classical theory differs from quantum theory where an intrinsic limit is set by the special requirements of indeterminacy. This is not to be confused with practical difficulties in specifying the phase: errors in momentum and position specifications are uncorrelated in classical theory whereas they are intrinsically related according to quantum arguments.

While fine-grained distributions are useful in the description of equilibrium systems it will be found later that course-grained distributions, where $\delta\mathbf{p}^N \delta\mathbf{r}^N$ cannot be made smaller than some lower value, are necessary for the description of non-equilibrium conditions.[11]

Less knowledge than that supplied by $f^{(N)}$ will often be sufficient for our arguments, and can be deduced from $f^{(N)}$ by integrating away the unwanted information. Thus, the specific probability distribution for a subset of $h(< N)$ particles, and written $f^{(h)}$, may be adequate for some purposes. Then

$$f^{(h)}(\mathbf{p}^h, \mathbf{r}^h) = \int \cdots \int f^{(N)}(\mathbf{p}^N, \mathbf{r}^N) \prod_{j=h+1}^{N} d\mathbf{p}_j \, d\mathbf{r}_j. \qquad (2.24)$$

Specific distributions in position (configuration) alone will be found to be of particular importance in the theory to be developed, all the information about particle momentum being excluded. The importance of such distributions will be clear from the previous distinction between the three states of matter in terms of particle spatial distributions.

The configuration distribution functions can be defined in ways analogous to those used to define the phase distributions. Thus, the probability of finding particle 1 at the point $\mathbf{r}_1$, within the limit $d\mathbf{r}_1$, and simultaneously the particle 2 at the point $\mathbf{r}_2$ within the limit $d\mathbf{r}_2$, and so on for all the N particles of the system, will be written at the time t,

$$n^{(N)}(\mathbf{r}^N, t) \, d\mathbf{r}_1 \, d\mathbf{r}_2 \cdots d\mathbf{r}_N, \qquad (2.25)$$

in conformity with (2.20). $n^{(N)}$ defined this way has the dimensions of inverse volume to the Nth power. It is convenient to replace $n^{(N)}$ by a dimensionless distribution, or correlation function, denoted by $g^{(N)}(\mathbf{r}^N)$. For a system of N particles that are completely independent of each other,

$$n^{(N)}(\mathbf{r}^N) = \prod_{j=1}^{N} n^{(1)}(\mathbf{r}_j).$$

For a fluid in equilibrium, the singlet distribution is not a function of the actual position so that

$$n^{(N)} \to n^N,$$

where $n = N/V$ is the average number density. This applies where all the particle separation distances are indefinitely large (i.e. in the limit of infinite particle dilution). Deviations from microscopic spatial particle uniformity arise because of particle interactions and are shown explicitly by replacing $n^{(N)}$ in (2.25) by

$$n^{(N)}(\mathbf{r}^N) = n^N g^{(N)}(\mathbf{r}^N). \qquad (2.26)$$

Consequently,

$$n^N g^{(N)}(\mathbf{r}^N, t) = \int \cdots \int f^{(N)}(\mathbf{p}^N, \mathbf{r}^N) \prod_{j=1}^{N} d\mathbf{p}_j. \qquad (2.27)$$

Reduced functions follow from these expressions, and typically,

$$n^h g^{(h)}(\mathbf{r}^h) = \int \dots \int f^{(h)}(\mathbf{p}^h, \mathbf{r}^h) \prod_{j=1}^{h} d\mathbf{p}_j. \tag{2.28}$$

The distinction between equilibrium and non-equilibrium conditions is made in the form assigned to $f^{(N)}$. In addition, n referring to the mean particle number per unit volume may need to be replaced by some local value of the number density. Thus n in (2.26), (2.27), and (2.28) may need to be associated with a specific spatial location for non-equilibrium conditions.

In order to reproduce measured macroscopic properties, $f^{(N)}$ must be assigned an appropriate dependence on the constants of the macroscopic system. For equilibrium conditions $f^{(N)}$ will depend only upon the energy since it is invariant to space translation and rotation: it then has the canonical form to be introduced in the next chapter. For non-equilibrium, translation and rotation are not necessarily irrelevant, and $f^{(N)}$ will not have the canonical form.

It is important to realise that, unlike $f^{(N)}$, the configuration distribution $n^{(N)}$ is not left unaffected by the phase flow. Consequently, $n^{(N)}$ does not satisfy an equation of the type (2.23) which applies for $f^{(N)}$. Equations for the configurational distribution can, however, be deduced from the appropriate form of the Liouville equation by performing integrations over the momenta, as will be seen later. We shall enter into more detailed discussion of the distribution functions later, when we encounter the need to determine these functions explicitly for particular physical fluid situations.

2.6. MICROSCOPIC AVERAGES

According to the standpoint of the kinetic theory, the properties of macroscopic bulk matter are to be deduced from the microscopic particle properties already briefly described. The astronomically large number of microscopic data involved in the molecular arguments makes it quite unrealistic to attempt to link macroscopic properties directly with the details of the microscopic particle trajectories. Instead, it is the mean values of appropriate microscopic properties that are to be interpreted as the gross macroscopic properties of matter. For example, the macroscopic energy of a physical system, possibly interpreted through its temperature, is to be linked to the mean energy of the microscopic model representing the gross system. Trajectories in certain regions of phase space will contribute more strongly to this average than those in other phase regions due to variations in γ-phase density. In determining the mean energy, therefore, independent knowledge of the distribution functions is necessary for linking the micro- and macro-physical works: this is true for the derivation of any mean value of physical significance. We shall assert, therefore, that the magnitude of a macroscopic gross feature of matter $\langle Q \rangle$ is to be derived by performing an ensemble phase average over an appropriate microscopic phase function $Q(\mathbf{p}^N, \mathbf{r}^N)$: that is:[12]

$$\langle Q \rangle = \int \ldots \int Q(\mathbf{p}^N, \mathbf{r}^N) f^{(N)} (\mathbf{p}^N, \mathbf{r}^N) \prod_{j=1}^{N} d\mathbf{p}_j \, d\mathbf{r}_j. \qquad (2.29)$$

For equilibrium conditions, the distribution $f^{(N)}$ is to be assigned the canonical form (see section 3.2): thus the distribution depends only on the energy for a given temperature and is independent of the time. For non-equilibrium conditions the canonical form does not apply, the distribution depending also on the details of the physical non-uniformities imposed on the system from outside. For steady non-equilibria $f^{(N)}$, and also $\langle Q \rangle$, are independent of the time (like equilibrium) but $f^{(N)}$ does not have the canonical form. The various macroscopic fluid properties result from appropriate assignments of the phase function $Q(\mathbf{p}^N, \mathbf{r}^N)$. It is supposed that this dynamical phase variable is not an explicit function of the time. If Q is replaced by unity, the expression (2.29) reduces to the normalisation condition for the distribution function $f^{(N)}$. For equilibrium, equating Q to the Hamiltonian $\mathcal{H}$ provides the macroscopic internal energy; for the entropy Q is associated with the expression $-k \ln f^{(N)}$. For non-equilibrium the equations of motion are obtained eventually from a time differentiation of (2.29) but with Q interpreted successively as the mass density, the momentum density, and the energy density, each of which is a function of the position and in general also of the time.

We have now two types of average available: one over phase (the ensemble), where we have denoted the corresponding mean quantity by angular brackets as in (2.29); and the other over the time, where the average is denoted by a bar as in equation (2.14).

The equivalence or otherwise of these two types of average will be found later to be intimately associated with considerations respectively of equilibrium or non-equilibrium.

With the mean values in phase defined by (2.29) the micro- and macro-worlds are therefore formally related theoretically. This relation involves a knowledge of the distribution functions appropriate to a fluid under specific macroscopic conditions: the determination of the appropriate distribution functions for a specific fluid state is, therefore, one of the central problems of microscopic statistical physics.

If the particle interaction forces are primarily those between small groupings of particles, for instance between pairs of particles, a knowledge of the full phase distribution $f^{(N)}$ may not always be necessary in the calculation of phase averages appropriate to certain physical situations. In particular, for mutual particle interactions described by (2.1) in configuration space, the full specification of the doublet phase function $f^{(2)}$ may be enough. For essentially free particles a knowledge of the singlet function $f^{(1)}$ may be sufficient.

Important forms of (2.29) result when the phase function for the total system of N particles is separable into simultaneous interactions between smaller groupings of particles. Two special results for fluids are when

$$Q(\mathbf{p}^N, \mathbf{r}^N) = NQ_1(\mathbf{p}_1, \mathbf{r}_1), \qquad (2.30a)$$

and when

$$Q(\mathbf{p}^N, \mathbf{r}^N) = \frac{N(N-1)}{2} Q_2(\mathbf{p}_1, \mathbf{p}_2, \mathbf{r}_1, \mathbf{r}_2). \qquad (2.30b)$$

Successive insertion into (2.29) yields the two results:

$$\langle Q_1 \rangle = N \int\!\!\int Q_1(\mathbf{p}_1, \mathbf{r}_1) f^{(1)} d\mathbf{p}_1 \, d\mathbf{r}_1, \qquad (2.31a)$$

and

$$\langle Q_2 \rangle = \frac{N(N-1)}{2} \int \ldots \int Q_2(\mathbf{p}_1, \mathbf{p}_2, \mathbf{r}_1, \mathbf{r}_2) f^{(2)} \, d\mathbf{p}_1 \, d\mathbf{p}_2 \, d\mathbf{r}_1 \, d\mathbf{r}_2 \qquad (2.31b)$$

where (2.24) has been used with h set successively equal to 1 and 2. These expressions can, in fact, be resolved further since the momentum and configuration contributions can be separated. The expression (2.31a) applies to gases at sufficient dilution; the configuration contribution is weak and the singlet distribution describes the particle momentum. For more dense gases and liquids a separation is still possible but now, although the singlet distribution is sufficient for the treatment of the momentum components (as for a dilute gas), the configuration components can be discussed only within the doublet distribution. Only in this way can the particle pair interactions be accounted for. Consequently, the expression (2.31b) can apply to general fluid densities and will show two contributions; one will refer to conditions of high fluid dilution (which is described by (2.31a)) and the other will show explicitly the action of the interparticle force potential.

A result of phase averaging can be derived which has a marked similarity with that of the virial expression of section 2.4.

Suppose $Q(\mathbf{p}^N, \mathbf{r}^N)$ is some phase function for a system of N interacting particles which does not explicitly involve the time and which always remains finite throughout the motion. Consider the total time derivative dQ/dt, and suppose we inquire of the form of the macroscopic average according to the expression (2.29). Then

$$\left\langle \frac{dQ}{dt} \right\rangle = \sum_{j=1}^{N} \int \cdots \int \left[\left(\frac{\partial Q}{\partial \mathbf{p}_j} \cdot \mathbf{F}_j \right) + \left(\frac{\partial Q}{\partial \mathbf{r}_j} \cdot \frac{\partial \mathcal{H}}{\partial \mathbf{r}_j} \right) \right]$$
$$\times f^{(N)}(\mathbf{p}^N, \mathbf{r}^N) \prod_{k=1}^{N} d\mathbf{p}_k \, d\mathbf{r}_k,$$

where the equations of motion have been used in the same way as in section 2.4. The left hand side of this expression vanishes because Q is not explicitly a function of time and all phase is to be encompassed in the motion. With the Hamiltonian given by (2.9) we are left with the relation between phase averages

$$-\left\langle \left(\frac{\partial Q}{\partial \mathbf{p}_j} \cdot \mathbf{F}_j \right) \right\rangle = \left\langle \frac{\partial Q}{\partial \mathbf{r}_j} \cdot \frac{\mathbf{p}_j}{m} \right\rangle, \tag{2.32a}$$

for all j in the range 1 to N.

This expression bears a striking similarity (though not identity) with the previous expression (2.16). As in section 2.4 so now the forms of (2.32) which result from specific choices of Q can be of physical importance.

For instance if

$$Q = \sum_{j=1}^{N} (\mathbf{p}_j \cdot \mathbf{r}_j), \tag{2.33}$$

then (2.32) has the form

$$-\left\langle \sum_{j=1}^{N} (\mathbf{r}_j \cdot \mathbf{F}_j) \right\rangle = \left\langle \sum_{j=1}^{N} \frac{p_j^2}{m} \right\rangle. \tag{2.32b}$$

This expression relates the phase average of twice the total kinetic energy of the system to the phase virial.

The expressions (2.16) and (2.32a) are of the same form but involve different averaging procedures. The identity of these two procedures has now been established for equilibrium conditions[13] through arguments involving the ergodic theory and in practice by the identity of data calculated by each formulation. The two averaging procedures are not identical for non-equilibrium conditions, and this difference has been used as a means of describing the structure of non-uniform fluids. Attempts to account for the ergodic theorem on the basis of molecular dynamical arguments have not so far been entirely successful, but any adequate discussion of these circumstances is beyond the scope of our present arguments.

2.7. REAL FLUIDS AND MIXTURES

Particle dynamics enters the statistical theory independently of whether the mass and size of all particles is the same or not. Provided the relative particle orientations are properly accounted for, the particle shape does not affect the basic structure of the theory. The simplest case certainly is when all the particles of the model are identical, with each particle showing complete spherical symmetry. This situation is realised physically in the monatomic rare gases, of which argon, neon, and xenon are examples. The case of mixtures of particles is more complicated in practice although it offers no difference in principle. Besides accounting for interactions between like particles, interactions between unlike particles must also be accounted for. The law of particle interaction becomes more complicated but not impossible. Expressions such as (2.4) for the pair potential are still applicable but the parameters ε and σ cease to have a simple relation with the features of each particle taken separately.

For two particles A and B we may take

$$\sigma_{AB} = \frac{\sigma_A + \sigma_B}{2}, \quad \text{and} \quad \varepsilon_{AB} = \sqrt{\varepsilon_A \varepsilon_B}. \tag{2.34}$$

The expression for σ_{AB} is exact for rigid spheres; the expression for ε_{AB} accounts, at least crudely, for particle polarisability. These expressions have been found useful in the qualitative and semiquantitative treatment of dense fluids. As a consequence, the formulae to be developed for a system of identical particles can be supposed to apply to each component of a mixture separately, and also to interactions between pairs of unlike particles. The formula for the total mixed system is then the simple sum of the separate contributions. In this way the theory is arranged into a form able to be applied to situations of physical interest.

The microscopic representation of dense fluids is not yet in a final form and its quantitative application to real fluids can be made at present only for the simplest cases and with restricted accuracy. Two difficulties stand in the way at the very beginning: one is the present lack of an idealised molecular model of a liquid, comparable to the harmonic crystal model on the one hand and the disordered binary encounter approximation for dilute gases on the other; and the other difficulty is the present lack of a detailed and simple representation for the interaction force between even relatively simple particles. The theory of dense fluids is at the stage of groping towards an elementary understanding in principle of the quantitative nature of a real fluid in molecular terms. Detailed application to the peculiarities of specific fluid features having technological interest is still for the future. Nevertheless, a statistical theory of simple classical dense fluids now exists which leads to numerical predictions for comparison with experimental data. The further development of the present theory can be expected to lead eventually to an improved general theory able to treat complex liquids in detail. The present theory can in this way be regarded as the embryo of a branch of statistical physics of enormous technological interest. It is in this spirit that the assessment is made in this report of the present state of the statistical theory of simple dense fluids.

CHAPTER 3

FLUID STATISTICAL THERMODYNAMICS

THE kinetic theory asserts that both the relations between, and the values of, the measured macroscopic thermodynamic functions can be uniquely determined from a knowledge of the appropriate molecular data. The procedure by which this is to be achieved is called statistical thermodynamics,[1] and is based on the arguments of statistical mechanics. By its very nature, statistical thermodynamics is not able to associate measured thermodynamic functions with individual microscopic molecular events. Rather, these functions are identified with certain most probable or average collective microscopic properties. Because the number of degrees of freedom of the system is very large (since the system is composed of a very large number of particles) significant deviations from the mean value will be sufficiently rare events to ignore (law of large particle numbers). In this way the theoretical values of the thermodynamic functions, although calculated from arguments of probability, will nevertheless show a constancy fully compatible with experimental data.

Statistical thermodynamics falls naturally into two parts; viz. that part designed to relate the thermodynamic functions one with another and also formally with molecular data; and that part concerned with the separate calculation of the individual thermodynamic functions from molecular data. There is a sharp practical distinction to be drawn between these two related aspects of the theory due to purely mathematical difficulties. The relations between the several thermodynamic functions are of wide validity applying to all equilibria (both classical and quantal); these relations are well known but are included in the appendices for later reference.[3] The second aspect is the explicit relation of individual thermodynamic functions to microscopic data (and particularly the interparticle force). It is this aspect that concerns us in the present chapter in its application to general fluid densities.

It will be found that difficulties arise because each fluid particle is continuously in the force field of the neighbours. The severe mathematical difficulties in the general calculation of the thermodynamics for all dense matter arise because of this continuous coupling between large particle groupings. Simplification is introduced into the calculations by decoupling the total interaction between the N particles of the system into the sum of interactions between smaller groups of particles. For fluids where the reduction (2.1) is valid, the general thermodynamic expressions derived from the theory can be rearranged to show explicitly the relation between pairs of particles in the fluid. In this way the fluid spatial features described by the radial distribution function (or its generalisation) can be introduced explicitly into the theoretical formulae. This restricts the validity of the formulae to the description of simple fluids systems, but they are then amenable to evaluation. The problem of determining adequate information about the radial distribution is left for the next chapter, the present chapter being devoted to the deduction of expressions for the fluid thermodynamic functions themselves.

3.1. SPECIFIC AND GENERIC DISTRIBUTIONS

The macroscopic thermodynamic functions are to be derived from equation (2.29) by making appropriate choices of the phase function Q. But before any evaluation can be attempted the specific N-th order phase distribution $f^{(N)}$ must be defined explicitly in terms of the phase.

The mechanical system with which we deal is assumed to be composed of N identical particles and individual particles cannot be recognised. Consequently a slight reinterpretation of the N-th order distribution is appropriate. Instead of defining the probability that each of the N particles taken separately shall be found within the dimensionless phase volume $h^{-3N}(dp^N \, dr^N)$ for the set of N particles (where h is Planck's constant of action), we now introduce the N-th order distribution function $f^{(N)}$ such that

$$h^{-3N}f^{(N)}(\mathbf{p}^N, \mathbf{r}^N)d\mathbf{p}^N \, d\mathbf{r}^N \qquad (3.1)$$

shall be the probability that *any* one of the N particles will be found to lie within the phase element $d\mathbf{p}_1 d\mathbf{r}_1$ while simultaneously *any* other particle will lie within the phase element $d\mathbf{p}_2 d\mathbf{r}_2$, and so on until all the particles are allotted a phase placing. In (3.1) the obvious notation has been used that

$$\mathbf{p}^N = (\mathbf{p}_1, \mathbf{p}_2, \mathbf{p}_3, \ldots \mathbf{p}_N),$$

$$\mathbf{r}^N = (\mathbf{r}_1, \mathbf{r}_2, \mathbf{r}_3, \ldots \mathbf{r}_N), \qquad (3.2)$$

$$d\mathbf{p}^N = \prod_{j=1}^{N} d\mathbf{p}_j, \quad \text{and} \quad d\mathbf{r}^N = \prod_{j=1}^{N} d\mathbf{r}_j,$$

so that $\mathbf{p}^N$ and $\mathbf{r}^N$ can be regarded as vectors in a hypothetical $6N$-dimensional phase space. For the partial phase element to be associated with $h(< N)$ particles we have the obvious notation

$$\mathbf{p}^h = (\mathbf{p}_1, \mathbf{p}_2, \mathbf{p}_3, \ldots \mathbf{p}_h),$$
$$\mathbf{r}^h = (\mathbf{r}_1, \mathbf{r}_2, \mathbf{r}_3, \ldots \mathbf{r}_h), \tag{3.3}$$
$$d\mathbf{p}^h = \prod_{j=1}^{h} d\mathbf{p}_j, \quad \text{and} \quad d\mathbf{r}^h = \prod_{j=1}^{h} d\mathbf{r}_j.$$

To distinguish the distribution $f^{(N)}$ from the previous specific distribution $f^{(N)}$, $f^{(N)}$ is often called the generic N-th order phase distribution since reference is not made to specific particles.

The generic and specific distributions are related by the formulae

$$f^{(N)}(\mathbf{p}^N, \mathbf{r}^N) = N! f^{(N)}(\mathbf{p}^N, \mathbf{r}^N), \tag{3.4a}$$

$$f^{(h)}(\mathbf{p}^N, \mathbf{r}^N) = \frac{N!}{(N-h)!} f^{(h)}(\mathbf{p}^h, \mathbf{r}^h). \tag{3.4b}$$

Further $f^{(h)}$ and $f^{(N)}$ are related by

$$f^{(h)}(\mathbf{p}^h, \mathbf{r}^h) = \frac{1}{(N-h)!} \int \ldots \int f^{(N)}(\mathbf{p}^N, \mathbf{r}^N) \prod_{j=h+1}^{N} d\mathbf{p}_j \, d\mathbf{r}_j. \tag{3.5}$$

It follows from the normalisation condition (2.21) that

$$1 = \frac{1}{h^{3N}} \frac{1}{N!} \int \ldots \int f^{(N)}(\mathbf{p}^N, \mathbf{r}^N) \prod_{j=1}^{N} d\mathbf{p}_j \, d\mathbf{r}_j. \tag{3.6}$$

Phase distributions of consecutive order are related by the expression

$$f^{(h)}(\mathbf{p}^h, \mathbf{r}^h) = \frac{1}{(N-h)!} \int \ldots \int f^{(h+1)}(\mathbf{p}^{h+1}, \mathbf{r}^{h+1}) \, d\mathbf{p}_{h+1} \, d\mathbf{r}_{h+1}. \tag{3.7}$$

The singlet and doublet distributions are especially important from the statistical description of fluids, $f^{(1)}$ for dilute gases and $f^{(2)}$ for dense gases and liquids.

Generic configurational distributions are derived by integrating the corresponding phase distributions over the momenta. The particle configuration distribution (i. e. the distribution in position) provides a means of distinguishing between the three main phases of matter. Denoting the generic spatial distributions by $g^{(h)}$ ($h \le N$) we have the expressions from Chapter 2:

$$n^h g^{(h)}(r^h) = \int f^{(h)}(\mathbf{p}^h, \mathbf{r}^h) \, d\mathbf{p}^h, \tag{3.8a}$$

(where $h \leqslant N$),

$$g^{(h)}(\mathbf{r}^h) = \frac{n}{(N-h)} \int g^{(h+1)}(\mathbf{r}^{h+1}) \, d\mathbf{r}_{h+1}. \qquad (3.8b)$$

It follows immediately that the pair and triplet configuration distributions are given by

$$g^{(2)}(\mathbf{r}_1, \mathbf{r}_2) = \frac{n}{(N-2)} \int g^{(3)}(\mathbf{r}_1, \mathbf{r}_2, \mathbf{r}_3) \, d\mathbf{r}_3, \qquad (3.9a)$$

$$n^2 g^{(2)}(\mathbf{r}_1, \mathbf{r}_2) = \frac{n^N}{(N-2)!} \int \cdots \int g^{(N)}(\mathbf{r}^N) \prod_{j=3}^{N} d\mathbf{r}_j, \qquad (3.9b)$$

$$n^3 g^{(3)}(\mathbf{r}_1, \mathbf{r}_2, \mathbf{r}_3) = \frac{n^N}{(N-3)!} \int \cdots \int g^{(N)}(\mathbf{r}^N) \prod_{j=4}^{N} d\mathbf{r}_j. \qquad (3.9c)$$

These expressions will be of great importance in the later development of the theory.

There is one boundary condition that is satisfied by $g^{(h)}$ that can be immediately recognised. If the h particles are moved apart to a very large distance they behave like independent particles, correlation having broken down between them. This situation is described by the condition

$$g^{(h)}(\mathbf{r}^{(h)}) \to 1 \quad \text{as} \quad |\mathbf{r}_i - \mathbf{r}_j| \to \infty \qquad (3.10)$$

for all particles i and j of the group of h particles.

The pair distribution function $g^{(2)}(\mathbf{r}_1, \mathbf{r}_2)$, which is sometimes called alternatively the correlation function because of its dimensionless form, gives the relative probability for the occurrence of two particles separated by the vector distance $\mathbf{r} = \mathbf{r}_2 - \mathbf{r}_1$. It reduces to the radial distribution function defined in (1.6) when the particle relative orientation is either irrelevant (spherical particles) or has been integrated away.

3.2. THE CANONICAL FORM

The phase and configuration distribution functions set down so far apply to any steady situation whether it refers to equilibrium or not. To make them apply specifically to equilibrium conditions it is necessary to add a supplementary statement that non-equilibrium is explicitly excluded, and this is achieved by assigning a special form to the N-th order phase distribution $f^{(N)}$.

Consider the case of a system of a constant number N of identical particles. We suppose throughout that N is very large so that we deal with asymptotic distributions. The most detailed information about the mechanical system is obtained by defining $f^{(N)}$: this is chosen as the standard distribution for the hierarchy of equations (3.7). For equilibrium, $f^{(N)}$ is assigned[2] the canonical form

$$f^{(N)}(\mathbf{p}^N, \mathbf{r}^N) = \frac{1}{Z} \exp \left\{ -\frac{\mathscr{H}(\mathbf{p}^N, \mathbf{r}^N)}{kT} \right\}, \qquad (3.11)$$

where Z is a normalisation constant called the phase partition function or sometimes the sum-over-states. Z is to be determined from the normalisation condition (3.6):

$$Z = \frac{1}{h^{3N}} \frac{1}{N!} \int \cdots \int \exp \left\{ -\frac{\mathscr{H}(\mathbf{p}^N, \mathbf{r}^N)}{kT} \right\} d\mathbf{p}^N \, d\mathbf{r}^N. \qquad (3.12)$$

The phase partition function plays a vital role in the general theory of equilibrium matter since if Z is known explicitly as function of volume and temperature then the corresponding thermodynamic Helmholtz free energy is known (see next section). The extreme mathematical difficulties encountered in equilibrium statistical theory arise from the problem of evaluating the configurational part of the integral (3.12).

When the canonical form (3.11) is inserted into the previous definition (2.20) for $f^{(N)}$, using also (3.4a), the Gibbs distribution results, giving the asymptotic probability distribution for finding the particles of the mechanical system close to prescribed values of the phase.

The phase partition function (3.12) can be separated into component momentum and configuration parts. Using the form (2.9) for the Hamiltonian and considering only interparticle contributions to the potential energy of the system, we have

$$Z = Z_r Z_p, \qquad (3.13)$$

where

$$Z_p = \frac{1}{h^{3N}} \int \cdots \int \exp \left\{ -\sum_{j=1}^{N} \frac{p_j^2}{2mkT} \right\} d\mathbf{p}^N, \qquad (3.14a)$$

$$Z_r = \frac{1}{N!} \int \cdots \int \exp \left\{ -\frac{\Psi(\mathbf{r}_1, \mathbf{r}_2, \ldots \mathbf{r}_N)}{kT} \right\} d\mathbf{r}^N. \qquad (3.14b)$$

Z_p depends upon the particle momenta but not the configuration, while Z_r depends upon the particle configuration but not the momenta. By their definitions, it is seen that the total partition function Z is dimensionless, the momentum partition function Z_p has the dimensions (volume)$^{-N}$, while the configurational partition function Z_r has the dimensions (volume)^N. According to (3.13), the total partition function is the product of the separate momentum and configurational functions, and this result is quite general for all equilibria. The Nth order distribution function $f^{(N)}$ is fully known only when the partition function Z has been evaluated.

The evaluation of the momentum partition function Z_p is readily achieved since the total integral for N particles is now the product of identical integrals each referring to a single particle. Then:

$$Z_p = \prod_{j=1}^{N} \left[\frac{1}{h^3} \int_{-\infty}^{\infty} \exp\left\{ \frac{p_j^2}{2mkT} \right\} dp_j \right] = \left(\frac{2\pi mkT}{h^2} \right)^{3N/2}. \quad (3.15)$$

This expression is quite general and applies to all equilibrium.

The evaluation of the configuration partition function Z_r is an entirely different story. The integral in (3.14b) can be equated to the product of identical integrals only in the special case of completely uncoupled particles (when $\Psi = 0$). In this case

$$Z_r = \frac{V^N}{N!},$$

so that the total partition function for this case is

$$Z = \left(\frac{2\pi mkT}{h^2} \right)^{3N/2} \frac{V^N}{N!}. \quad (3.16)$$

For the general case, the nature of the statistical integral (3.14b) depends upon the details of the potential function Ψ and we have

$$Z = \frac{1}{N!} \left(\frac{2\pi mkT}{h^2} \right)^{3N/2} \int \cdots \int \exp\left\{ -\frac{\Psi(r_1, r_2, \ldots r_N)}{kT} \right\} dr^N. \quad (3.17)$$

The central problem in the calculation of thermodynamic functions by the methods of statistical physics is that of performing the evaluation of the statistical integral in (3.17).

3.3. THE ROLE OF THE PARTITION FUNCTION

The link between the microscopic statistical theory and macroscopic thermodynamics is made by considering the entropy, S. The microscopic phase function here is $-k \ln f^{(N)}$ so that

$$S = -k \langle \ln f^{(N)} \rangle. \quad (3.18)$$

The canonical form (3.11) for $f^{(N)}$ leads to the expression

$$S = k \ln Z + \frac{\langle E \rangle}{T},$$

where $\langle E \rangle$ is the phase average of the Hamiltonian function. Interpreting this average as the internal energy U of the system then we have the well-known thermodynamic relation[3]

$$F = U - TS, \quad (3.19)$$

provided the Helmholtz free energy F is defined by

$$F = -kT \ln Z(V, T). \tag{3.20}$$

This relation between F and Z is basic to statistical thermodynamics. Thus, using (3.14b) and (3.17) we have

$$F = -kT \ln Z_r - \frac{3NkT}{2} \ln \left(\frac{2\pi mkT}{h^2} \right). \tag{3.21}$$

If the partition function is known as function of the volume V and the temperature, for fixed N, then the Helmholtz free energy $F(V, T)$ is known, and further thermodynamic functions can be deduced. Those of interest for our later arguments are the expressions for pressure p, internal energy U, entropy, S, specific heat C, and chemical potential μ. From (3.19) we have

$$p = -\frac{\partial F}{\partial V}\bigg|_T = kT \frac{\partial}{\partial V} (\ln Z(V, T)), \tag{3.22a}$$

$$U = F - T \frac{\partial F}{\partial T}\bigg|_V = kT^2 \frac{\partial}{\partial T} (\ln Z(V, T)), \tag{3.22b}$$

$$S = -\frac{\partial F}{\partial T}\bigg|_V = k \ln Z + kT \frac{\partial}{\partial T} (\ln Z), \tag{3.22c}$$

$$C_V = \frac{\partial U}{\partial T}\bigg|_V = kT \left[T \frac{\partial^2}{\partial T^2} (\ln Z) + 2 \frac{\partial}{\partial T} (\ln Z) \right]$$

$$= kT \frac{\partial}{\partial T} \left[T \frac{\partial}{\partial T} (\ln Z) + \ln Z \right], \tag{3.22d}$$

$$\mu = \frac{\partial F}{\partial N}\bigg|_{V,\,T} = F(V, T, N) - F(V, T, N-1). \tag{3.22e}$$

Formulae such as these apply to all equilibria and remain valid in both classical and quantum physics, provided in the latter case that Z is interpreted as the Slater sum.

The important role played by the partition function in the equilibrium theory of matter is now quite plain. And the statement made before that the modern equilibrium theory provides problems of mathematics, but not of physics, is also quite apparent. The central problem is the evaluation of the partition function. The integral (3.14b) can be evaluated exactly only for the special case when the N particles of the system can be uncoupled. This is not possible for dense fluids where each particle is constantly in the force field of neighbours, and the exact evaluation of Z_r proves not to be possible at the present time. The evaluation of the thermodynamic formulae for liquids must be arranged to circumvent the direct evaluation of Z_r: this is to be achieved by introducing mathematical approximations based on the physics of the structure of fluids. But before entering this discussion it is convenient here to consider a generalisation of the canonical form.

3.4. GRAND CANONICAL FORM

The canonical form (3.11) applies for a mechanical system having a fixed number of particles. The more general situation is that where the number of particles is not fixed[4], and is described by the grand canonical ensemble. The generic distribution for the system to replace (3.11) is denoted by $f_G^{(N)}$ and is to involve N as well as the particle phase. Explicitly, we write

$$f_G^{(N)}(\mathbf{p}^N, \mathbf{r}^N) = \frac{1}{\Xi} \exp \left\{ \frac{\mu N - \mathcal{H}(\mathbf{p}^N, \mathbf{r}^N)}{kT} \right\}, \qquad (3.23)$$

where μ is a parameter yet to be indentified, and Ξ is a normalising constant called the grand partition function. The insertion of (3.23) into (2.20), using also the combinatorial expression (3.4a), provides an expression for the probability that an open mechanical system in equilibrium will be found to contain N particles with phases close to $(\mathbf{p}^N, \mathbf{r}^N)$. The thermodynamical formulae are obtained if μ in (3.23) is identified with the macroscopic chemical potential.

The grand partition function is the sum over all possible particle numbers of the average over the phase. Explicitly,

$$\Xi(V, T) = \sum_{N \geq 0} \exp \left\{ \frac{\mu N}{kT} \right\} Z(N), \qquad (3.24)$$

where $Z(N)$ is (3.12) applying to that system having N particles. Clearly, if the number of particles in the system is constant, then (3.23) reduces to the canonical form (3.11).

It is convenient to introduce two new quantities, related to the chemical potential: we define the absolute activity λ and the fugacity z by

$$\lambda = \exp \left\{ \frac{\mu}{kT} \right\}, \quad \text{and} \quad z = \frac{Z(1)}{V} \lambda. \qquad (3.25)$$

According to the definition (3.12) for Z, it follows that

$$Z(0) = 1, \qquad (3.26a)$$

and for a single particle (and so without particle interaction)

$$Z(1) = \left(\frac{2\pi mkT}{h^2} \right)^{3/2} V; \qquad (3.26b)$$

for the general case of N particles including interaction

$$Z(N) = \left(\frac{Z(1)}{V}\right)^N Z_r(N), \qquad (3.26c)$$

where V is the volume of the system, and Z_r is given by equation (3.14b). From (3.24) it follows that

$$\Xi = \sum_{N \geq 0} \lambda^N \left(\frac{Z(1)}{V}\right)^N Z_r(N) = \sum_{N \geq 0} z^N Z_r(N). \qquad (3.27a)$$

Consequently, the grand partition function can be written in the form of a series:

$$\Xi = 1 + z Z_r(1) + z^2 Z_r(2) + \dots \qquad (3.27b)$$

This expansion is of considerable interest in the theory of imperfect gases.

Thermodynamic functions follow from a knowledge of Ξ just as previously they followed from a knowledge of Z_r.

Thus, the pressure p is given by

$$\frac{pV}{kT} = \ln \Xi(z, V, T), \qquad (3.28a)$$

and the average number N of particles in the volume V is given by

$$N = z \frac{\partial}{\partial z} \ln \Xi(z, V, T). \qquad (3.28b)$$

The equation of state is the equation which expresses p as function of N, V, and T: this is derived from the equations (3.28) by eliminating the fugacity z.

The internal energy, being the ensemble average of the particle Hamiltonian, is given by

$$U = -k \frac{\partial}{\partial(1/T)} \ln \Xi(z, V, T), \qquad (3.29)$$

and this expression becomes a function of (N, V, T) after z is eliminated using (3.28). Finally, the Helmholtz free energy follows from (3.19) and is

$$F = NkT \ln \lambda - kT \ln \Xi(z, V, T), \qquad (3.30)$$

where once again z is to be eliminated by using (3.28). Using (3.30) and (3.28a) the Gibbs free energy G is given by

$$G = F - V \frac{\partial F}{\partial V}\bigg|_{T, N} = NkT \ln \lambda = N\mu. \qquad (3.31)$$

The full range of thermodynamic functions can then be related directly to the partition functions.

The importance of the grand canonical form as compared with the canonical form is that the former applies to open systems whereas the latter does not. The grand canonical form, therefore, is able to describe more general situations (like the simultaneous equilibrium between different phase of matter) than is the canonical form. Both forms will be found important later in the development of the statistical theory of fluids.

3.5. APPEAL TO THE PAIR DISTRIBUTION

The central mathematical problem in calculating the thermodynamic functions according to the arguments of statistical thermodynamics is the evaluation of the partition function in either the canonical or grand canonical form. Since the evaluation of Ξ involves the evaluation of Z_r, the latter function alone need be considered now.

In Chapter 1 it was found that an essential distinction between the main three phases of matter could be expressed by details of the particle spatial arrangement. For simple fluids the essential arrangement is that of pairs of particles, described empirically by the radial distribution function of equation (1.6) and described theoretically by the pair distribution (3.9). For the theoretical calculation of macroscopic thermodynamic functions, the general formulae involving the partition function will be replaced by formulae based on the explicit appearance of the pair distribution.

The insertion of (3.11) into (3.8a) with h set equal to N leads to the appropriate expression for the N-th order configuration function $g^{(N)}$. This is

$$n^N g^{(N)}(\mathbf{r}^N) = \frac{1}{N!Z_r} \exp\left\{-\frac{\Psi(\mathbf{r}^N)}{kT}\right\}. \tag{3.32}$$

The use of (3.9b) then provides the expression for the pair distribution $g^{(2)}$ $(\mathbf{r}_1, \mathbf{r}_2)$. Assuming the total potential can be replaced by the sum of pair contributions according to (2.1) it follows[5] easily that

$$n^2 g^{(2)}(\mathbf{r}_{12}) = \frac{1}{(N-2)!} \frac{1}{Z_r} \int \cdots \int \exp\left\{-\sum_{1\leq i<j\leq N} \chi(\mathbf{r}_{ij})\right\} \prod_{j=3}^{N} d\mathbf{r}_j, \tag{3.33}$$

where $\mathbf{r}_{12} = \mathbf{r}_1 - \mathbf{r}_2$ is the relative pair separation and we have introduced the dimensionless potential function χ according to

$$kTX = \sum_{i,j} kT\chi(\mathbf{r}_{ij}) = \sum_{i,j} \psi(\mathbf{r}_{ij}) = \Psi. \tag{3.34}$$

To show that $g^{(2)}$ introduced this way is in fact to be identified with the measured radial distribution, consider the relation between $g^{(2)}$ given by

(3.33) and Z_r defined in (3.14b). From the latter equation it follows that

$$Z_r = \frac{(N-2)!}{N!} Z_r \left\{ \frac{1}{(N-2)!Z_r} \int \cdots \int \exp\left\{ -X(\mathbf{r}^N) \right\} d\mathbf{r}^N \right\},$$

where $kTX(\mathbf{r}^N) = \Psi(\mathbf{r}^N)$, so that for a fluid

$$N(N-1) = \int\int n^2 g^{(2)}(\mathbf{r}_{12}) d\mathbf{r}_1\, d\mathbf{r}_2.$$

For spherical particles this expression reduces to

$$\int 4\pi r^2 n g^{(2)}(r)\, dr = N-1.$$

Interpreting $g^{(2)}(r)$ as being the radial distribution for particles about one particle chosen as origin (see section 1.5), the left hand side of the expression is equal to the number of particles other than the origin particle. But this is precisely the number of particles on the right of the equation. $g^{(2)}$ introduced in equation (3.33) has in fact the same physical interpretation and use as the experimental radial distribution. The expression (3.33), therefore, relates the radial distribution of experiment to the molecular data, which is to say the actual interparticle force potential.

Higher order functions, such as the triplet function $g^{(3)}$ and the quartuplet function $g^{(4)}$, can be defined in an analogous way. A knowledge of these functions will be necessary for the purposes of the next chapter but we do not need them here. It will be realised that the configurational partition function appears in these expressions and it will be necessary to deal with this appearance later. For the present we need not concern ourselves with this difficulty, remembering that the pair distribution can anyway be obtained experimentally according to the methods of section 1.5 even if the calculations prove intractable. The question of whether the experimental data can be provided to sufficient accuracy for theoretical purposes will not be considered here. Suffice it to admit that the pair distribution can provide an alternative method for the evaluation of the formulae for the thermodynamical properties of a fluid, and that the direct determination of the partition function can be avoided. We turn now to the problem of expressing the formulae such as (3.22) in terms of the pair distribution.

The partition function has the form (3.17) and

$$\ln Z = \frac{3N}{2} \ln \left(\frac{2\pi mkT}{h^2} \right) + \ln Z_r. \tag{3.35}$$

An expression for the internal energy follows from the insertion of (3.35) into (3.22b), and using (3.14b) and (3.33). The result is

$$U = \frac{3NkT}{2} + \frac{n^2}{2} \int g^{(2)}(\mathbf{r}_{12})\psi(\mathbf{r}_{12}) \, d\mathbf{r}_{12}.$$

For spherical particles where the relative particle orientation is irrelevant, this expression becomes[6]

$$\frac{U}{V} = \frac{3nkT}{2} + \frac{n^2}{2} \int g^{(2)}(r)\psi(r)4\pi r^2 \, dr, \tag{3.36}$$

where N is assumed sufficiently large for there to be no distinction between $(N-1)$ and N. The first term on the right hand side of this expression arises from the movement of single particles and is the predominant term for dilute gases. The second term on the right hand side arises from the interaction between pairs of particles, and it is this term that predominates at liquid densities. The formula (3.36) can be expected to apply also in the region of the gas–liquid transition. U given by (3.36) is a function of both the temperature and the density. This dependence is shown explicitly in the first term of the equation; it appears implicitly in the second term through the temperature and density dependence of the pair distribution.

The rearrangement of the expression (3.22a) for the pressure is a more difficult task because the differentiation over the volume involves explicitly the limits of the integration of the partition function. This difficulty can be overcome by applying a mathematical artifice; alternatively, the pressure can be derived directly from the virial theorem. For equilibrium conditions, the time and phase averaging processes are equivalent, according to the ergodic theorem. Consequently, the equation (2.19) is equivalent to (2.32a): we use the later expression now.

We choose for the phase function Q, the form (2.33), so that (2.32b) applies. And $\mathbf{F}_j$ is given by (2.17), where the potential V is the sum (2.8a). The particle interaction contribution Ψ has the pair form (2.1) and the potential $\mathfrak{K}$ of external origin arises from the interaction between the particles of the system and the containing boundary wall. With p as the pressure and V the volume of the system, then

$$\left\langle \sum_{j=1}^{N} \left(\mathbf{r}_j \cdot \frac{\partial \mathfrak{K}}{\partial \mathbf{r}_j} \right) \right\rangle = 3pV, \tag{3.37a}$$

and

$$\left\langle \sum_{j=1}^{N} \left(\mathbf{r}_j \cdot \frac{\partial \Psi}{\partial \mathbf{r}_j} \right) \right\rangle = \frac{1}{2} \frac{1}{N!} \frac{1}{Z_r} \int \cdots \int \sum_{1 \leq i < j \leq N} \left(\mathbf{r}_{ij} \cdot \frac{\partial \psi(\mathbf{r}_{ij})}{\partial \mathbf{r}_{ij}} \right) \tag{3.37b}$$

$$\times \exp\{-X(\mathbf{r}^N)\} \, d\mathbf{r}^N.$$

With

$$\left\langle \sum_{j=1}^{N} \frac{p_j^2}{m} \right\rangle = 3NkT, \tag{3.37c}$$

and using the definition of the pair distribution (3.33), then the expression (2.32) becomes:

$$3pV = 3NkT - \frac{n^2}{2} \int \int g^{(2)}(\mathbf{r}_{12}) \left(\mathbf{r}_{12} \cdot \frac{\partial \psi(\mathbf{r}_{12})}{\partial \mathbf{r}_{12}} \right) d\mathbf{r}_1 \, d\mathbf{r}_2.$$

For spherically symmetric particles we have, in the limit of very large N,

$$p = nkT - \frac{n^2}{6} \int_0^\infty g^{(2)}(r) \frac{\partial \psi(r)}{\partial r} 4\pi r^3 \, dr. \tag{3.38}$$

This expression will be referred to as the virial expression for the pressure.[6] As for the expression (3.36) for the internal energy, so now from (3.38) for the pressure, the first term on the right hand side refers to conditions for a dilute gas while the second term is concerned with conditions appropriate to dense gases and liquids. Thus (3.38) can describe the full range of fluid conditions.

It should be made clear that the expressions (3.36) and (3.38) are exact within the pair potential assumption (2.1), no terms having been neglected. The appearance of $g^{(2)}$ alone, and not higher order distributions, in these expressions is a direct consequence of the assumed validity of the mutual particle interaction. If the interaction between triplets had been taken as the basic interaction instead of that between pairs, then the triplet distribution would have taken the place of the pair distribution in the formulae. For this reason the formulae involving the pair distribution are somewhat restricted in safe application; while they can certainly be supposed to apply to simple liquids (such as liquid argon), there is no immediate guarantee that they will be directly applicable except approximately to the more complex organic liquids, or to molten metallic elements or compounds. But the rearrangement of the formulae to include higher order interactions is readily performed. The general range of validity of the equations involving the pair distribution for the various types of fluid is likely to be wider for a gas where the particle number density is lower than for a liquid, and the interparticle force potential is less likely to involve more than particle pairs simultaneously.

Other expressions for the thermodynamic functions can be expressed in terms of the pair distribution. As an example, the specific heat at constant volume C_v is given by

$$\frac{C_v}{V} = \frac{3nk}{2} + \frac{n^2}{2} \int_0^\infty \psi(r) \frac{\partial g^{(2)}(r)}{\partial T} 4\pi r^2 \, dr. \tag{3.39}$$

Further examples will not be written down here but expressions for quantities like the Joule–Thomson coefficient and speed of sound in a fluid can be deduced in terms of the pair distribution for comparison with specific experimental situations.

3.6. FLUCTUATIONS

The formulae derived so far lead to values of the thermodynamic functions which are unambiguous for each temperature and in this respect satisfy a primitive experimental requirement. But the arguments on which the theory is based rely on considerations of probability according to which the measured properties of the actual physical system are explained in terms of the most probable or average properties of the representative ensemble. Unique deductions from the theory are possible only if the arguments lead to a unique average of microscopic functions. The ergodic hypothesis equates ensemble to time average, but the ensemble average is not necessarily the same as the most probable value interpreted as that value which is possessed by the largest number of systems in the ensemble. The value of a phase function possessed by the largest number of systems in the ensemble can be equated to the ensemble average only if the mean of the square of the function is exactly equal to the square of its mean value. This would never be the case exactly in mechanical systems of physical interest because it would involve for its validity an infinite mechanical system. But for real systems the number of particles is astronomically large although technically not infinite, so that the above condition can apply only approximately. The degree of approximation can, however, be very high so that for a function Q the condition $\langle Q^2 \rangle = \langle Q \rangle^2$ can be obeyed to very great accuracy. Actual measurements are subject to experimental errors and this situation saves the day. For the experimental errors of macroscopic functions may be such as to overlap the inequality of the two ensemble averages $\langle Q^2 \rangle$ and $\langle Q \rangle^2$: even though they are not exactly equal to each other in fact, the difference between them can then be small enough to be neglected. This will be the case if

$$\frac{\langle Q^2 \rangle - \langle Q \rangle^2}{\langle Q \rangle^2} \ll 1, \tag{3.40}$$

which is the condition that the mean square deviation is very small compared with the square of the mean value. This condition is well known to statisticians as being necessary for average values to have unique interpretation.

The phase average in (3.40) is that defined in (2.29): if (3.40) is valid then the measured values can be linked uniquely to calculated average values. If (3.40) is not valid then there is no unique way of specifying how the measured macroscopic value can be calculated from molecular data.

The fact that the left hand side of (3.40) is very small but does not vanish has important consequences. For it suggests a fine fluctuating nature to calculated values that may have counterparts in measured data. These fluctuations can be important in leading to a different method of relating the microscopic and macroscopic properties of matter. These considerations are well known for equilibrium conditions[7] and will be reviewed briefly here. They also lead to important consequences for non-equilibrium conditions that are perhaps less well known; the study for non-equilibrium fluid conditions will be left for a later chapter.

(a) Energy Fluctuations

Let us consider the fluctuation of the internal energy of a closed system of N particles. The calculation therefore involves a phase average of the Hamiltonian over a canonical ensemble. Remembering the basic relation (3.20) we have

$$U = \exp\left\{\frac{F}{kT}\right\} \int \mathscr{H}(\mathbf{p}^N, \mathbf{r}^N) \exp\left\{-\frac{\mathscr{H}(\mathbf{p}^N, \mathbf{r}^N)}{kT}\right\} d\mathbf{p}^N \, d\mathbf{r}^N,$$

so that

$$\int\int d\mathbf{p}^N \, d\mathbf{r}^N [U - \mathscr{H}(\mathbf{p}^N, \mathbf{r}^N)] \exp\left\{\frac{F}{kT} - \frac{\mathscr{H}(\mathbf{p}^N, \mathbf{r}^N)}{kT}\right\} = 0, \quad (3.41)$$

where in evaluating the integral it is to be remembered that $F = F(V, T)$ is the macroscopic free energy. The integral (3.41) applies at a definite temperature T: the variation with temperature follows by differentiation. Using (3.19) the result is

$$kT^2 \frac{\partial U}{\partial T} = \langle (U - \mathscr{H})^2 \rangle = \langle \mathscr{H}^2 \rangle - \langle \mathscr{H} \rangle^2. \quad (3.42)$$

For conditions of constant volume $\partial U/\partial T = C_V$, the specific heat at constant volume, so that finally

$$kT^2 C_v = \langle \mathscr{H}^2 \rangle - \langle \mathscr{H} \rangle^2. \quad (3.42a)$$

The macroscopic specific heat at constant volume is a measure of the mean square deviation of the energy. Expressed another way, if $\Delta U = \langle (U - \mathscr{H})^2 \rangle$,

$$\Delta U = \sqrt{kT^2 C_v}. \quad (3.42b)$$

For a real physical system of N particles $\mathcal{H}$ is proportional to N and so is U. Let us consider the relative fluctuation (3.40) for the energy. Clearly

$$\delta U^2 \equiv \frac{\langle \mathcal{H}^2 \rangle - \langle \mathcal{H} \rangle^2}{\langle \mathcal{H} \rangle^2} = \frac{kT^2 C_v}{\langle \mathcal{H} \rangle^2} \, \alpha \, \frac{1}{N}. \tag{3.43}$$

Apparently the deviation in the relative energy (which is the square root of the left hand side of this expression) decreases like $N^{-1/2}$. For real condensed matter $N \sim 10^{23}$ so that $\delta U \sim 10^{-12}$, which is certainly very small although it is not formally zero. The conclusion to be drawn from (3.43) is that most of the members of the ensemble have the same energy, so that it reduces effectively to the microcanonical ensemble in calculations. But this is true, because the number of degrees of freedom of the mechanical system (or the number of particles) is very large.

b) Density Fluctuations

A most important aspect of a dense fluid is that of particle density fluctuations in any spatial volume contained within the main fluid volume. The particle kinetic energy is not negligible in a fluid in comparison with the potential energy. The interaction between particles prevents the random distribution of particles about any one chosen as centre. The ordering of the particles is affected by the kinetic energy that they possess: a combined study of the particle spatial ordering about any location in the fluid, and of the fluctuation of the particles in a chosen volume about this location, can give information about the physical conditions within a liquid.

For the study of the local particle density the appropriate distribution is the grand canonical form. The total system, of N particles contained in volume V, is described by the canonical distribution. For the local volume $V_1 (\ll V)$ within V, the phase distribution is the grand canonical form.

The statistical deviation for the particles in V_1 is obtained using (3.23) and (3.27a):

$$\langle N^2 \rangle = \frac{1}{\Xi} \sum_{N \geq 0} N^2 z^N Z_r(N) = \frac{1}{\Xi} \frac{\partial^2 \Xi}{\partial (\ln z)^2}, \tag{3.44a}$$

$$\langle N \rangle = \frac{1}{\Xi} \sum_{N \geq 0} N z^N Z_r(N) = \frac{\partial \ln \Xi}{\partial \ln z}. \tag{3.44b}$$

Consequently,

$$\langle N^2 \rangle - \langle N \rangle^2 = \frac{\partial \langle N \rangle}{\partial \ln z} = z \frac{\partial \langle N \rangle}{\partial z}, \tag{3.44c}$$

where on the right hand side differentiation is to be performed for con stant volume and temperature.

Two further relations are deduced. First we find

$$\int n^2 g^{(2)}(\mathbf{r}_{12}) \, d\mathbf{r}_1 \, d\mathbf{r}_2 = \langle N^2 \rangle - \langle N \rangle, \qquad (3.45a)$$

$$n^2 \int g^{(2)}(\mathbf{r}_1) g^{(2)}(\mathbf{r}_2) \, d\mathbf{r}_1 \, d\mathbf{r}_2 = \langle N \rangle^2, \qquad (3.45b)$$

where $g^{(1)}$ is the singlet distribution. In a fluid, $g^{(1)}(\mathbf{r}_1) = g^{(1)}(\mathbf{r}_2) = 1$. The second relation of importance is

$$z \frac{\partial \langle N \rangle}{\partial z} = kT \frac{\partial \langle N \rangle}{\partial \mu} = V kT n^2 \varkappa, \qquad (3.45c)$$

where $\varkappa = \dfrac{\partial n}{\partial p}\bigg|_T$ is the isothermal compressibility.

Combining the equations (3.44) and (3.45) there results the importan equation for spherical particles:

$$kT \frac{\partial n}{\partial p}\bigg|_{T, N} = 1 + 4\pi n \int_0^\infty [g^{(2)}(r) - 1] r^2 \, dr. \qquad (3.46a)$$

The integrand contains the correlation function $[g^{(2)}(r) - 1]$ which we previously denoted by $h(r)$ so that

$$kT \frac{\partial n}{\partial p}\bigg|_T = 1 + 4\pi n \int_0^\infty h(r) r^2 \, dr. \qquad (3.46b)$$

This equation relates the fluid compressibility and the correlation betwee pairs of particles.[8] It will be of great importance in later arguments.

The function $h(r)$ varies with r because the particle distribution is a func tion of the separation distance. For a completely uniform distribution $h(r) = 0$, and the right hand side of equation (3.46b) reduces to unity Consequently, the integral in (3.46b) is physically important because i describes the degree to which space is available for particle movement In these terms important conclusions about the molecular spatial distribu tion in simple fluids can be drawn from a study of the function $(kT\varkappa - 1)$ Experimental information concerning this function is particularly interest ing in the construction of a theory of dense fluids.

The expression (3.44c) has an important consequence.

For

$$\frac{\langle N^2 \rangle - \langle N^2 \rangle}{\langle N \rangle^2} = z \frac{\partial \langle N \rangle}{\partial z} \frac{1}{\langle N \rangle^2}. \qquad (3.47)$$

Consequently, the root mean square deviation is proportional to $\langle N \rangle^{-1/2}$ which is essentially zero for the large particle numbers appropriate to macroscopic matter. It is seen that most of the members of the grand canonical ensemble contain the same number of particles. Thus in practice, for the calculation of thermodynamic properties, the grand canonical distribution is virtually a closed canonical ensemble containing a number of particles equal to the average for the associated grand ensemble.

3.7. THE VIRIAL EXPANSION

The arguments and formulae developed to this point are to be true generally for fluids within the range of validity of the concept of the radial distribution as a continuous function of the particle separation distance. For dense fluids, the formulae are subject to severe restrictions in their practical application to numerical studies because of the extreme mathematical difficulties encountered in calculating the trajectory of a particle which is in continuous interaction with neighbouring particles. In the theory this difficulty shows itself in the evaluation of the integrals defining the partition function. The simultaneous interaction between an astronomically large number of particles must be accounted for, and our present mathematical techniques (even augmented by modern electronic computational aids) are unable to do this exactly. It is true that the recognition of the importance of the pair distribution for simple fluids has allowed the partition function to be eliminated formally from the expressions for the thermodynamic functions. This is an important simplification if experimental knowledge of the radial distribution is adequate for the evaluation of these formulae (and we must say here that generally it is not adequate). But in any case the complete theory must be capable of providing data for the particle pair distribution in terms of microscopic data (and particularly involving the interparticle force potential) so that the calculation of the appropriate pair distribution is unavoidable. The integral in the expression (3.9b) for $g^{(2)}$ contains the contributions from only two particles fewer than that of (3.12) for Z_r, so that all that has been said about the problem of evaluating the partition function for dense fluids applies also to the problem of evaluating the corresponding pair distribution. Approximation is inevitable in such a case, and the methods at present available for the calculation of $g^{(2)}$ over the full range of fluid density will be discussed in detail in the two chapters to follow. In the meantime it is appropriate to precede these considerations by some discussion of the special case of low fluid density. For here the direct evaluation of the partition function is possible within useful limits of accuracy and the general formulae of the theory can be applied directly to the calculation of the macroscopic thermodynamics of gases at sufficiently low density. The associated argu ments have some value for the general study of fluids at higher densities in that they provide some encounter with the viable problems at low den sities which become unmanageable at higher densities.

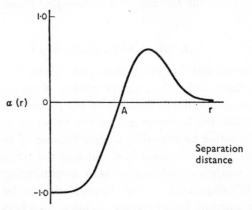

FIG. 6. Typical curve for $\alpha(r)$ as function of separation distance.

The partition function and the pair distribution are both dependent upon the function
$$\exp\left\{-\sum_{1\leq i<j\leq N}\chi(\mathbf{r}_{ij})\right\}.$$
This can be expanded formally:
$$\exp\left\{-\sum_{1\leq i<j\leq N}\chi(\mathbf{r}_{ij})\right\} = \prod_{1\leq i<j\leq N}\exp\left\{-\chi(\mathbf{r}_{ij})\right\} = \prod_{1\leq i<j\leq N}\left(1+\alpha(i,j)\right), \quad (3.48)$$
where the function $\alpha(i,j)$ is defined by
$$\alpha(i,j) \equiv \alpha(\mathbf{r}_{ij}) = \exp\left\{-\chi(\mathbf{r}_{ij})\right\}-1. \qquad (3.49)$$
The dependence of α on the separation distance depends upon the detail of the interparticle force. For short-range forces of the type which charac terise simple fluids, α itself is also a short-range function of the separation distance and vanishes after a couple of particle diameters (Fig. 6). In con sequence, the various terms appearing in the expansion (3.48) involve separately very restricted regions of space and are sensibly zero over much of the physical volume available to the fluid.

By using (3.34), the insertion of the expansion (3.48) into the expression (3.12) provides the expansion for the partition function:
$$Z = \frac{1}{N!}\int\left[1+\sum\alpha(i,j)+\sum\sum\alpha(i,j)\alpha(l,m)+\ldots\right]d\mathbf{r}^N. \qquad (3.50)$$

'he first term in the expansion (3.50) refers to single particles having no interaction with neighbours; physically this describes a gas at infinite ilution. The second term refers to the interaction between pairs of particles; the third term between particle triplets and quadruplets, and so on throughout the series. This hierarchy of interaction between the particles of successively larger groupings is the theoretical description of the effect of increasing the macroscopic density. The expansion (3.50) can, indeed, be interpreted physically in terms of an expression in terms of powers of the density. Using (3.50) in conjunction with the previous equations (3.22a) or (3.22b) provides an expansion for fluid pressure or internal energy in powers of the density. More details of the calculation are collected in Appendix 3.9, and we quote here only the final results.

The succession of terms in (3.50), interpreted as a hierarchy of terms describing the interaction between successively larger groupings of particles, is replaced by the so-called irreducible integrals. The irreducible integral for a group of $(k+1)$ particles, written β_k, is defined as the integral over the configuration available to the $(k+1)$ particles:

$$\beta_k = \frac{1}{k!} \frac{1}{V} \int \cdots \int \sum_{1 \leq j < i \leq N} \Pi \, \alpha(i, j) \prod_{s=1}^{k+1} d\mathbf{r}_s. \qquad (3.51)$$

The total interaction between a group of N particles is then expressed as the sum of interactions between constituent subgroupings. The dimensions of β_k are V^k: the effect of the particle interaction can be judged by the degree by which β_k differs from the value $V^N/k!$. In terms of (3.51), the partition function is given by

$$\ln Z_r = N \left[1 + \sum_{k \geq 1} \left(\frac{1}{k+1} \right) \beta_k n^k - \ln n \right], \qquad (3.52a)$$

and the Helmholtz free energy by

$$F = NkT \left[\ln \left(\frac{h^2}{2\pi m kT} \right)^{3/2} n - \sum_{k \geq 1} \beta_k n^k \right]. \qquad (3.52b)$$

This expression involves powers of the particle number density n. Explicit expressions for pressure and internal energy follow from the formulae (3.22). Thus,

$$p = nkT \left[1 - \sum_{k \geq 1} \left(\frac{k}{k+1} \right) \beta_k n^k \right], \qquad (3.53a)$$

$$\frac{U}{V} = \frac{3nkT}{2} \left[1 + \frac{2T}{3} \sum_{k \geq 1} \left(\frac{1}{k+1} \right) \frac{\partial \beta_k}{\partial T} n_k \right]. \qquad (3.53b)$$

Expressed alternatively, the expansions (3.53) are written

$$p = nkT \left[1 + \sum_{k \geq 1} B_{j+1} n^j \right], \tag{3.54a}$$

$$\frac{U}{V} = \frac{3}{2} nkT \left[1 + \sum_{j \geq 1} U_j n^j \right], \tag{3.54b}$$

where

$$B_{j+1} = -\left(\frac{j}{j+1} \right) \beta_j, \quad \text{and} \quad U_j = \frac{2T}{3} \left(\frac{1}{j+1} \right) \frac{\partial \beta_j}{\partial T}. \tag{3.54c}$$

These are the virial expansions well known[10] in the empirical thermodynamics of gases where the density is not too high.[11] The coefficients in the expansion are functions of the temperature and of the exact details of the constituent molecules of the gas (which means particularly of the intermolecular force potential); they are not functions of the volume even though the dimensions of B_{j+1} and U_j are each volume raised to the j-th power. The coefficients B_{j+1} in the expansion for the pressure are usually called the virial coefficients, starting with B_2 which is the second virial coefficient (pedantically, the first virial coefficient is unity in the expansion (3.54a)). Sometimes the second, third, fourth, fifth, ... virial coefficients are denoted alternatively by respectively B, C, D, E, ...

The insertion of (3.51) into (3.54c) allows expressions to be derived which relate directly the measured virial data to the details of the interparticle force. In particular, we have the important formulae for the first three virial coefficients for spherical particles:

$$B \equiv B_2 = -2\pi \int_0^\infty \alpha(r) r^2 \, dr, \tag{3.55a}$$

$$C \equiv B_3 = -\frac{1}{3V} \iiint \alpha(1, 2) \, \alpha(1, 3) \, \alpha(2, 3) \, d\mathbf{r}_1 \, d\mathbf{r}_2 \, d\mathbf{r}_3, \tag{3.55b}$$

$$D \equiv B_4 = -\frac{1}{8V} \iiiint [\alpha(1, 2) \, \alpha(1,3) \, \alpha(2, 3) \, \alpha(1, 4) \, \alpha(2, 4) \, \alpha(3, 4)$$

$$+ 6\alpha(1, 2) \, \alpha(2, 3) \, \alpha(1, 3) \, \alpha(1, 4) \, \alpha(2, 4) \tag{3.55c}$$

$$+ 3\alpha(1, 2) \, \alpha(2, 3) \, \alpha(3, 4) \, \alpha(1, 4)] \, d\mathbf{r}_1 \, d\mathbf{r}_2 \, d\mathbf{r}_3 \, d\mathbf{r}_4.$$

The next member of the set, E, is highly complicated and lengthy. The expressions (3.55) are exact, no approximations having been involved in their derivation.

An alternative method of deriving the virial expansions for pressure and internal energy as power series in particle number density, is that using the relation (3.28a) between the pressure and the grand partition function, together with (3.24) which relates Ξ to Z_r. For an exact theoretical description, the virial coefficients appearing in (3.54a) must be the same whether calculated from (3.22a) or from (3.28a). The criterion can be of value in assessing the value of any approximation that it may be expedient to introduce into the theory.

One further expression of the internal consistency of the theory involves both the pressure and internal energy. A comparison between the coefficients in (3.54a) and (3.54b) show that the relation

$$\frac{\partial B_{j+1}}{\partial T}\bigg|_V = -\frac{3j}{2T}\, U_j\bigg|_T \qquad (3.56a)$$

is valid: in the alternative notation,

$$\frac{\partial B}{\partial T} = -\frac{3}{2}\frac{U_1}{T}, \quad \frac{\partial C}{\partial T} = -\frac{3U_2}{T}, \quad \frac{\partial D}{\partial T} = -\frac{9}{2}\frac{U_3}{T}, \,\dots \qquad (3.56b)$$

In this way, the coefficients in the density expansion for the energy are related directly to the temperature derivatives at constant volume of the corresponding coefficients in the density expansion for the pressure. The relations (3.56) apply to dilute gases where the density expansions (3.54) are valid, but in fact these relations are special examples of a more general statement which is applicable to any fluid density. Thus from the basic thermodynamic relation (3.19) together with (3.22) we find

$$\frac{\partial}{\partial V}\left(\frac{U}{T^2}\bigg|_T\right) = \frac{\partial}{\partial T}\left(\frac{p}{T}\bigg|_V\right). \qquad (3.56)$$

The relation is potentially of great interest in the theory of liquids and will be evoked later in our arguments.

The virial expansions (3.54) have been deduced by considering the form of the partition function (the statistical integral) expanded in the form (3.50). The virial expansions also follow from the expansion of the expression (3.33) for the pair distribution, used in conjunction with the equations (3.36) and (3.38). The density expansion of the pair distribution will be considered in detail in the next chapter.

3.8. CORRESPONDING STATES

In finishing this chapter we shall not attempt any direct evaluation of the partition function but instead will consider its structure in respect to scaling procedures. Such a procedure is of value for obtaining quickly fairly rough information about totally unknown thermodynamic data for one fluid from known data applying to some other suitably related fluid. The two fluids are said to be in corresponding states: the principle of corresponding states has played a very valuable role in empirical thermodynamics in the past and is still of value in the initial exploration of complicated fluids.

Suppose the interparticle force potential has the form of the product of an energy and a function of the separation distance. If σ is the characteristic length describing the particle size, and ε is depth of the potential well, then we assume

$$\psi(r) = \varepsilon f(r^*), \tag{3.57}$$

where $r = \sigma r^*$. The parameter ε fixes the overall magnitude of the potential while the function $f(r^*)$ fixes its general spatial range. Many potential functions used in calculations have this two-parameter form and although they are usually rather ill-founded theoretically they have a definite utility in connection with theoretical arguments. As an example the (12–6) potential (2.4) and its generalisations (2.5) and (2.6) have exactly the form (3.57), where for the general case of an $(m-6)$ potential

$$f(r^*) = \left(\frac{m}{6}\right)^{\frac{6}{m-6}} \left(\frac{m}{m-6}\right) [(r^*)^{-m} - (r^*)^{-6}]. \tag{3.58}$$

The law of corresponding states is particularly associated with the potential form (3.57). The differences in the interparticle force potential for fluids having the same function form (3.57) are due only to differences in ε and σ. In particular, the configurational partition function is a direct function of the interparticle force potential so that the derived thermodynamic data are functions of ε and σ directly, which are the scale factors in the given law of interparticle force.

Four dimensional quantities can be constructed from the trio (N, ε, σ); viz. (1) an energy $N\varepsilon$; (ii) a volume $N\sigma^3$; (iii) a temperature ε/k, where k is the Boltzmann constant; and (iv) a pressure ε/σ^3. If N refers to a mole of matter then these can be designated as molar quantities. We can now introduce the dimensionless thermodynamic quantities (p^*, V^*, T^*, U^*) according to

$$p^* = \left(\frac{\sigma^3}{\varepsilon}\right) p, \quad V^* = \frac{V}{N\sigma^3}, \quad T^* = \frac{Tk}{\varepsilon}, \quad U^* = \frac{U}{N\varepsilon}. \tag{3.59}$$

It follows immediately that

$$\frac{pV}{RT} = \frac{p^*V^*}{T^*}, \quad \text{and} \quad \frac{pV}{U} = \frac{p^*V^*}{U^*}, \tag{3.60}$$

so that the scale parameters do not appear in these dimensionless ratios.

Consider next the configurational partition function. In parametric form,

$$Z = \left(\frac{2\pi m \varepsilon \sigma^2}{h^2}\right)^{\frac{3N}{2}} T^{*\frac{3N}{2}} Z_r^*, \tag{3.61a}$$

where

$$Z_r^* = \frac{1}{N!} \int \cdots \int \exp\left\{-\sum_{1 \le i < j \le N} \frac{f(r_{ij}^*)}{T^*}\right\} \mathbf{dr}^{*N}, \tag{3.61b}$$

i.e.

$$Z_r^* = Z_r^*(V^*, T^*, N). \tag{3.61c}$$

In this form Z_r^* is dimensionless and so is the expression enclosed by the brackets in (3.61a).

Noting the relations

$$\frac{\partial}{\partial T} = \frac{k}{\varepsilon}\frac{\partial}{\partial T^*}, \quad \text{and} \quad \frac{\partial}{\partial V} = \frac{1}{N\sigma^3}\frac{\partial}{\partial V^*}, \tag{3.62}$$

then it follows directly from the relations (3.22a) and (3.61) that:

$$p^* = -\frac{T^*}{N}\frac{\partial}{\partial V^*}[\ln Z_r^*], \tag{3.63a}$$

$$U^* = \frac{3}{2}\frac{T^*}{N} + \frac{T^{*2}}{N}\frac{\partial}{\partial T}[\ln Z_r^*]. \tag{3.63b}$$

It follows from the expressions in (3.63a) that we can write generally for a closed system of N particles:

$$p^* = p^*(V^*, T^*), \quad \text{and} \quad U^* = U^*(V^*, T^*), \tag{3.64}$$

for all particle interactions characterised by the general pair potential form (3.57), irrespective of the numerical values of the two scale parameters ε and σ. The relations (3.64) follow from the general form of the configurational partition function (3.17), although subject to the pair decomposition of the potential (2.1).

The expressions (3.64) are an expression of the deduction that the pressure and internal energy are each a universal function of the volume and the temperature for a group of substances characterised by interaction potentials of the same form.[12] This is a statement of the law of corresponding states. The thermodynamic properties expressed in dimensionless form of such a group of substances are identical: the measured thermodynamic properties of the various members of the group differ only as regards magnitude relative to the single appropriate scale (3.59).

This dimensionless approach to the empirical study of fluids has great value in practice, but its range of validity is ill defined and it must be used with caution for all but the simplest substances such as the noble gases. One important difficulty is that the interparticle force laws envisaged theoretically are only approximations to those applying in practice, and it is essential to make sure that any group of fluids being discussed collectively do in fact fall under the heading of having essentially the same two-parameter force law, and that no critical features of the force are neglected in such a representation. It is seen, however, that the statistical theory of fluids is able to provide a theoretical basis for the law of corresponding states and is able to offer definite guidance concerning the general conditions of its safe application.

Approaches to fluid thermodynamics other than those considered in this chapter are also available and have value under restricted circumstances. These are considered in Appendix 3.13; see also reference 14.

CHAPTER 4

THEORY OF EQUILIBRIUM SHORT-RANGE ORDER: CLOSURE APPROXIMATION

THE macroscopic thermodynamic functions have been related to appropriate molecular properties by the arguments of the last chapter. For sufficiently low fluid densities it is possible to expand the thermodynamic formulae in powers of the density, although for higher densities this is not possible. Fluid thermodynamics can be calculated by simple differentiation for all densities if the configurational partition function is known explicitly in terms of the fluid volume and temperature. Alternatively, the fluid equilibrium properties can be calculated directly at a given temperature from a knowledge of the appropriate pair distribution, defined by (3.9b). A direct evaluation of the partition function is not possible even for the simplest fluid. The direct evaluation of the pair distribution is scarcely an easier problem but it appears in the theory after the necessary volume and temperature differentiations have been conducted. Consequently, less detailed information is sufficient concerning the pair distribution than is necessary if the partition function itself is to be used. And again, the pair distribution (averaged over an angular dependence if necessary) is to be identified with the experimental radial distribution. It is seen that a close study of the function $g^{(2)}$ introduced in (3.9) is important both for the calculation of fluid thermodynamic properties and for the theoretical elucidation of the fluid structure itself.

The theoretical description of fluid spatial structure can be approached either mathematically by way of the hierarchy of the formulae defining the distribution functions or equivalently by starting from a direct physical study of the direct and indirect contributions to the total particle correlation. This duality is, of course, only one of emphasis and not of principle but the details of the associated mathematics are rather different and this is important in the present unfinished state of the theory. It will prove convenient in our arguments to use this duality to approach the calculation of $g^{(2)}$ in two different ways, and we shall devote two chapters to this development. In the present chapter we approach the calculation of $g^{(2)}$

mathematically starting from the elementary definitions of the lower order particle distributions. A hierarchy of coupled equations results and the calculation of $g^{(2)}$ requires some closure expression to break the chain of equations. This is the superposition approximation, introduced at first primarily as a mathematical closure device but which can be given a physical interpretation and certain restricted defence in its application to fluids. In the next chapter we consider the specification of fluid spatial structure alternatively from the study of the direct and indirect correlations between the particles comprising the fluid. The superposition approximation is not then explicitly involved in the development of the theory. Certain numerical predictions of the arguments are collected in Chapter 6.

4.1. THE SUPERPOSITION APPROXIMATION

The lower order distribution functions are defined for equilibrium conditions by inserting (3.11) into (3.5) and (3.8a). For the interparticle force decomposition (2.1) in terms of the interaction between pairs of particles we derive the expressions for the pair, triplet, and quadruplet functions:

$$n^2 g^{(2)}(\mathbf{r}_{12}) = \frac{1}{(N-2)!} \frac{1}{Z_r} \int \cdots \int \exp\left\{-\sum_{i=1}^{N}\sum_{j>i}^{N} \chi(\mathbf{r}_{ij})\right\} \prod_{k=3}^{N} d\mathbf{r}_k, \qquad (4.1a)$$

$$n^3 g^{(3)}(\mathbf{r}_1, \mathbf{r}_2, \mathbf{r}_3) = \frac{1}{(N-3)!} \frac{1}{Z_r} \int \cdots \int \exp\left\{-\sum_{i=1}^{N}\sum_{j>i}^{N} \chi(\mathbf{r}_{ij})\right\} \prod_{k=4}^{N} d\mathbf{r}_k, \qquad (4.1b)$$

$$n^4 g^{(4)}(\mathbf{r}_1, \mathbf{r}_2, \mathbf{r}_3, \mathbf{r}_4) = \frac{1}{(N-4)!} \frac{1}{Z_r} \int \cdots \int \exp\left\{-\sum_{i=1}^{N}\sum_{j>i}^{N} \chi(\mathbf{r}_{ij})\right\} \prod_{k=5}^{N} d\mathbf{r}_k. \qquad (4.1c)$$

In these equations χ is defined by (3.34). For simple fluids with spherical particles the vectorial character of the distributions is irrelevant so that

$$g^{(2)}(\mathbf{r}_{12}) = g^{(2)}(r_{12}).$$

The situation is more complicated at any boundary region and we explicitly exclude this now.

It follows immediately from the equations (4.1) that the distribution function describing the correlation between a group of $h\,(< N)$ particles is related to that for a group of $(h+1)$ particles by

$$g^{(h)}(\mathbf{r}^h) = \frac{n}{(N-h)} \int g^{(h+1)}(\mathbf{r}^{h+1})\, d\mathbf{r}_{h+1}. \qquad (4.2)$$

It follows, then, that $g^{(2)}$ can be determined if $g^{(3)}$ is known explicitly as function of the configuration of the three particles, $g^{(3)}$ can be determined from a knowledge of the configuration of four particles, and so on. Finally, $g^{(N-1)}$ can be determined from the canonical form of $g^{(N)}$. Although exact, this scheme cannot be used in direct calculations because of the extended and continuous particle interaction for fluids and it is necessary to cut off the procedure after a very few steps. The theory is not yet in a position to give an exact closure procedure and an approximate mathematical procedure must be invoked: this is the superposition approximation first introduced by Kirkwood[1] in connection with the pair function $g^{(2)}$. According to the superposition approximation, the correlation between a group of h particles can be reduced to a superposition of the correlations between smaller constituent particle groupings. For fluids, the total interaction Ψ can be reduced to the sum of the interaction between the constituent particle pairs according to (2.1) so that the superposition statement implies that the correlation between a group of fluid particles can ultimately be reduced to the superposition of the separate correlations between pairs of particles. In the limit of vanishing density (i.e. indefinitely great particle separation), the superposition statement reduces to a trivial exact statement concerning essentially independent particles.

The probability that any chosen three particles (1, 2, 3) of the system will be found in the configuration element $d\mathbf{r}_1\,d\mathbf{r}_2\,d\mathbf{r}_3$ about the configuration point $(\mathbf{r}_1, \mathbf{r}_2, \mathbf{r}_3)$ is $n^{(3)}\,(\mathbf{r}_1, \mathbf{r}_2, \mathbf{r}_3)\,d\mathbf{r}_1\,d\mathbf{r}_2\,d\mathbf{r}_3$. The superposition approximation is that this is to be proportional to the product of the separate pair probabilities, the typical member for the pair of particles (1,2) being $n^{(2)}\,(\mathbf{r}_1, \mathbf{r}_2)d\mathbf{r}_1\,d\mathbf{r}_2$. Consequently, in an obvious notation we write

$$n^{(3)}(1, 2, 3)\,d\mathbf{r}_1\,d\mathbf{r}_2\,d\mathbf{r}_3 = A\big[n^{(2)}(1, 2)\,d\mathbf{r}_1\,d\mathbf{r}_2\big]\big[n^{(2)}(1, 3)\,d\mathbf{r}_1\,d\mathbf{r}_3\big]$$
$$\times\big[n^{(2)}(2, 3)\,d\mathbf{r}_2\,d\mathbf{r}_3\big].$$

The constant of proportionality is to be chosen so that this expression reduces to the appropriate statement when the three separation distances become indefinitely great, i.e.

$$A = \frac{1}{n^{(1)}(1)\,d\mathbf{r}_1\,n^{(1)}(2)\,d\mathbf{r}_2\,n^{(1)}(3)\,d\mathbf{r}_3}.$$

For a fluid in equilibrium, $n^{(1)}(1) = n^{(2)}(2) = n^{(2)}(3) = n$. This means that

$$n^3 n^{(3)}(1, 2, 3) = n^{(2)}(1, 2)\,n^{(2)}(1, 3)\,n^{(2)}(2, 3). \tag{4.3a}$$

The dimensionless correlation functions can be introduced according to the relations (2.26), (2.27), and (2.28), i.e.

$$n^{(3)}(1, 2, 3) = n^3 g^{(3)}(1, 2, 3), \quad \text{and} \quad n^{(2)}(1, 2) = n^2 g^{(2)}(1, 2).$$

The superposition approximation then becomes:

$$g^{(3)}(1, 2, 3) = g^{(2)}(1, 2) \, g^{(2)}(1, 3) \, g^{(2)}(2, 3). \tag{4.3b}$$

This statement of the form of $g^{(3)}$ in terms of $g^{(2)}$ will be called the Kirkwood superposition approximation. It is a special case of a more general statement which will be considered later. According to this statement, the correlation between three particles in interaction is to be replaced by the correlations between the constituent particle pairs taken separately. Expressed alternatively, the correlation between any pair of particles is to be unaffected by the presence of a third particle, indirect correlation effects being assumed to be virtually zero.

The relation (4.3) is clearly true in the limit where all the separation distances are very great, for then the influence of one particle on another is negligible. The relation is also clearly true when any two of the triplet of particles are close together but the third is a very great distance away. For now the interaction between the pair is not influenced by the presence of the third, which is one interpretation of the assumption (4.3). It is now asserted, according to (4.3), that the same conditions apply even when all three particles are close together, such as is considered to be the case in a liquid. This is a more drastic assumption than when no more than two particles are close together. The expression (4.3) (and the more general later statement (4.11) but with S_h set equal to unity) can be viewed as a statement of self-consistency in calculation. In this respect the implied assumption is less drastic than expressing the triplet distribution in terms of those for single particles.

The mathematical approximation (4.3) can be expressed as a statement about the potential of the mean force for a particle pair Φ_2, and for a particle triplet Φ_3. Remembering the earlier equation (1.14) we write in an obvious notation:

$$\Phi_2(i, j) = -kT \ln g^{(2)}(i, j), \tag{4.4a}$$

$$\Phi_3(i, j, k) = -kT \ln g^{(3)}(i, j, k). \tag{4.4b}$$

Consequently the Kirkwood assumption (4.3) can be written as a relation between the mean potential between three and two particles:

$$\Phi(1, 2, 3) = \Phi(1, 2) + \Phi(1, 3) + \Phi(2, 3). \tag{4.5}$$

Apparently, the mean force for a particle triplet is to be equated to the sum of the mean forces for the comprising particle pairs.

An exact statement about the mean potentials is

$$\Phi(1, 2, 3) = \Phi(1, 2) + \Phi(1, 3) + \Phi(2, 3) + W_3(1, 2, 3), \tag{4.6}$$

where $W_3(1, 2, 3)$ is a triplet indirect correlation for the mean force. The corresponding relation between the distribution functions which replaces (4.3) is:

$$g^{(3)}(1, 2, 3) = g^{(2)}(1, 2)\, g^{(2)}(1, 3)\, g^{(2)}\, (2, 3)\, S_3(1, 2, 3), \qquad (4.7)$$

where

$$S_3(1, 2, 3) = \exp \left\{ -\frac{W_3(1, 2, 3)}{kT} \right\}. \qquad (4.8)$$

The Kirkwood superposition approximation then amounts to setting W_3 equal to zero in (4.6). Modifications of the approximation (4.3) follow from the inclusion of W_3 as some function whose form is deduced alternatively: these considerations will be postponed until later in this chapter.[2]

The superposition statement can be applied to more than three particles although this extension is not necessarily uniquely achieved in the absence of auxiliary arguments. As a general statement we have for a group of $h(< N)$ particles:

$$\Phi_h(1, 2, 3, \ldots h) = -kT \ln g^{(h)}(1, 2, 3, \ldots h), \qquad (4.9)$$

so that the problem is that of the appropriate decomposition of Φ_h. Various possibilities present themselves. For instance, Φ_h can be expressed as the sum of the comprising functions Φ_{h-1}, so that

$$\Phi_h(1, 2, 3, \ldots h) = \sum_{\substack{\text{all } (h-1) \\ \text{in } h}} \Phi_{h-1}(1, 2, 3, \ldots h-1) + W_h(1, 2, 3, \ldots h).$$

$$(4.10)$$

This leads to a relation between the distribution functions of the form (using an obvious notation):

$$g^{(h)}(1, 2, \ldots h) = \left[\prod_{1 \le i < j \le h} g^{(h-1)}(i, j \ldots) \right] S_h(1, 2, \ldots h). \qquad (4.11)$$

This expression is the prototype of a hierarchy and ultimately $g^{(h)}$ can be expressed as the product of the corresponding $g^{(2)}$ functions multiplied by a composite indirect correlation function. The superposition approximation then is associated with details of taking approximate account of the indirect correlation. The indirect correlation functions must all satisfy the condition at indefinitely large separation distance:

$$S_h(r^h) \to 1, \quad \text{as} \quad |r_i - r_j| \to 0. \qquad (4.11\,a)$$

This condition is always assumed to hold in what follows.

For four particles we can replace the approximation (4.3) for the triplet by the expression:

$$g^{(4)}(1, 2, 3, 4) = g^{(3)}(1, 2, 3)\, g^{(3)}(1, 2, 4)\, g^{(2)}(2, 3, 4)\, g^{(3)}(1, 3, 4)\, S_4(1, 2, 3, 4).$$

$$(4.12)$$

The requirements of normalisation for $g^{(4)}$ can be accounted for explicitly, using arguments entirely analogous to those leading to equation (4.3a), by introducing a new function S_{14} according to

$$S_{14} = \left[\prod_{i>j=1}^{4} g^{(2)}(i,j) \right] S_4. \qquad (4.13a)$$

The elementary approximation is to set $S_{14} = 1$, but there are other possibilities.

For instance, we can assume

$$g^{(4)}(1, 2, 3, 4) = g^{(3)}(1, 2, 3) \prod_{j=1}^{4} g^{(2)}(j, 4), \qquad [(4.14a)$$

so that using (4.3) we have

$$g^{(4)}(1, 2, 3, 4) = \prod_{1 \leq i < j \leq 4} g^{(2)}(i, j), \qquad (4.14b)$$

where we have also set $S_3 = 1$. This expression follows from (4.13) by making an appropriate choice of S_{14}.

The expression for $g^{(h)}$ should be such as to treat all particles equally, that is the expression should be symmetric with respect to the constituent particles. This is true of both (4.13) and (4.14b) for $g^{(4)}$, although (4.14a) treats particle 4 differently from the other three. We will consider the superposition approximation further, later in the chapter.

The present chapter is concerned with the application of the superposition approximation to the calculation of the distribution of fluid particles in space. Numerical consequences of the theory are considered in Chapter 6.

4.2. DIFFERENTIAL EQUATIONS FOR THE PAIR DISTRIBUTION

The superposition approximation cannot usefully be inserted directly into the relation (4.2) unless the indirect correlation is known. For consider the case $h = 2$, and insert (4.7) into this form of the equation. The result is:

$$1 = \frac{1}{V} \int g^{(2)}(1, 3) g^{(2)}(2, 3) S_3(1, 2, 3) \, d\mathbf{r}_3, \qquad (4.15a)$$

which is exact if S_3 is specified exactly. But the specification of S_3 is equivalent to the specification of $g^{(3)}$ and the superposition approximation was introduced to avoid just this problem. The choice $S_3 = 1$, which reduces (4.7) to the original Kirkwood form (4.3), has the merit of mathematical simplicity but reduces (4.15a) to the inconsistent form

$$1 = \frac{1}{V} \int g^{(2)}(1, 3) g^{(2)}(2, 3) \, d\mathbf{r}_3. \qquad (4.15b)$$

The integral here is not generally independent of r_{12} and equal to the fluid volume which is necessary if the equation is to be true.

It is concluded that approximate information about $g^{(h+1)}$ is not generally sufficient for providing adequate information about $g^{(h)}$ directly, using (4.2). In particular, the approximation (4.3) cannot be directly inserted into (4.2) with h set equal to 2. In the absence of exact information about $g^{(h+1)}$ it is necessary to attempt a rearrangement of the theory into a form able to use approximate data for $g^{(h+1)}$ satisfactorily in the elucidation of $g^{(h)}$. It has been found useful in the past to convert the integral expression (4.2) into an integro-differential equation for this purpose.

The reason for this may be seen as follows. The integral expressions such as (4.1) and (4.2) describe the spatial distribution of particles in terms of the controlling interparticle forces. The relation between the neighbouring particle positions is fairly critically dependent upon the characteristics of the force (see Chapter 6). On the other hand, once the distribution of particles in space is established, the interparticle forces will be less effective in controlling small displacements about the mean particle position than in controlling the mean position itself. The superposition approximation explicitly neglects certain (indirect) effects of the particle interaction: it can be expected, then, that the superposition approximation may prove valuable in treating the effect of elementary changes on the correlation between the particles of a group even though it is not valuable in the deduction of the relative particle positions themselves.

We therefore construct integro-differential equations by considering the effect on the h-th order distribution function of an elementary displacement of one of the constituent particles. For the pair distribution, we seek the effect on $g^{(2)}$ of an elementary movement of one of the pair of particles, say particle 1. The important mathematical simplification introduced by the superposition approximation is, therefore, made possible by rearranging the formulae of theory into a form where the interparticle force is less dominant in controlling the physically acceptable solutions of the equations.

(a) *Born–Green–Yvon Equation (BGY)*

We base our discussion on the canonical distribution although the grand canonical form could equally well be the starting point. Consider the general case of a sub-group of $h (< N)$ particles: eventually we will be interested in the case $h = 2$. The h-th order distribution $g^{(h)}$ is defined by

$$n^h g^{(h)}(\mathbf{r}^h) = \frac{1}{(N-h)!} \frac{1}{Z_r} \int \cdots \int \exp\left\{-\sum_{i=1}^{N}\sum_{j>1}^{N} \chi(\mathbf{r}_{ij})\right\} d\mathbf{r}^{N-h}, \quad (4.16)$$

where

$$d\mathbf{r}^{N-h} = d\mathbf{r}_{h+1}\, d\mathbf{r}_{h+2} \cdots d\mathbf{r}_N.$$

Differentiation with respect to the position of particle 1 gives the equation

$$n^h \frac{\partial g^{(h)}}{\partial \mathbf{r}_1} = \frac{1}{(N-h)!} \frac{1}{Z_r} \int \cdots \int \left[-\frac{\partial}{\partial \mathbf{r}_1} \sum_{j>1}^{N} \chi(\mathbf{r}_{ij})\, \exp\left\{-\sum\sum\chi(\mathbf{r}_{ij})\right\}\right] d\mathbf{r}^{N-h}.$$
$$(4.17)$$

This is simplified in form by introducing the $(h+1)$-th order distribution on the right hand side with the result:

$$\frac{\partial g^{(h)}}{\partial \mathbf{r}_1} = -\frac{\partial}{\partial \mathbf{r}_1}\left[\sum_{j=2}^{h} \chi(\mathbf{r}_{ij})\right] g^{(h)} - \frac{n}{(N-h)} \int g^{(h+1)} \frac{\partial \chi(\mathbf{r}_{1,h+1})}{\partial \mathbf{r}_1}\, d\mathbf{r}_{h+1}. \quad (4.18)$$

This is the general vector equation relating the gradient of $g^{(h)}$ to the functions $g^{(h)}$ and $g^{(h+1)}$. If $g^{(h+1)}$ is known as a function of $g^{(h)}$ then (4.18) is an integro-differential equation with the single unknown function $g^{(h)}$. Equation (4.18) is the representative of a hierarchy of equations obtained by letting h take all possible values. For the case of a particle pair we set $h = 2$ and (4.18) becomes

$$\frac{\partial g^{(2)}(\mathbf{r}_{12})}{\partial \mathbf{r}_1} = -\left[\frac{\partial \chi(\mathbf{r}_{12})}{\partial \mathbf{r}_1}\right] g^{(2)}(\mathbf{r}_{12}) - \frac{n}{\left(1-\dfrac{2}{N}\right)} \int \frac{\partial \chi(\mathbf{r}_{13})}{\partial \mathbf{r}_1} g^{(3)}(\mathbf{r}_{12}, \mathbf{r}_{13}, \mathbf{r}_{23})\, d\mathbf{r}_3.$$
$$(4.19)$$

For spherical particles appropriate to a simple fluid these formulae can be written more simply. Remembering that N is very large, (4.19) becomes:

$$\frac{\partial g^{(2)}(r_{12})}{\partial r_{12}} + \frac{\partial \chi(r_{12})}{\partial r_{12}} g^{(2)}(r_{12}) = -n \int \frac{\partial \chi(r_{13})}{\partial r_{13}} g^{(3)}(r_{12}, r_{13}, r_{23})\, d\mathbf{r}_3. \quad (4.20)$$

On the left hand side of this equation, particle 2 has been chosen as origin of coordinates, while for the separate problem of evaluating the integral on the right hand side, particle 3 is chosen as origin of coordinates. Division throughout (4.20) by the function $g^{(2)}(r_{12})$ leads to the alternative form:

$$\frac{\partial}{\partial r_{12}}\left[\ln g^{(2)}(r_{12}) + \chi(r_{12})\right] = -n \int \frac{\partial \chi(r_{13})}{\partial r_{13}} \frac{g^{(3)}(r_{12}, r_{13}, r_{23})}{g^{(2)}(r_{12})} 4\pi r_{13}^2\, dr_{13}.$$
$$(4.21)$$

The equations set down so far are exact within the validity of decomposition (2.1) of the total interaction potential into pair contributions.

In the absence of detailed information about $g^{(3)}$, the remaining equations of the hierarchy (4.18) are not to be invoked: instead, the superposition approximation (4.3) is introduced. The resulting equation is

$$\frac{\partial g^{(2)}(r_{12})}{\partial r_{12}} + \frac{\partial \chi(r_{12})}{\partial r_{12}} g^{(2)}(r_{12}) =$$

$$- n g^{(2)}(r_{12}) \int \frac{\partial \chi(r_{13})}{\partial r_{13}} g^{(2)}(r_{13}) g^{(2)}(r_{23}) 4\pi r_{13}^2 \, dr_{13}, \qquad (4.22a)$$

which is a non-linear integro-differential equation. In the alternative form corresponding to (4.21), the equation (4.22a) is

$$\frac{\partial}{\partial r_{12}} [\ln g^{(2)}(r_{12}) + \chi(r_{12})] = -n \int \frac{\partial \chi(r_{13})}{\partial r_{13}} g^{(2)}(r_{13}) g^{(2)}(r_{23}) 4\pi r_{13}^2 \, dr_{13}.$$

$$(4.22b)$$

An alternative form of this equation is also useful for later discussion in Chapter 5, viz:

$$\frac{\partial}{\partial r_{12}} [\ln y(r_{12})] = -n \int E(1, 2, 3) 4\pi r_{13}^2 \, dr_{13}, \qquad (4.22c)$$

where

$$y(r) = g^{(2)}(r) \exp \{\chi(r)\}, \qquad (4.22d)$$

$$E(1, 2, 3) = \frac{\partial \chi(r_{13})}{\partial r_{13}} g^{(2)}(r_{13}) g^{(2)}(r_{23}). \qquad (4.22e)$$

The solutions of (4.22) of interest for the description of fluid properties are those showing short-range order. Thus $g^{(2)}$ derived from (4.22) is to satisfy the requirement that it become unity at large separation distances, i.e.

$$g^{(2)}(r) \to 1, \quad \text{as} \quad r \to \infty. \qquad (4.22f)$$

This is the particular case of the general requirement for the group of h particles:

$$g^{(h)}(r^h) \to 1 \quad \text{as} \quad |r_i - r_j| \to \infty \qquad (4.22g)$$

for all particles. In addition, the particle impenetrability requires that the pair distribution should vanish as the relative separation of all the h particles each approach zero. The equation (4.22) was derived[3] independently by Born and Green, by Yvon, and by Bogoliubov. It is most often called the Born–Green–Yvon equation. Bogoliubov treated it also in the form (4.20) under special circumstances that we will consider in section 4.3.

The equation (4.18) is open to an important physical interpretation which gives certain information about liquid structure through the potential of the mean force for a subgroup of h ($< N$) particles.[4] For, according to the arguments associated with the equation (4.9), the negative gradient of Φ_h applying to a group of h particles of the system of N particles gives the average force on one particle of the group for the particular fixed locations of the remaining particles of the subgroup. Explicitly, the mean force on the particle at the location $\mathbf{r}_1$ is

$$-\frac{\partial}{\partial \mathbf{r}_1}\Phi_h(\mathbf{r}^h) = kT\frac{\partial}{\partial \mathbf{r}_1}\left[\ln g^{(h)}(\mathbf{r}^h)\right] = kT\frac{1}{g^{(h)}}\frac{\partial g^{(h)}}{\partial \mathbf{r}_1}.$$

Consequently, for sufficiently large N

$$-\frac{\partial \Phi_h}{\partial \mathbf{r}_1} = -kT\frac{\partial X(\mathbf{r}^h)}{\partial \mathbf{r}_1} - nkT\int \frac{\partial \chi(\mathbf{r}_{1,h+1})}{\partial \mathbf{r}_1}\frac{g^{(h+1)}(\mathbf{r}^{h+1})}{g^{(h)}(\mathbf{r}^h)}\,d\mathbf{r}_{h+1}.$$

In this way the potential of the mean force for a member of the subgroup of particles is related to the distribution of the remaining particles of the system. In particular, for the pair distribution, equation (4.21) is to be interpreted physically by writing it alternatively:

$$-\frac{\partial \chi(\mathbf{r}_{12})}{\partial \mathbf{r}_{12}} - n\int \frac{\partial \chi(\mathbf{r}_{13})}{\partial \mathbf{r}_{13}}\frac{g^{(3)}(\mathbf{r}_{12},\mathbf{r}_{13},\mathbf{r}_{23})}{g^{(2)}(\mathbf{r}_{12})}\,d\mathbf{r}_{13}$$

$$= \frac{\partial}{\partial \mathbf{r}_{12}}\ln g^{(2)}(\mathbf{r}_{12}) = -\frac{1}{kT}\frac{\partial \Phi_2}{\partial \mathbf{r}_{12}}. \qquad (4.22\mathrm{h})$$

The right hand side of this equation is the mean force on the particle at $\mathbf{r}_1$ divided by kT: the left hand side is the sum of two contributions, one describing direct interaction with the second particle of the pair, and the other describing the interaction with the remaining particles. In the notation of the previous equation (1.15):

$$\langle \mathbf{F}_1 \rangle = -\frac{\partial \psi(\mathbf{r}_{12})}{\partial \mathbf{r}_{12}} - n\int \frac{\partial \psi(\mathbf{r}_{13})}{\partial \mathbf{r}_{13}}\frac{g^{(3)}(\mathbf{r}_{12},\mathbf{r}_{13},\mathbf{r}_{23})}{g^{(2)}(\mathbf{r}_{12})}\,d\mathbf{r}_3,$$

where the actual potential ψ has replaced the reduced potential χ according to the previous equation (3.34).

(b) The Kirkwood Equation (K)

The Born–Green–Yvon equation was derived by considering the effect of the elementary displacement of one particle of a group on the collective correlations of the group. In effect we change the coupling between one chosen particle and the remainder by the movement. This can be achieved more directly by expanding the total potential in terms of the pair potential function but in such a way that the actual coupling between one chosen particle (say particle 1) and the remainder can be varied continuously explicitly from the actual value corresponding to the real fluid and zero. For this purpose, introduce a coupling factor ξ, with $0 \le \xi \le 1$, and expand the total potential in the form

$$X(\mathbf{r}^N) = \xi \sum_{j=2}^{N} \chi(\mathbf{r}_{1j}) + \sum_{i=2}^{N} \sum_{j>i}^{N} \chi(\mathbf{r}_{ij}). \tag{4.23}$$

When $\xi = 0$ there is no coupling; when $\xi = 1$ the coupling is complete. Partial coupling with particle 1 can be varied by varying the parameter ξ. The effect on $g^{(2)}$ of varying the coupling with particle 1 is obtained from (4.16) by differentiation with respect to ξ. Remembering that $g^{(2)}(r, \xi)$ approaches unity as $\xi = 0$ and also as $r \to \infty$ there results the equation:

$$\frac{\partial}{\partial \xi} \ln g^{(2)}(\mathbf{r}_{12}, \xi) = -\chi(\mathbf{r}_{12}) g^{(2)}(\mathbf{r}_{12}, \xi) - n \int \chi(\mathbf{r}_{13}) T(1, 2, 3) \, d\mathbf{r}_3, \tag{4.24a}$$

where

$$T(1, 2, 3) = \left[\frac{g^{(3)}(\mathbf{r}_{12}, \mathbf{r}_{13}, \mathbf{r}_{23})}{g^{(2)}(\mathbf{r}_{12}, \xi)} - 1 \right] g^{(2)}(\mathbf{r}_{12}, \xi). \tag{4.24b}$$

We next insert the superposition approximation (4.3) and integrate with respect to ξ to obtain finally for spherical particles:

$$\ln g^{(2)}(\mathbf{r}_{12}, \xi) = -\xi \chi(\mathbf{r}_{12}) - n \int_0^{\xi} \int \chi(\mathbf{r}_{13}) g^{(2)}(\mathbf{r}_{13}, \xi)$$
$$\times [g^{(2)}(\mathbf{r}_{23}) - 1] 4\pi r_{13} \, d r_{13} \, d\xi. \tag{4.25}$$

Interest is with solutions of (4.25) for $\xi = 1$, subject also to the spatial conditions (4.22f) applying to large particle separation. This equation was derived by Kirkwood and Boggs[5] and is equivalent to the Born–Green–Yvon equation (4.22b). The two equations are completely equivalent until the superposition approximation is involved: but they differ in the way that this approximation is introduced. This can be seen as follows.

First write the Born–Green–Yvon equation (4.22) in terms of the coupling parameter:

$$\frac{\partial}{\partial r_{12}} \ln g^{(2)}(\mathbf{r}_{12}, \xi) = -\xi \frac{\partial \chi(r_{12})}{\partial r_{12}} - n\xi \int \frac{\partial \chi(r_{13})}{\partial r_{13}} g^{(2)}(r_{13}, \xi) g^{(2)}(r_{23}) 4\pi r_{13}^2 \, dr_{13}, \tag{4.26a}$$

and next differentiate the Kirkwood equation with respect to $\mathbf{r}_1$:

$$\frac{\partial}{\partial \mathbf{r}_{12}} \ln g^{(2)}(\mathbf{r}_{12}, \xi) = -\xi \frac{\partial \chi(r_{12})}{\partial r_{12}} - n \int_0^{\xi} \int \frac{\partial}{\partial r_{13}} [\chi(\mathbf{r}_{13}) g^{(2)}(\mathbf{r}_{13}, \xi)]$$
$$\times g^{(2)}(\mathbf{r}_{23}) \, d r_{13} \, d\xi, \tag{4.26b}$$

since

$$\frac{\partial}{\partial \mathbf{r}_{13}} \int \chi(\mathbf{r}_{13}) g^{(2)}(\mathbf{r}_{13}, \xi) \, 4\pi r_{13} \, d r_{13} = 0. \tag{4.26c}$$

Comparison between (4.26a) and (4.26b) shows that the later equation contains the non-vanishing term:

$$n \int_0^\xi \int \chi(\mathbf{r}_{13}) \frac{\partial g^{(2)}(\mathbf{r}_{13}, \xi)}{\partial \mathbf{r}_{13}} g^{(2)}(\mathbf{r}_{23}) 4\pi r_{13}^2 \, d r_{13} \, d\xi,$$

which does not appear in the former equation (4.26a). The two equations are therefore different because of this term. Numerical solutions of the Kirkwood equation will be considered in Chapter 6.

(c) Cole Equations

The Born, Green, Yvon and Kirkwood equations describe $g^{(2)}$ as function of the separation distance in terms of the triplet function alone. A more precise description of fluid structure can be expected to result from the inclusion of distributions of order higher than the triplet, and an equation can readily be constructed which involves also the quadruplet distribution. The Born–Green–Yvon equation is obtained by differentiating (4.1a) once with respect to changes in the position of particle 1. In this way $g^{(3)}$ is introduced: further distributions are introduced by further differentiation, successively one more for each additional differentiation. Cole[6] has given a second-order equation which shows the principle and we consider this now.

We start with the general expression (4.16) and differentiate twice with respect to $\mathbf{r}_1$. This gives the expression:

$$\frac{\partial^2}{\partial \mathbf{r}_1^2} g^{(h)}(\mathbf{r}^h) = \sum_{j=2}^{N} \left[\frac{\partial^2}{\partial \mathbf{r}_1^2} \chi(\mathbf{r}_{ij}) + \left(\frac{\partial \chi(\mathbf{r}_{ij})}{\partial \mathbf{r}_1} \right) \left(\frac{\partial g^{(h)}(\mathbf{r}^h)}{\partial \mathbf{r}_1} \right) \right]$$

$$+ \int \left[\frac{\partial^2}{\partial \mathbf{r}_1^2} \chi(\mathbf{r}_{1,h+1}) g^{(h+1)}(\mathbf{r}^{h+1}) + \left(\frac{\partial \chi(\mathbf{r}_{1,h+1})}{\partial \mathbf{r}_1} \right) \frac{\partial g^{(h+1)}(\mathbf{r}^{h+1})}{\partial \mathbf{r}_1} \right] dr_{h+1}. \tag{4.27}$$

This is a tensor equation for $g^{(h)}$ in terms of both $g^{(h+1)}$ itself and its gradient. The gradient of $g^{(h+1)}$ can be replaced by $g^{(h+1)}$ and $g^{(h+2)}$ by inserting (4.18), with h replaced by $h+1$, into (4.27). Consequently,

$$\frac{\partial^2 g^{(h)}(\mathbf{r}^h)}{\partial \mathbf{r}_1^2} + A(\mathbf{r}^h) \frac{\partial g^{(h)}(\mathbf{r}^h)}{\partial \mathbf{r}_1} + B(\mathbf{r}^h) g^{(h)}(\mathbf{r}^h) = C(\mathbf{r}^h), \tag{4.28a}$$

where

$$A(\mathbf{r}^h) = 2 \sum_{j=2}^{h} \frac{\partial \chi(\mathbf{r}_{1j})}{\partial \mathbf{r}_1}, \tag{4.28b}$$

$$B(\mathbf{r}^h) = \sum_{j=1}^{h} \frac{|\partial^2 \chi(\mathbf{r}_{ij})}{\partial \mathbf{r}_1^2} + \left(\sum_{j=2}^{h} \frac{\partial \chi(\mathbf{r}_{ij})}{\partial \mathbf{r}_1} \right)^2 \equiv \sum_{j=1}^{h} B(1, j), \tag{4.28c}$$

$$C(\mathbf{r}^h) = C_1(\mathbf{r}^h) + C_2(\mathbf{r}^h), \tag{4.28d}$$

with

$$C_1(\mathbf{r}^h) = -n \int B(1, h+1) g^{(h+1)}(\mathbf{r}^{h+1}) \, d\mathbf{r}_{h+1},$$

$$C_2(\mathbf{r}^h) = -n^2 \int \frac{\partial \chi(\mathbf{r}_{1, h+1})}{\partial \mathbf{r}_1} \frac{\partial \chi(\mathbf{r}_{1, h+2})}{\partial \mathbf{r}_1} g^{(h+2)}(\mathbf{r}^{h+2}) \, d\mathbf{r}_{h+1} \, d\mathbf{r}_{h+2}. \tag{4.28e}$$

Discussion of $g^{(2)}$ is to proceed by setting $h = 2$ in the expressions (4.28). A knowledge of $g^{(2)}$ then requires also a knowledge of the two functions $g^{(3)}$ and $g^{(4)}$. For this purpose we invoke the superposition approximation for both distributions $g^{(3)}$ and $g^{(4)}$. For $g^{(3)}$ there is no ambiguity: we assume the Kirkwood form (4.3). For $g^{(4)}$ the situation is not so clear cut. One possibility is to invoke the expression (4.12) but with the indirect correlation S_4 set equal to unity. In terms of the pair distribution this implies the validity of equation (4.13a) but with $S_{14} = 1$. Alternatively, we can move directly to pair distribution through equations (4.14a) and (4.14b). The first alternative is presumably the correct choice for reasons of consistency, but the second choice is the simplest of the two. For later reference we write down now the form of equation (4.28) in its application to the pair distribution and using the superposition approximation in the form (4.14):

$$-\frac{\partial^2 g^{(2)}}{\partial \mathbf{r}_1^2} = \left[\left(\frac{\partial \chi(\mathbf{r}_{12})}{\partial \mathbf{r}_1} \right)^2 + \frac{\partial^2 \chi(\mathbf{r}_{12})}{\partial \mathbf{r}_1^2} \right] g^{(2)} + 2 \left(\frac{\partial \chi(\mathbf{r}_{12})}{\partial \mathbf{r}_1} \right) \left(\frac{\partial g^{(2)}(\mathbf{r}_{12})}{\partial \mathbf{r}_1} \right)$$

$$+ n \int \left[\frac{\partial^2 \chi(\mathbf{r}_{13})}{\partial \mathbf{r}_1^2} - \left(\frac{\partial \chi(\mathbf{r}_{13})}{\partial \mathbf{r}_1} \right)^2 \right] g^{(2)}(\mathbf{r}_{13}) g^{(2)}(\mathbf{r}_{23}) \, d\mathbf{r}_3$$

$$- n^2 \int \int \frac{\partial \chi(\mathbf{r}_{13})}{\partial \mathbf{r}_1} \frac{\partial \chi(\mathbf{r}_{14})}{\partial \mathbf{r}_1} g^{(2)}(\mathbf{r}_{13}) g^{(2)}(\mathbf{r}_{23}) g^{(2)}(\mathbf{r}_{14})$$

$$\times g^{(2)}(\mathbf{r}_{24}) g^{(2)}(\mathbf{r}_{34}) \, d\mathbf{r}_3 \, d\mathbf{r}_4. \tag{4.29}$$

This tensor equation is incomparably more difficult to handle than the vector Born–Green–Yvon equation. With the proper superposition approximation the equation (4.28) can be expected to provide better data about the pair distribution than the corresponding first order equation (4.18).

Further distribution functions in the hierarchy of lower order functions can be introduced by continued differentiation of equation (4.27). This could also possibly be associated with other members of the set of equations (4.27). The analytical difficulties in handling such a set of equations, however, are such as to make the scheme interesting only if more simple methods prove insufficient.

(d) *Fisher Equations*

Up to this point the superposition approximation has been used in the form that equates the indirect correlation terms S_j to unity. The adequacy of neglecting the indirect particle correlation has not been assessed, but it can be included into the scheme. One way of achieving this has been described by Fisher.[7]

We start with the general expression (4.18) relating to a chosen group of h particles. But whereas before we considered only the single member of the hierarchy for which $h = 2$, we now consider the two cases $h = 2$ and $h = 3$. The two configurational distribution functions $g^{(3)}$ and $g^{(4)}$ are both involved, so that closure for the calculation involves both the expressions (4.7) and (4.12). Approximation again enters through the specification of the indirect correlation functions S_3 and S_4. Fisher proposes that S_3 should be determined exactly from the theory so that the triplet distribution is included exactly: the quadruplet distribution is introduced into the theory through the approximation $S_{14} = 1$. Written explicitly we assert that

$$\prod_{i,j=1}^{4} g^{(2)}(i,j)\, g^{(4)}(1,2,3,4) = g^{(3)}(1,2,3)\, g^{(3)}(1,2,4)\, g^{(3)}(2,3,4)\, g^{(3)}(1,3,4),$$
$$(4.30a)$$

$$g^{(3)}(1,2,3) = g^{(2)}(1,2)\, g^{(2)}(1,3)\, g^{(2)}(2,3)\, S_3(1,2,3). \qquad (4.30b)$$

Using these formulae in the two equations which result from equation (4.18) with h set successively equal to 2 and 3, we obtain two coupled vector non-linear equations for the two unknown functions $g^{(2)}$ and S_3. These are, for spherical particles:

$$-\frac{\partial \ln g^{(2)}(1,2)}{\partial \mathbf{r}_1} = \frac{\partial \chi(\mathbf{r}_{12})}{\partial \mathbf{r}_1} + n \int \frac{\partial \chi(\mathbf{r}_{13})}{\partial \mathbf{r}_1}\, g^{(2)}(\mathbf{r}_{13}) g^{(2)}(\mathbf{r}_{23})\, S_3(1,2,3)\, d\mathbf{r}_3,$$
$$(4.31a)$$

$$\frac{\partial \ln S_3(1,2,3)}{\partial \mathbf{r}_1} = n \int \frac{\partial \chi(\mathbf{r}_{14})}{\partial \mathbf{r}_1}\, g^{(2)}(\mathbf{r}_{14}) Б(1,2,3,4)\, d\mathbf{r}_4, \qquad (4.31b)$$

and in an obvious notation

$$Б(1,2,3,4) = g^{(2)}(2,4)\, g^{(2)}(3,4)\, S_3(1,2,4)\, S_3(2,3,4)\, S_3(1,3,4)$$
$$-\, g^{(2)}(2,4)\, S_3(1,2,4) - g^{(2)}(3,4)\, S_3(1,3,4). \qquad (4.31c)$$

The two functions $g^{(2)}$ and S_3 must be such as to satisfy the two conditions at large separation distances:

$$g^{(2)}(r_{12}) \to 1$$

$$S_3(r_{12}, r_{13}, r_{23}) \to 1, \tag{4.32}$$

as any r_{ij} becomes indefinitely large, that is as any one of the particles goes off to infinity. These conditions ensure the proper normalisation at large distances.

The great merit of the Fisher analysis over the previous development of the equations for the pair distribution is that the triplet function is introduced exactly, the superposition approximation being necessary only in connection with the correlation between four particles. The Fisher equations are extremely difficult to apply in calculations and they have not so far been used in anything other than the formal aspects of the theory. The method is, however, important and can be extended for use with equations other than the Born–Green–Yvon equation (4.18). Severe mathematical difficulties preclude any easy extension of the method, however, and it will not be considered further here. But it would seem to provide a method of developing a theory of equilibrium fluids able to provide, eventually, accurate quantitative information.

4.3. FORMAL THEORY FOR GASES

The equations derived so far are exact up to the stage where the superposition approximation is introduced. For the development of a theory of fluids based directly on the definitions of the lower order distribution functions it is not possible at the present time to avoid the use of some superposition closure approximation. But for the special range of sufficiently low density, where a (virial) expansion of the thermodynamic quantities in powers of the density (such as the expression (3.53a)) is valid, the theory can be developed systematically without reference to a superposition approximation. The physical reason for this is not difficult to find. The superposition approximation is a mathematical device of restricting the coupling between particle groupings in a way that makes the formulae of the theory tractable in calculations; but for a sufficiently dilute gas the actual interparticle coupling is already weak and no special theoretical problems arise once this physical situation is recognised. In the present section we derive expressions which define the expansion of the particle distribution functions in powers of the density. The coefficients in the hierarchy of expansions are derived successively by an application of the relations derived in the last section but without the superposition approximation. The case of the pair distribution will be treated at the end.[8]

Assume that $g^{(h)}$, applying to a group of $h < N$ particles, can be expanded in the form:

$$g^{(h)}(\mathbf{r}^h) = \sum_{j=0}^{\infty} A_j^{(h)}(\mathbf{r}^h) n^j, \qquad (4.33a)$$

where the coefficients $A_j^{(h)}$ are functions of the particle coordinates ($\mathbf{r}^h$ being the collective configuration vector with components ($\mathbf{r}_1$, $\mathbf{r}_2$, $\mathbf{r}_3$, ... $\mathbf{r}_h$)) and n is the mean number density ($= N/V$). The $A_j^{(h)}$ are to be determined by invoking one of the exact equations for $g^{(h)}$: in the present instance we use the Born–Green–Yvon formalism. The standard normalisation requirement is to apply, viz.

$$g^{(h)}(\mathbf{r}^h) \to 1 \quad \text{for} \quad |\mathbf{r}_i - \mathbf{r}_j| \to \infty. \qquad (4.33b)$$

The case $h = 1$ (single particle distribution) is included in the expansion (4.33a). For this case we have the obvious conditions

$$\underset{V \to \infty}{Lt} \frac{1}{V} \int A_0^{(1)}(\mathbf{r})\, d\mathbf{r} = 1, \qquad (4.33c)$$

$$\underset{V \to \infty}{Lt} \frac{1}{V} \int A_j^{(1)}(\mathbf{r})\, d\mathbf{r} = 0 \quad \text{for} \quad j \ge 1. \qquad (4.33d)$$

We are to determine the coefficients appearing in the expansion (4.33a) by inserting this expansion directly into equation (4.18) and systematically setting to zero the coefficients of the successive powers of n. In this process it is important to notice that the integral term in equation (4.18) will contribute terms one power higher in n than the corresponding contributions of the two remaining terms.

The terms independent of the density in equations (4.17) and (4.33a) provide the relation:

$$\frac{\partial A_0^{(h)}}{\partial \mathbf{r}_1} + A_0^{(h)} \frac{\partial}{\partial \mathbf{r}_1} \left(\sum_{j=2}^{h} \chi(\mathbf{r}_{1j}) \right) = 0. \qquad (4.34a)$$

As solution of this equation write

$$A_0^{(h)}(\mathbf{r}^h) = a_0^{(h)}(\mathbf{r}^h) \exp\left\{ -X(\mathbf{r}^h) \right\}; \qquad (4.34b)$$

this is a solution, provided $a_0^{(h)}$ satisfies the condition

$$\frac{\partial a_0^{(h)}}{\partial \mathbf{r}_1} = 0. \qquad (4.34c)$$

Because $a_0^{(h)}$ must be symmetric in its dependence on all the particles of the group of h particles, if it is not affected by changes in the position of particle 1, then it must also be insensitive to change in the position of any particle. Consequently a_0 must be a constant, and the normalisation condition (4.33b) fixes its value to be unity. Therefore

$$A_0^{(h)}(\mathbf{r}^h) = \exp\left\{-X(\mathbf{r}^h)\right\}. \tag{4.34d}$$

For the lower order distribution functions, we have the set of expressions:

$$A_0^{(1)} = 1, \tag{4.35a}$$

$$A_0^{(2)} = \exp\left\{-\chi(\mathbf{r}_{12})\right\}, \tag{4.35b}$$

$$A_0^{(3)} = \exp\left\{-\sum_{1\leq i<j\leq 3}\chi(\mathbf{r}_{ij})\right\}, \tag{4.35c}$$

$$A_{0\ .}^{(4)} = \exp\left\{-\sum_{1\leq i<j\leq 4}\chi(\mathbf{r}_{ij})\right\}, \tag{4.35d}$$

and so on for all values of h up to N for the system.

The next coefficient in the expansion (4.33a) for the distribution functions is that directly proportional to the density and again follows from equation (4.18): it is

$$\frac{\partial A_1^{(h)}(\mathbf{r}^h)}{\partial \mathbf{r}_1} + A_1^{(h)}(\mathbf{r}^h)\frac{\partial}{\partial \mathbf{r}_1}\sum_{j=2}^{h}\chi(\mathbf{r}_{1j}) - \int \frac{\partial\chi(\mathbf{r}_{1,\,h+1})}{\partial \mathbf{r}_1}A_0^{(h+1)}\,d\mathbf{r}_{h+1} = 0. \tag{4.36a}$$

We next insert the appropriate form of the result (4.34d) into the integral in (4.36a) and notice that

$$\frac{\partial\chi(1,h+1)}{\partial \mathbf{r}_1}\exp\left\{-X(\mathbf{r}^{h+1})\right\}$$

$$= -\exp\left\{-X(\mathbf{r}^h)\right\}\frac{\partial}{\partial \mathbf{r}_1}\left[\exp\left\{-\sum_{i=1}^{h}\chi(i,h+1)\right\}\right]. \tag{4.36b}$$

Introducing the function $\alpha(\mathbf{r}_i, \mathbf{r}_j)$ defined by equation (3.49) into the expression (4.36b) provides the alternative form for this latter expression:

$$\frac{\partial\chi(1,h+1)}{\partial \mathbf{r}_1}\exp\left\{-X(\mathbf{r}^{h+1})\right\} = \exp\left\{-X(\mathbf{r}^h)\right\}\left[\frac{\partial}{\partial \mathbf{r}_1}\left\{\prod_{j=1}^{h}\left(1+\alpha(j,h+1)\right)\right\}\right].$$
$$\tag{4.36c}$$

Because the interparticle force potential is assumed to be of only short range, then the function α itself will decrease rapidly with separation distance. Consequently, the configuration integral having (4.36c) as integrand will be absolutely convergent and we have equation (4.36a) in the alternative form:

$$\frac{\partial A_1^{(h)}}{\partial \mathbf{r}_1} + A_1^{(h)}\frac{\partial X(\mathbf{r}^h)}{\partial \mathbf{r}_1} = \exp\left\{-X(\mathbf{r}^h)\right\}\int\frac{\partial}{\partial \mathbf{r}_1}\prod_{j=1}^{h}\left(1+\alpha(j,h+1)\right)\,d\mathbf{r}_{h+1}. \tag{4.36d}$$

We can now take the final step of rewriting the integral of the gradient of the function in this last equation as the gradient of the integral of the function, so that

$$\frac{\partial A_1^{(h)}}{\partial \mathbf{r}_1} + A_1^{(h)} \frac{\partial X(\mathbf{r}^h)}{\partial \mathbf{r}_1} = \exp\left\{-X(\mathbf{r}^h)\right\} \frac{\partial}{\partial \mathbf{r}_1} \int \prod_{j=1}^{h} \left(1 + \alpha(j, h+1)\right) d\mathbf{r}_{h+1}. \quad (4.36e)$$

As solution of this equation write

$$A_1^{(h)}(\mathbf{r}^h) = a_1^{(h)}(\mathbf{r}^h) \exp\left\{-X(\mathbf{r}^h)\right\}. \quad (4.37)$$

Then the function a_1 must satisfy the equation

$$\frac{\partial a_1^{(h)}}{\partial \mathbf{r}_1} - \frac{\partial}{\partial \mathbf{r}_1} \int \prod_{j=1}^{h} \left[1 + \alpha(j, h+1)\right] d\mathbf{r}_{h+1} = 0. \quad (4.38)$$

This leads to the expression for $a_1^{(h)}$:

$$a_1^{(h)}(\mathbf{r}^h) = \int \prod_{j=1}^{h} \left[1 + \alpha(j, h+1)\right] d\mathbf{r}_{h+1} + \mathcal{A}, \quad (4.39a)$$

where $\mathcal{A}$ is a constant to be chosen in conformity with the condition (4.33b).

To determine $\mathcal{A}$ we require the separate terms in the integrand of $a_1^{(h)}$ to vanish at large separation distances; consequently, $\mathcal{A}$ will have the form of an integral. Explicitly,

$$\mathcal{A} = -\int \left[1 + \sum_{1=j}^{h} \alpha(j, h+1)\right] d\mathbf{r}_{h+1}, \quad (4.39b)$$

and it is easily found that $\dfrac{\partial \mathcal{A}}{\partial \mathbf{r}_1} = 0$. Consequently, we have for $a_1^{(h)}$:

$$a_1^{(h)}(\mathbf{r}^h) = \int \left\{ \prod_{j=1}^{h} \left[1 + \alpha(j, h+1)\right] - \sum_{1=j}^{h} \alpha(j, h+1) - 1 \right\} d\mathbf{r}_{h+1}. \quad (4.40)$$

The coefficient of the term proportional to n^2 in the expansion (4.33a) can be obtained by repeating this procedure, together with the remaining coefficients in the expansion. The formulae are rather complicated and lengthy and we do not write them down now because we shall not need them explicitly in our arguments. Suffice it to recognise that the expansion (4.33a) can be written in the form:

$$g^{(h)}(\mathbf{r}^h) = \exp\left\{-X(\mathbf{r}^h)\right\}[1 + a_1^{(h)}(\mathbf{r}^h)n + \ldots], \quad (4.41a)$$

i.e.

$$g^{(h)}(\mathbf{r}^h) \exp\left\{X(\mathbf{r}^h)\right\} = 1 + \sum_{j \geq 1} a_j^{(h)}(\mathbf{r}^h)n^j. \quad (4.41b)$$

One important point to notice for later use is that the particular combination

$$g^{(h)}(\mathbf{r}^h) \exp\left\{X(\mathbf{r}^h)\right\}$$

plays an important role in the theory.

For the fluid pair distribution we set h equal to 2. In this case,[9] writing $a_j^{(2)}$ simply as a_j for convenience, we have

$$g^{(2)}(r) \exp \{\chi(r)\} = 1 + \sum_{j \geq 1} a_j(r) n^j, \qquad (4.42)$$

where the first coefficient in the expansion, $a_1(r)$, is given by

$$a_1(\mathbf{r}_{12}) = \int \alpha(\mathbf{r}_{23}) \, \alpha(\mathbf{r}_{13}) \, d\mathbf{r}_3. \qquad (4.43)$$

The expansion (4.42) for the pair distribution can be used to obtain an expansion expression for the pressure, and internal energy, in terms of the density. Indeed, such expressions immediately follow from the insertion of (4.42) into the appropriate formulae of Chapter 3. Thus for the pressure, using either (3.38) or (3.46) indifferently we find by this method:

$$p = nkT[1 + Bn + Cn^2 + Dn^3 + \ldots], \qquad (4.44a)$$

where

$$B = -\frac{1}{2V} \int \int \alpha(1,2) \, d\mathbf{r}_1 \, d\mathbf{r}_2, \qquad (4.44b)$$

$$C = -\frac{1}{3V} \int \int \int \alpha(2,3) \, \alpha(1, 3) \, \alpha(1, 2) \, d\mathbf{r}_1 \, d\mathbf{r}_2 \, d\mathbf{r}_3, \qquad (4.44c)$$

$$D = -\frac{1}{8V} \int \int \int \int [\alpha(1, 2) \, \alpha(1, 3) \, \alpha(2, 3) \, \alpha(1, 4) \, \alpha(2, 4) \, \alpha(3, 4)$$
$$+ 6\alpha(1, 2) \, \alpha(2, 3) \, \alpha(1, 3) \, \alpha(1, 4) \, \alpha(3, 4)$$
$$+ 3\alpha(1, 2) \, \alpha(2, 3) \, \alpha(3, 4) \, \alpha(1, 4)] \, d\mathbf{r}_1 \, d\mathbf{r}_2 \, d\mathbf{r}_3 \, d\mathbf{r}_4 \qquad (4.44d)$$

It will be seen that the integrations become more complicated with each new member of the series, due to combinatorial characteristics of the particle groupings. Corresponding expressions can be set down for the various coefficients in the density expansion of the internal energy, and other thermodynamic functions.

One thing is important to notice here. The expressions (4.44) for the virial coefficients are arrived at whether the pressure equation (3.38) or the compressibility equation (3.46b) is invoked: this is a manifestation of the internal consistency in the theory associated with the use of the expansion (4.42) which is exact. Inexact information about $g^{(2)}$ will still lead to a virial series but the numerical values for the virial coefficients derived from the virial pressure equation (3.38) will generally differ from those derived from the compressibility pressure equations (3.46), the seriousness of the discrepancy increasing as the information about $g^{(2)}$ becomes less exact. The calculation of the virial coefficients from the two pressure equations has proved to be a valuable method of testing the accuracy of approximation about the fluid pair distribution (see Chapter 6).

4.4. USE OF THE SUPERPOSITION APPROXIMATION

The arguments of the last section apply when a density expansion is valid, but this is not the case for dense gases and liquids. The development of a general theory of simple fluids is, therefore, to involve more general arguments than those leading to the expression (4.42) although the resulting general information about the pair distribution must reduce to the form (4.42) in the limit of low density.

We have seen before, the need to introduce approximations into the general statistical theory of fluids and in particular the superposition approximation was proposed in section 4.1. In the present section the use of this approximation is considered further. The method of application of the approximation will depend upon the density of the fluid under consideration. This means in particular that the indirect correlation function S_{h} of equation (4.11) will be introduced approximately.

(a) *Liquid Densities*

For liquid densities there is, at the present time and on the present approach, no way of using an exact superposition statement. The method proposed by Fisher, and considered in section 4.2(d), involves approximation in connection with the quadruplet function but not in connection with the triplet function. The method can be extended to involve approximation first in connection with still higher order functions, but the method has limitations in practice. Indeed, approximation is at present necessary in connection with the triplet function, and for liquids it is necessary to invoke the superposition approximation in the form (4.3). This means that the equations (4.22), (4.25), or (4.29) are to be used directly at liquid densities. Future work must be devoted to improving the superposition approximation.

(b) *Dilute Gas*

The situation is rather better if the density is sufficiently low for a density expansion like (4.42) to be valid. In this case, quantities like the virial coefficients for the pressure can be derived exactly as function of the interparticle force, such as in the formulae (4.44). Although the lower order coefficients can be expressed exactly in this way, the associated formulae are so complicated as to have little practical use for numerical calculations if any realistic interparticle force potential is to be used. For practical reasons, therefore, alternative methods of calculation are necessary. But in ıny case the various formulae derived in the present chapter should be ıpplicable at low densities, and so can lead to calculated virial coefficients :apable of comparison with exact, or at least more accurate, data.

According to the arguments of section 4.3, the triplet function can be :xpanded directly in terms of powers of the density in this case and the 'ormulae of the present section applied exactly as far as the lower powers. By determining the function

$$K = \frac{g^{(3)}(1, 2, 3)}{g^{(2)}(1, 2)g^{(2)}(1, 3)g^{(2)}(2, 3),}, \tag{4.45}$$

ı direct test of the superposition approximation becomes possible in the 'orm

$$K = 1 + Y_1 n + Y_2 n^2 + \ldots, \tag{4.46}$$

where the coefficients Y_j are functions of the triplet of particle relative separations and also functions of the interparticle force and the temperature. The function K is now to be identified with the general function S_3 of the expression (4.7). For the present case, the arguments of section 4.3 lead to the following exact formula for Y_1:

$$Y_1 = Y_{11} - Y_{12}, \tag{4.47a}$$

where

$$Y_{11} = \int dr_4 \{ \alpha(1, 4)\alpha(2, 4)\alpha(3, 4) + \alpha(1, 4)\alpha(2, 4) $$
$$+ \alpha(1, 4)\alpha(3, 4) + \alpha(2, 4)\alpha(3, 4) \}, \tag{4.47b}$$

and

$$Y_{12} = \int dr_3 \{ 3\alpha(1, 3) \, \alpha(2, 3) \}. \tag{4.47c}$$

The expressions for the higher coefficients are extremely complicated and will not be written down here. The difficulties to be expected in any direct evaluation of these expressions for realistic potential functions make it useful to contemplate the use of approximate information about the functions Y_j in the expansion (4.46). It is therefore useful to have expressions for the coefficients a_j in the expansion (4.42) for the pair function $g^{(2)}$, and we give some formulae now.

Later discussion (in Chapter 6) will centre around the Born–Green–Yvon equation (4.22) and we consider this equation alone now. To calculate the coefficients in the expansion (4.42) for the pair distribution, insert (4.42) and (4.46) into (4.20). The result is an equation containing ascending powers of n. Equating the coefficient of each power of n separately to zero, we arrive at the expressions for the coefficients a_j in (4.42). For particles showing spherical symmetry, and using the conventional notation $r \equiv r_{12}$, $s \equiv r_{13}$, $t \equiv r_{23}$, we are led to the following expressions[10] for a_j as far as the cube power of n:

$$a_1(r) = -\frac{\pi}{r} \int_0^\infty \int_{-s}^s (t+r)(s^2-t^2)\alpha(t+r)\,dt\,\alpha'(s)\,ds \qquad (4.48)$$

$$a_2(r) = a_2^K(r) + \Xi_2(r), \qquad (4.49a)$$

where

$$a_2^K(r) = \frac{1}{2}a_1^2(r) - \frac{\pi}{r} \int_0^\infty \int_{-s}^s (t+r)(s^2-t^2)a_1(t+r)[\alpha(t+r)+1]\,dt\alpha'(s)\,ds,$$

$$- \frac{\pi}{r} \int_0^\infty \int_{-s}^s (t+r)(s^2-t^2)\,\alpha(t+r)\,dt\,a_1(s)\,\alpha'(s)\,ds; \qquad (4.49b)$$

and

$$\Xi_2(r) = -\frac{\pi}{r} \int_0^\infty \int_{-s}^s Y_1(r,s,t)(t+r)(s^2-t^2)\alpha(t+r)\alpha'(s)\,dt\,ds; \qquad (4.49c)$$

$$a_3(r) = a_3^K(r) + \Xi_3(r), \qquad (4.50a)$$

where

$$a_3^K(r) = a_1 a_2^K - \frac{a_1^3}{3} - \frac{\pi}{r} \int_0^\infty \int_{-s}^s (t+r)(s^2-t^2)a_2^K(t+r)\alpha(t+r)\,dt\alpha'(s)\,ds$$

$$- \frac{\pi}{r} \int_0^\infty \int_{-s}^s (t+r)(s^2-t^2)\,a_1(t+r)\alpha(t+r)\,dta_1(s)\alpha'(s)\,ds$$

$$- \frac{\pi}{r} \int_0^\infty \int_{-s}^s (t+r)(s^2-t^2)\alpha(t+r)\,dta_2^K(s)\alpha'(s)\,ds$$

$$- \frac{\pi}{r} \int_0^\infty \int_{-s}^s (t+r)(s^2-t^2)\,a_2^K(t+r)\,dt\alpha'(s)\,ds$$

$$- \frac{\pi}{r} \int_0^\infty \int_{-s}^s (t+r)(s^2-t^2)\,a_1(t+r)\,dt\,a_1(s)\alpha'(s)\,ds, \qquad (4.50b)$$

and

$$\Xi_3(r) = -\frac{\pi}{r} \int_0^\infty \int_{-s}^s Y_1(r,s,t)(t+r)(s^2-t^2)\,a_1(t+r)[\alpha(t+r)+1]\,dt\alpha'(s)\,ds$$

$$- \frac{\pi}{r} \int_0^\infty \int_{-s}^s Y_1(r,s,t)(t+r)(s^2-t^2)\alpha(t+r)\,dta_1(s)\alpha'(s)\,ds$$

$$- \frac{\pi}{r} \int_0^\infty \int_{-s}^s Y_2(r,s,t)(t+r)(s^2-t^2)\alpha(t+r)\,dt\alpha'(s)\,ds; \qquad (4.50c)$$

and so on. It will be seen that only the single coefficient a_1 is independent of the functions Y_j. From the formulae (3.38) for the pressure and (4.42) for the pair function it follows that a knowledge of the coefficient a_1 for a given potential ψ is required to determine the third virial coefficient C but higher coefficients than a_1 are required in the calculation of the fourth and higher functions. The calculation of the second virial coefficient B does not require any knowledge of the coefficients a_j, only a knowledge of the function ψ being necessary. We can conclude, therefore, that the value of a_1 is not affected by superposition considerations and that the Kirkwood superposition approximation (4.3) gives C exactly. Exact information concerning the function K defined in equation (4.45) leads to exact information about the higher virial coefficients because the expressions (4.50) are exact then. Approximate information about the function K will lead to approximate calculated thermodynamic data. This will be considered further in Chapter 6.

It is seen, then, that there is a difference in the practical use of the superposition approximation for liquids on the one hand, and dilute gases on the other, at the present time. The future development of the theory on the lines of the present chapter must be towards the improvement of the closure procedure exemplified by the superposition approximation.[11] This can take the form either of the application of the arguments of section 4.2(d) or of the refined study of the closure procedure at liquid densities.[12] In this way, the theories of liquids and gases are to be joined into a single formulation instead of showing the duality that seems necessary at the present time.

CHAPTER 5

THEORY OF EQUILIBRIUM
SHORT-RANGE ORDER:
TOTAL CORRELATION

IN THE last chapter we approached the problem of calculating the liquid structure by a direct appeal to the lower order distribution functions. The method leads rigorously to a hierarchy of equations but the difficulties arose with the problems of closure. An approximation was introduced, the superposition approximation, for mathematical reasons, and a physical basis was sought for it only after it was certain that the mathematical difficulties had actually been reduced by the approximation. This procedure is defensible on mathematical grounds but is hardly satisfactory from the point of view of physics. In the present chapter we look at the problem of calculating the liquid short-range order afresh but from a different point of view.

The chapter is in two distinct parts. The first part (comprising sections 5.1 and 5.2) is concerned with the calculation of the pair distribution directly by using the concept of the total correlation. Two equations will result (viz. the so-called hypernetted chain equation and the equation of Percus and Yevick) which are different from those derived in the last chapter. The remainder of the chapter is then devoted to the task of synthesising the various equations that are available in an attempt to arrive at a single procedure for the calculation of the pair distribution.

5.1. THE DIRECT AND INDIRECT CORRELATION

The correlation between a pair of particles due to the action of the interparticle force is described by the function $[g^{(2)}(r)-1]$, defined by the symbol $h(r)$ in equation (1.11), i.e.

$$h(r) = g^{(2)}(r)-1. \qquad (5.1)$$

If the interparticle force were inoperative, then $g^{(2)}$ would have the value unity: this is the value for the pair correlation at large distances according to the concept of fluid short-range order. The function $h(r)$ will be called the total correlation function, to distinguish it from the correlation function $g^{(2)}$. Liquid short-range order is described by the condition that $h(r)$ shall become zero for large values of the interparticle distance r.

The total influence of one particle, say particle 1, on a second particle 2 in a collection of $N(> 2)$ interacting particles is the result of two distinct effects, viz. the direct effect of particle 1 on particle 2, and the indirect effect of particle 1 on 2 through the intermediate effect of particle 1 on the other particles 3, 4, ... N with the consequent effect of these particles on particle 2. Thus in the indirect contribution, particle 1 will affect a representative third particle directly, and this effect will in turn be transmitted to the particle 2. The indirect contribution for the total system is the sum of all the separate indirect contributions for particles 3, 4, ... N, averaged over all positions available to these particles in the volume V.

This argument has been used to define a direct correlation function $c(r)$ between two particles, distance r apart, and in the presence of the remaining particles by the expression:

$$h(\mathbf{r}_{12}) = c(\mathbf{r}_{12}) + n \int h(\mathbf{r}_{23}) \, c(\mathbf{r}_{13}) \, d\mathbf{r}_3. \qquad (5.2)$$

The concept of the direct correlation seems first to have been considered by Ornstein and Zernike.[1] It is important to realise that, as introduced here, the direct correlation function has no simple physical meaning for an isolated pair of particles: it must relate to a pair of particles in the presence of the remaining particles of the system. If the direct correlation function is known as function of the separation distance then (5.2) is an integral equation for the function h and so, from equation (5.1), for the pair distribution. The problem of calculating $g^{(2)}(r)$ is now converted to that of calculating the function $c(r)$. The situation is reminiscent of that of the last chapter where the problem of calculating $g^{(2)}$ hinged upon the successful solution of the problem of obtaining knowledge about the triplet function $g^{(3)}$. There it was necessary to use approximate information for $g^{(3)}$: in the present case it is necessary to use approximate information about $c(r)$. Two important approximate forms for $c(r)$ have been proposed so far and these will be considered in turn in a moment.

Before passing on to consider the equations to be derived from equation (5.2), some comment is appropriate. The equation (3.46b) relates the compressibility to the function $h(r)$ directly. By using the expression (5.2), the compressibility equation can be rearranged to include the direct correlation $c(r)$, and is

$$\frac{\partial p}{\partial n}\bigg|_T = kT\left[1 - n \int c(r)r^2 \, dr\right]. \qquad (5.3)$$

It is seen that a knowledge of the direct correlation is sufficient for determining the fluid pressure. If $c(r)$ is specified exactly then equation (5.3) is exact: equations (5.3) and (3.38) then provide two exact expressions for the fluid pressure. The degree of inconsistency between them for any inexact function $c(r)$ can be used as a test of the level of accuracy to be accorded to this inexact function. A direct consequence of these arguments is that $c(r)$ must involve the pair function $g^{(2)}$ directly.

5.2. TWO EQUATIONS FOR THE PAIR DISTRIBUTION

The relation (5.2) has yielded two equations for the pair distribution which have proved valuable in the theory of fluids. These two equations arise from two alternative assumptions about the particle pair direct correlation. The original deduction of these equations involved rather complicated cluster arguments which are summarised in the Appendices. In the present text we use formal definitions of $c(r)$. The cluster deductions are primarily associated with a density expansion but these cannot be expected to apply directly to a liquid. But it can be that cancellation of terms in a high density expansion can fortuitously allow the application to liquid densities of an equation derived primarily for lower densities. This will be considered later in Chapter 6.

(a) *The Hypernetted Chain Equation (HNC)*

The direct pair correlation function is concerned with the direct effect between two chosen particles arising from the action of the interparticle forces. Equations for the pair distribution follow from particular choices of the direct correlation. For gases at low density, arguments involving clusters of particles (see Appendix 5.2) lead to the approximate expression for the pair correlation in terms of the pair distribution:

$$c_H(r) = h(r) - \ln g^{(2)}(r) - \frac{\psi(r)}{kT}, \tag{5.4}$$

where $\psi(r)$ is the actual pair interaction potential. The terms accounted for in deriving the expression (5.4) for gases are likely also to be of controlling importance at higher densities. Consequently, let us assert that the direct correlation function for a particle pair in a liquid is to be given by the expression (5.4). The insertion of (5.4) into (5.2) provides an equation whose solution, subject to the condition (4.22f), is the fluid pair distribution.

The formula (5.4) can be rearranged to show explicitly the function $y(r)$ defined by:

$$y(r) = g^{(2)}(r) \exp \chi(r), \qquad (5.5)$$

met with earlier in the expansion (4.42). Thus,

$$c_H(r) = h(r) - \ln y(r), \qquad (5.6a)$$

or alternatively using $\alpha(r)$ defined by equation (3.49)

$$c_H(r) = \alpha(r)y(r) + [y(r) - 1 - \ln y(r)]. \qquad (5.6b)$$

The insertion of c_H, in any of the forms (5.4) or (5.6), into the relation (5.2) provides an equation for $g^{(2)}$ in terms of the interparticle potential ψ. This is:

$$h(\mathbf{r}_{12}) = h(\mathbf{r}_{12}) - \ln y(\mathbf{r}_{12}) + n \int h(\mathbf{r}_{23})[h(\mathbf{r}_{13}) - \ln y(\mathbf{r}_{13})] \, d\mathbf{r}_3, \qquad (5.7)$$

i.e.

$$\ln y(\mathbf{r}_{12}) = n \int [h(\mathbf{r}_{13}) - \ln y(\mathbf{r}_{13})] h(\mathbf{r}_{23}) \, d\mathbf{r}_3. \qquad (5.7a)$$

Explicitly in terms of $g^{(2)}$:

$$\ln g^{(2)}(\mathbf{r}_{12}) + \chi(\mathbf{r}_{12}) = n \int [g^{(2)}(\mathbf{r}_{13}) - \ln g^{(2)}(\mathbf{r}_{13}) - 1 - \chi(\mathbf{r}_{13})]$$
$$\times [g^{(2)}(\mathbf{r}_{23}) - 1] \, d\mathbf{r}_3. \qquad (5.7b)$$

This is to be solved subject to the boundary condition at large distances (4.22f). The equation (5.7) is called the hypernetted chain equation. The name is hardly appropriate in the present statement of the equation as a simple consequence of the definition (5.4) for $c(r)$ but is descriptive of the original deduction involving diagram considerations (see Appendix 5.2.). Comparison between the equation (5.7b) and the Born–Green–Yvon equation (4.22) is instructive. The gradient of the left hand side of equation (5.7b) is exactly the left hand side of the previous equation (4.22): the gradient of the right hand side of (5.7b) is not identical to the right hand side of (4.22). The difference lies in the form assumed for the superposition approximation used in the latter equation.

By taking the gradient of equation (5.7b) with respect to $\mathbf{r}_1$ we obtain the equation:

$$\frac{\partial y(\mathbf{r}_{12})}{\partial \mathbf{r}_1} = -n \int \frac{\partial \chi(\mathbf{r}_{13})}{\partial \mathbf{r}_1} g^{(2)}(\mathbf{r}_{13}) \, g^{(2)}(\mathbf{r}_{23}) \, d\mathbf{r}_3 + Y(\mathbf{r}_{12}), \qquad (5.7c)$$

where

$$Y(\mathbf{r}_{12}) = n \int \left[\frac{\partial g^{(2)}(\mathbf{r}_{13})}{\partial \mathbf{r}_1} - \frac{\partial}{\partial \mathbf{r}_1} \ln g^{(2)}(\mathbf{r}_{13}) - \frac{\partial \chi(\mathbf{r}_{13})}{\partial \mathbf{r}_1} \right] [g^{(2)}(\mathbf{r}_{23}) - 1] \, d\mathbf{r}_3$$

(5.7d)

$$+ n \int \frac{\partial \chi(\mathbf{r}_{13})}{\partial \mathbf{r}_1} g^{(2)}(\mathbf{r}_{13}) g^{(2)}(\mathbf{r}_{23}) \, d\mathbf{r}_3.$$

The function Y represents the difference between the Born–Green–Yvon and hypernetted chain equations.

The comparison between (5.7c) and (4.22) could be treated as the reason for making the assumption (5.4) about the direct pair correlation function. This form provides an equation directly such that the space gradient of its left hand side is identical to the left hand side of the exact Born–Green–Yvon equation, irrespective of the particular choice of superposition approximation. But this argument is not unique as becomes clear from the form of the Percus–Yevick equation to follow: the derivation in terms of diagrams indicated in Appendix 5.2 is the best alternative substantiation of the form (5.6) for $c(r)$.

The information that (5.7) gives for the pair distribution for different densities is considered in Chapter 6.

(b) The Percus–Yevick Equation (PY)

Other equations for the pair distribution follow from alternative assumptions about the direct correlation $c(r)$. Another important equation arises from the form $c(r)$ deduced as follows.

The equation (5.7) depended, for its deduction, on the subtraction of the interaction between the particle pair in question and the remaining particles from the fluid. Equation (4.42) can be interpreted as expressing the interaction between the particle pair and the remainder; and the expression $y(r) - 1$ is the interaction neglecting that between the pair. Consequently assume for $c(r)$ the expression,[3] written $c_P(r)$,

$$c_P(r) = h(r) - [g^{(2)}(r) \exp \chi(r) - 1] = g^{(2)}(r) \exp \{\chi(r)\} [\exp \{-\chi(r)\} - 1],$$

i.e.

$$c_P(r) = \alpha(r) y(r). \tag{5.8}$$

The insertion of equation (5.8) into the relation (5.2) gives

$$h(\mathbf{r}_{12}) = \alpha(\mathbf{r}_{12}) y(\mathbf{r}_{12}) + n \int h(\mathbf{r}_{23}) \alpha(\mathbf{r}_{13}) y(\mathbf{r}_{13}) \, d\mathbf{r}_3. \tag{5.9}$$

Written in terms of $g^{(2)}$ we have the equation:

$$g^{(2)}(\mathbf{r}_{12}) \exp \chi(\mathbf{r}_{12}) = 1 - n \int [\exp \chi(\mathbf{r}_{13}) - 1] (g^{(2)}(\mathbf{r}_{23}) - 1)$$

$$\times g^{(2)}(\mathbf{r}_{13}) \, d\mathbf{r}_3. \qquad (5.10)$$

This non-linear integral equation was proposed first by Percus and Yevick. The original derivation of the equation involved the use of collective co-ordinates (see Appendix 5.4) and so is presumably concerned with liquid densities. Later (see Appendices 5.2 and 5.4) it was found that the equation can also be derived from an application of diagram techniques, and this would act as a substantiation for the lower range of gas density. It would seem, therefore, that the equation (5.10) can be defended over the full range of fluid density. In this it is better than equation (5.7b) which is associated in its deduction specifically with low fluid density. The equation (5.10) has proved of considerable value in the study of fluids, possibly also including liquid densities. Numerical predictions resulting from its use will be considered in Chapter 6.

The equation (5.10) differs from equation (5.7) in the expression assumed for the direct correlation $c(r)$. The comparison between the expressions (5.6) and (5.8) show that

$$c_H(r) - c_P(r) = y(r) - \ln y(r) - 1. \qquad (5.11)$$

This expression vanishes when the separation distance is large but is not necessarily zero at the distance when the function $\alpha(r)$ vanishes. The direct correlation used in connection with (5.8) does vanish when the pair interaction vanishes because of the presence of the factor $\alpha(r)$. Consequently the direct pair correlation involved with the Percus–Yevick equation has truly the range of the interparticle force, whereas the pair correlation involved with the hypernetted chain equation has a somewhat longer range. This is the essential difference between the two equations.

We can also ask the relation between the Born–Green–Yvon equation (both with and without the superposition approximation) and the Percus–Yevick and hypernetted chain equation. For such a comparison we need to take the gradient of the expression (5.2), assume successively the validity of the relations (5.4) and (5.8), and then compare with the equations (4.22). The gradient of (5.2) with respect to $\mathbf{r}_1$ is

$$\frac{\partial h(\mathbf{r}_{12})}{\partial \mathbf{r}_1} = \frac{\partial c(\mathbf{r}_{12})}{\partial \mathbf{r}_1} + n \int h(\mathbf{r}_{23}) \frac{\partial c(\mathbf{r}_{13})}{\partial \mathbf{r}_1} \, d\mathbf{r}_3. \qquad (5.12)$$

For the Percus–Yevick equation,

$$\frac{\partial c_P(\mathbf{r}_{12})}{\partial \mathbf{r}_1} = \frac{\partial}{\partial \mathbf{r}_1} [\alpha(\mathbf{r}_{12}) y(\mathbf{r}_{12})].$$

But

$$\alpha \frac{\partial y}{\partial \mathbf{r}_1} = \left\{ \frac{\partial g^{(2)}}{\partial \mathbf{r}_1} + g^{(2)} \frac{\partial \chi}{\partial \mathbf{r}_1} \right\} - \exp \chi \left\{ \frac{\partial g^{(2)}}{\partial \mathbf{r}_1} + g^{(2)} \frac{\partial \chi}{\partial \mathbf{r}_1} \right\},$$

$$y \frac{\partial \alpha}{\partial \mathbf{r}_1} = -g^{(2)} \frac{\partial \chi}{\partial \mathbf{r}_1},$$

i.e.

$$\frac{\partial c_P}{\partial \mathbf{r}_1} = \frac{\partial g^{(2)}}{\partial \mathbf{r}_1} - \exp \chi \left\{ \frac{\partial g^{(2)}}{\partial \mathbf{r}_1} + g^{(2)} \frac{\partial \chi}{\partial \mathbf{r}_1} \right\}. \tag{5.13}$$

Inserting (5.13) into (5.12) we have the equation:

$$\frac{\partial}{\partial \mathbf{r}_1} [\ln y(\mathbf{r}_{12})] + n \int \frac{\partial \chi(\mathbf{r}_{13})}{\partial \mathbf{r}_1} g^{(2)}(\mathbf{r}_{13}) g^{(2)}(\mathbf{r}_{23}) \, d\mathbf{r}_3$$

$$= -\frac{\partial}{\partial \mathbf{r}_1} [g^{(2)}(\mathbf{r}_{12}) \chi(\mathbf{r}_{12})] + \frac{\partial y(\mathbf{r}_{12})}{\partial \mathbf{r}_1}$$

$$+ n \int g^{(2)}(\mathbf{r}_{23}) \frac{\partial y(\mathbf{r}_{13})}{\partial \mathbf{r}_1} \, d\mathbf{r}_3$$

$$- n \int g^{(2)}(\mathbf{r}_{23}) \frac{\partial g^{(2)}(\mathbf{r}_{13})}{\partial \mathbf{r}_1} \, d\mathbf{r}_3$$

$$- n \int \frac{\partial \chi(\mathbf{r}_{13})}{\partial \mathbf{r}_1} g^{(2)}(\mathbf{r}_{23}) g^{(2)}(\mathbf{r}_{13}) \, d\mathbf{r}_3$$

$$+ n \int \frac{\partial y(\mathbf{r}_{13})}{\partial \mathbf{r}_1} \, d\mathbf{r}_3 + n \int \frac{\partial g^{(2)}(\mathbf{r}_{13})}{\partial \mathbf{r}_1} \, d\mathbf{r}_3. \tag{5.14}$$

Comparison with the Born–Green–Yvon equation (4.22) shows that the left hand side of equation (5.14) is exactly the Born–Green–Yvon equation under the superposition approximation (4.3). The Born–Green–Yvon and Percus–Yevick equations, therefore, differ by the terms on the right hand side of (5.14). The terms (5.7d) and (5.14) can be absorbed into the theory by some appropriate formulation of a superposition closure procedure. But since this would need to be based on somewhat hypothetical circumstances (the Percus–Yevick and hypernetted chain equations are themselves not exact) we do not pursue any formulation here.

Improvements on the forms (5.4) and (5.8) for the direct correlation can be made by successively modifying the right hand side of (5.11). For gases, $y(r)$ is to be expanded in the form (4.42), and the particular combination

$$y(r) - 1 - \ln y(r)$$

then becomes an expression in the density starting with the quadratic term. Since expression (5.8), regarded as a density expansion, is exact for the two leading terms $c_{P_0} = 1$ and $c_{P_1} = \alpha(r)a_1(r)$ (see Appendix 5.3), then from the form of (5.11) it follows that c_H is also exact up to the linear power of the density. In terms of equation (5.3), this means that c_P and c_H each give the second and third virial coefficients correctly but give incorrect data beyond this. Some preliminary attempts have been made to obtain at least consistency within the theory: see, for example, Chapter 6, section 2(e), and Appendix 6.45. For application to liquid densities, correction terms must be summed to all orders in the density. It is, therefore, expedient to attempt corrections using known functional summed forms such as are given by $y(r)$.

5.3. EQUATIONS FROM FUNCTIONAL DIFFERENTIATION

It has been known for about 20 years that a certain formal advantage can be gained in the formulation of the properties of a group of particles in interaction by using the mathematical tool of functional differentiation.[5] In more recent years the technique has been used to provide alternative derivations of the equations (such as the Born–Green–Yvon equation (4.20), the hypernetted chain equation (5.7), and the Percus–Yevick equation (5.10)) of the theory of fluids already known from alternative derivations. If this were as far as the story goes it would hardly provoke great interest but more is possible from the approach. Over the last year or so it has been found possible to extend its range so as to yield new equations not previously known. Each of the previously known three equations (4.20), (5.7), and (5.10) can be shown to be only the first member of three distinct sets of equations, and the next member of each set has improved the accuracy of calculated thermodynamic data (and particularly the virial coefficients) over that given by the first member of each set. This new approach has still to be fully explored and its potentialities realised, but it has already proved of sufficient interest for consideration here. We consider the matter in two parts. First we derive again the Percus–Yevick, hypernetted chain, and Born–Green–Yvon equations but now by the method of functional differentiation. And second, we shall explore the extension of the method in terms of an appropriate expansion to obtain what would be expected to be improved equations. We make a few comments on the possible prospects of the approach in the next section.

(a) *Alternative Approach to the Direct Correlation*

The idea behind the method is the replacement of a normal $(h+1)$th order distribution in the absence of an external potential of force by a singlet distribution but in some suitable external force potential determined by the remaining h particles of the subset of $(h+1)$ particles.

The starting point is the $(h+1)$th order distribution defined in the grand canonical ensemble: this is:

$$n^{(h+1)}(\mathbf{r}^{(h+1)}) = \frac{1}{\Xi} \sum_{N \geq h+1} \frac{z^N}{(N-h-1)!} \int \cdots \int \exp\left\{-X(\mathbf{r}^N)\right\} d\mathbf{r}^{N-h-1}$$

(5.15)

This contains the grand partition function: let us eliminate this by using the hth order distribution derived from the expression (5.15) by replacing $(h+1)$ by h. For this purpose form the ratio

$$\frac{n^{(h+1)}}{n^{(h)}} = \frac{\displaystyle\sum_{N \geq h+1} \frac{z^N}{(N-h-1)!} \int \cdots \int \exp\left\{-X(\mathbf{r}^N)\right\} d\mathbf{r}^{N-h-1}}{\displaystyle\sum_{N \geq h} \frac{z^N}{(N-h)!} \int \cdots \int \exp\left\{-X(\mathbf{r}^N)\right\} d\mathbf{r}^{N-h}}. \quad (5.16)$$

To proceed further we consider a rearrangement of the integrals appearing here by a particular separation of the various terms appearing in the interparticle potential function. Let us consider the interaction referring to the group of h particles explicitly: write the total interaction as the sum of a contribution of the h particles alone, a contribution of the remaining $(N-h) = t$ particles alone, and a contribution which accounts for the interaction between these two groupings. Thus we write:

$$X(\mathbf{r}^N) = X(\mathbf{r}^h) + X(\mathbf{r}^t) + X(h/t), \quad (5.17)$$

where the last term is a convenient notation for representing the interaction between the groups of h and $(N-h) = t$ particles.

The insertion of the separated form (5.17) into equation (5.16) gives an expression that can be rearranged to exclude direct reference to the group of h particles itself in the integration. Thus,

$$\frac{n^{(h+1)}}{n^{(h)}} = \frac{\displaystyle\sum_{t \geq 1} \frac{z^t}{(t-1)!} \int \cdots \int \exp\left\{-X(\mathbf{r}^t)-X(h/t)\right\} d\mathbf{r}^{t-1}}{\displaystyle\sum_{t \geq 0} \frac{z^t}{t!} \int \cdots \int \exp\left\{-X(\mathbf{r}^t)-X(h/t)\right\} d\mathbf{r}^t}. \quad (5.18)$$

This expression has an interesting interpretation, based on the recognition that the interaction term $X(h/t)$ transcends the integration process. The denominator on the right hand side of (5.18) can be interpreted as the grand canonical ensemble for a group of t particles in the field of force of the group of h particles that are now to be treated as external to the system of t particles. The total right hand side is then a singlet distribution referred to the group of particles t, in the now external force field of the group of h particles now treated as of external origin. To show this situation, ntroduce the notation

$$\frac{n^{(h+1)}(\mathbf{r}_1, \mathbf{r}_2, \ldots \mathbf{r}_h, \mathbf{r}_{h+1})}{n^{(h)}(\mathbf{r}_1, \mathbf{r}_2, \ldots \mathbf{r}_h)} = \varrho^{(1)}(h+1 \mid X(\mathbf{r}^h)). \tag{5.19}$$

The vertical bar in (5.19) is meant to indicate that this is the distribution function for one particle additional to the group t and under the influence of the force field of the group h.

We consider the simplest case where $h = 1$. In this case,

$$X(h/t) = \sum_{j=2}^{t+1} \chi(r_1, r_j), \tag{5.20}$$

so that the external field arises solely from the single particle 1, and the t particles of the system (where $t = N-1$ now) are labelled from particle 2 to $(t+1)(= N)$.

Apart from the trivial question of the numbering of particles, we recover the situation where the particle 1 is not operative in influencing the remainder if the interparticle force between particle 1 and the remainder is "cut-off". One way of achieving the theoretically interesting situation is to introduce a coupling parameter as was, for instance, done earlier by Kirkwood for alternative reasons (see section 4.2(b)). We do not do this now: rather we explore an alternative method involving the variation of the actual potential expression itself. Vary $\chi(\mathbf{r}_1, \mathbf{r}_j)$ in some way which changes it to $\chi_1(\mathbf{r}_1, \mathbf{r}_j)$ and suppose this change in the functional form to be only small. This can be expressed by

$$\chi_1(\mathbf{r}_1, \mathbf{r}_j) = \chi(\mathbf{r}_1, \mathbf{r}_j) + \delta\chi(\mathbf{r}_1, \mathbf{r}_j). \tag{5.21}$$

Further, let us denote $\chi(\mathbf{r}_1, \mathbf{r}_2)$ by χ from this point onwards. The insertion of (5.21) into the previous expressions (5.20), (5.18) and (5.19) provides an expression for the change $\varrho^{(1)}(2/\chi)$. Explicitly, this expression for the change $\delta\varrho^{(1)}$ in $\varrho^{(1)}$ is

$$\delta\varrho^{(1)}(2|\chi) = -\frac{\delta\chi}{\Xi} \sum_{t\geq 1} \frac{z^t}{(t-1)!} \int \exp\left\{-X(\mathbf{r}^t) - \sum_{j=2}^{t+1} \chi(\mathbf{r}_1, \mathbf{r}_j)\right\} d\mathbf{r}^{t-1}$$

$$-\frac{1}{\Xi} \sum_{t\geq 1} \frac{z^t}{(t-1)!} \int \exp\left\{-X(\mathbf{r}^t) - \sum_{j=2}^{t+1} \chi(\mathbf{r}_1, \mathbf{r}_j)\right\} \sum \delta\chi \, d\mathbf{r}^{t-1} - \varrho^{(2)}(2 \mid \chi) \frac{\delta\Xi}{\Xi}.$$

$$\tag{5.22}$$

Some immediate simplification of this expression is possible. For the second integral on the right hand side of equation (5.22) is the sum of $(t-1)$ identical contributions and reference to the defining expression (5.18) shows that the integrals appearing in (5.22) can be represented by distribution functions. Consequently, (5.22) can be recast into the simpler alternative form:

$$\delta\varrho^{(1)}(2\,|\,\chi) = -\varrho^{(1)}(2\,|\,\chi)\,\delta\chi$$

$$-\int \varrho^{(2)}(2,\,3\,|\,\chi)\,\delta\chi(\mathbf{r}_1,\,\mathbf{r}_2)\,d\mathbf{r}_3 - \varrho^{(1)}(2\,|\,\chi)\,\frac{\delta\varXi}{\varXi}. \quad (5.23)$$

In this equation the symbol $\varrho^{(2)}(2,\,3\,|\,\chi(\mathbf{r}_1,\,\mathbf{r}_2))$ is the pair function derived from the ratio $[n^{(h+2)}/n^{(h)}]$, with h set equal to 1, and particles 2 and 3 are considered to be in the external field of particle 1.

The variation of the grand partition function itself follows directly from the expression (5.23). For, integration over $\mathbf{r}_2$ gives

$$\int d\mathbf{r}_2\{\delta\varrho^{(1)}(2|\chi)\} = -\int d\mathbf{r}_2\varrho^{(1)}(2\,|\,\chi)\,\delta\chi$$

$$-\int\int d\mathbf{r}_2\,d\mathbf{r}_3\varrho^{(2)}(2,\,3\,|\,\chi)\,\delta\chi(\mathbf{r}_1,\,\mathbf{r}_3)\,d\mathbf{r}_3 - \int d\mathbf{r}_2\,\varrho^{(2)}(2\,|\,\chi)\frac{\delta\varXi}{\varXi}$$

from which it follows for large N that

$$\frac{\delta\varXi}{\varXi} = -\int \varrho^{(1)}(3\,|\,\chi)\,\delta\chi(\mathbf{r}_1,\,\mathbf{r}_3)\,d\mathbf{r}_3. \quad (5.24)$$

We now insert the expression (5.24) into the previous expression (5.23) to obtain

$$\delta\varrho^{(1)}(2|\chi) = -\int \varrho^{(1)}(2\,|\,\chi)\,\delta(\mathbf{r}_3-\mathbf{r}_2)\,\delta\chi(\mathbf{r}_1,\,\mathbf{r}_3)\,d\mathbf{r}_3$$

$$-\int \varrho^{(2)}(2,\,3\,|\,\chi)\,\delta\chi(\mathbf{r}_1,\,\mathbf{r}_3)\,d\mathbf{r}_3 + \varrho^{(1)}(2\,|\,\chi)\int \varrho^{(1)}(3\,|\,\chi)\,\delta\chi(\mathbf{r}_1,\,\mathbf{r}_3)\,d\mathbf{r}_3. \quad (5.25)$$

It is clear from equation (5.25) that the functional derivative of $\varrho^{(1)}(2/\chi)$ with respect to $\chi(\mathbf{r}_1,\,\mathbf{r}_3)$ is:

$$\frac{\delta\varrho^{(1)}(2\,|\,\chi)}{\delta\chi(\mathbf{r}_1,\,\mathbf{r}_3)} = -\varrho^{(1)}(2\,|\,\chi)\,\delta(\mathbf{r}_3-\mathbf{r}_2) - \varrho^{(2)}(2,\,3\,|\,\chi) + \varrho^{(1)}(2\,|\,\chi)\varrho^{(1)}(3\,|\,\chi). \quad (5.26)$$

When the particle 1 moves an indefinitely large distance away from the group of h particles the derivative expression (5.26) simplifies to become

$$-\frac{\delta\varrho^{(1)}(2\,|\,\chi)}{\delta\chi(\mathbf{r}_1,\,\mathbf{r}_3)}\bigg|_{\chi=0} = \varrho^{(1)}(2)\,\delta(\mathbf{r}_3-\mathbf{r}_2) + \varrho^{(2)}(2,\,3) - \varrho^{(1)}(2)\varrho^{(1)}(3). \quad (5.27)$$

We denote this derivative by $F_1(2,\,3)$.

The same arguments can be used to determine the inverse function:

$$\frac{\delta\chi(\mathbf{r}_1,\,\mathbf{r}_3)}{\delta\varrho^{(1)}(2\,|\,\chi)}\bigg|_{\chi=0} = (F_1)^{-1}. \quad (5.28)$$

The relation between a functional derivative and its inverse is

$$\int (F_1)\,(F_1)^{-1}\,d\mathbf{r}_2 = \int \frac{\delta\varrho^{(1)}(2)}{\delta\chi(\mathbf{r}_1,\mathbf{r}_3)}\,\frac{\delta\chi(\mathbf{r}_1,\mathbf{r}_4)}{\delta\varrho^{(1)}(2)}\,d\mathbf{r}_2 = \delta(\mathbf{r}_3-\mathbf{r}_4). \quad (5.29)$$

The relation between $\varrho^{(1)}(2/\chi)$ and the usual distribution functions should be recalled by reference to the definition (5.19). With the field particle located at $\mathbf{r}_1$ we have

$$\varrho^{(1)}(2\,|\,\chi) = \frac{n^{(2)}(\mathbf{r}_1,\mathbf{r}_2)}{n^{(1)}(\mathbf{r}_1)},$$

and $n^{(1)}$ is the number density at point $\mathbf{r}_1$. According to (3.33), we then write $n^{(2)} = n^2 g^{(2)}$ to obtain the usual pair distribution describing the correlation between the particles: $n^{(1)}$ is the number density n. The expression 5.28) can be given a physically important form if the inverse derivative 5.28) is written in the special way which defines the function c:

$$\left.\frac{\delta\chi(\mathbf{r}_1,\mathbf{r}_3)}{\delta\varrho^{(1)}(2\,|\,\chi)}\right|_{\chi=0} = -\frac{\delta(\mathbf{r}_2-\mathbf{r}_3)}{\varrho^{(1)}(3)} + c(2,3). \quad (5.30)$$

The physical interpretation of the quantity c follows from the insertion of the expression defining c, (5.30), into the relation between the functional derivative and its inverse (5.29). For, this gives

$$g^{(2)}(\mathbf{r}_{13}) = 1 + c(\mathbf{r}_{13}) + n \int \left[g^{(2)}(\mathbf{r}_{12}) - 1\right] c(\mathbf{r}_{23})\,d\mathbf{r}_2. \quad (5.31)$$

Comparison between the expressions (5.31) and the previous (5.2) shows that c defined in (5.30) is indeed the direct correlation function.

In applying the techniques of functional differentiation by the present method it is, then, necessary to make a general statement that some function of the configuration of a group of $(h+1)$ particles is a functional of another function of a constituent subgroup of h particles. We ask the relation between these two configurational functions as the remaining particle is moved a large distance away.

(b) *Rederivation of Known Equations*

With the direct correlation function defined in equation (5.30) directly in terms of a first order functional derivative we can develop the arguments to obtain a general relation between the pair distribution and the interparticle force. For this purpose we suppose some suitably chosen function of the pair distribution and the interparticle force to be a functional of the particle number density and also possibly the interparticle force potential. The skill is choosing the particular function and the particular functional, and different equations result from different choices.

Let us begin by assuming $\ln[\varrho^{(1)}(2/\chi)\exp\chi(\mathbf{r}_1,\mathbf{r}_2)]$ to be a functional of $\varrho^{(1)}(\mathbf{r}_3,\chi)$. The logarithmic function can be expanded in the functional Taylor series to give:

$$\ln g^{(2)}(\mathbf{r}_{12})+\chi(\mathbf{r}_{12}) =$$
$$+n\int [g^{(2)}(\mathbf{r}_{13})-1]\frac{\delta[\ln\varrho^{(1)}(2\,|\,\chi)\exp\chi]}{\delta\varrho^{(1)}(3\,|\,\chi)}\bigg|_{\chi=0}d\mathbf{r}_3+\ldots,\qquad(5.32)$$

where we have cut off the expansion after the first term. The reason for this is as follows. The two integral equations considered in section 5.2 involve the doublet distribution only, and not the triplet. It will be seen from the derivation of equation (5.26) involving only the first functional derivative that the second derivative will involve the triplet function, and so on. Higher terms in the expansion (5.32) will also involve higher derivatives than the first and so will introduce higher order distributions than the second. Since our equations (5.7) and (5.10) are not of this type, then the triplet and higher order distributions are to be explicitly excluded, which means that the expansion (5.32) is to be cut off at the first integral term.

Now,

$$\frac{\delta[\ln\varrho^{(1)}(2\,|\,\chi)\exp\chi]}{\delta\varrho^{(1)}(3\,|\,\chi)}\bigg|_{\chi=0} = \left[\frac{1}{\varrho^{(1)}(2\,|\,\chi)}\frac{\delta\varrho^{(1)}(2\,|\,\chi)}{\delta\varrho^{(1)}(3\,|\,\chi)}\right]_{\chi=0}+\frac{\delta\chi(\mathbf{r}_{12})}{\delta\varrho^{(1)}(3\,|\,\chi)}\bigg|_{\chi=0}$$
$$= \frac{\delta(\mathbf{r}_2-\mathbf{r}_3)}{\varrho^{(1)}(2\,|\,\chi)}+c(\mathbf{r}_2,\mathbf{r}_3)-\frac{\delta(\mathbf{r}_2-\mathbf{r}_3)}{\varrho^{(1)}(2\,|\,\chi)} = c(\mathbf{r}_2,\mathbf{r}_3),\qquad(5.33)$$

where the second form for the right hand side follows from the use of equation (5.30), defining the direct correlation function $c(\mathbf{r}_2,\mathbf{r}_3)$. The result (5.33) is first inserted into the expansion (5.32), and the function then eliminated by using the expression (5.31) defining c. The result is exactly the hypernetted chain equation (5.7), obtained earlier on the basis of a direct assumption about the form of the direct correlation function $c(r)$, viz. the expression (5.4). The derivation of this equation given in this section is apparently more respectable because it is more mathematical but it does depend upon the expression of one apparently arbitrary function as a linear functional of another arbitrary function. There is no physical criterion involved and why this particular development is made rather than another is at the present time obscure.

Other developments are interesting. Thus, if in place of $\ln[\varrho^{(1)}(2/\chi)\exp\chi]$ we suppose that $[\varrho^{(1)}(2/\chi)\exp\chi]$ itself is a linear functional of $[\varrho^{(1)}(3\,|\,\chi)$ in the limit $\chi=0$ (i.e. in the limit where the perturbing particle is removed to an indefinite distance), then the Percus–Yevick equation (5.10) results.

Other choices of function and functional provide other possible choices in the present limit of considering only the linear term in the func tional Taylor expansion. One choice of great importance is that of assuming $[\varrho^{(1)}(2/\chi)\partial\chi(\mathbf{r}_{12})/\partial\mathbf{r}_1]$ to be a linear functional of the function ln $[\varrho^{(1)}(2/\chi) \exp \chi]$. The result is the Born–Green–Yvon equation (4.22) including the superposition approximation. It is seen that the method of functional differentiation is able to provide an alternative derivation of the equations deduced earlier* whose solution is the fluid pair distribution.

(c) New Equations

Other choices of function and functional provide other possible choices in the approximation of retaining only the linear term in the functional Taylor expansion. For instance, if $[\varrho^{(1)}(2/\chi)\partial\chi/\partial\mathbf{r}]$ is treated as linear functional of $[\varrho^{(1)}(3\,|\,\chi)]$ the result is the equation:

$$\frac{\partial g^{(2)}(\mathbf{r}_{12})}{\partial\mathbf{r}_{12}} + \frac{\partial\chi(\mathbf{r}_{12})]}{\partial\mathbf{r}_{12}}\, g^{(2)}(\mathbf{r}_{12}) = -n \int \left[g^{(2)}(\mathbf{r}_{23}) - 1\right]g^{(2)}(\mathbf{r}_{13})\frac{\partial\chi(\mathbf{r}_{13})}{\partial\mathbf{r}_{13}}\, d\mathbf{r}_3.$$

$$(5.34a)$$

This equation alternatively follows from the earlier equation (5.2) by assuming for the gradient of the direct correlation function, the expression

$$-\frac{\partial c(\mathbf{r})|}{\partial\mathbf{r}} = g^{(2)}(\mathbf{r})\frac{\partial\chi(\mathbf{r})}{\partial\mathbf{r}}\mathbf{r}.$$

$$(5.34b)$$

Further equations can be constructed under the linear approximation but we do not pursue this matter further here. There is, indeed, a full correspondence between a specification of the direct correlation function on the one side, and an appropriate application of the procedures of functional differentiation on the other. But there is here no physical principle according to which the various functions can be chosen.

If this were the full story nothing would have been gained by the duality. Fortunately, functional differentiation would seem to offer the possibility of successively correcting the equations known already. This is achieved by including further terms in the Taylor expansion (5.32) beyond the linear term. In principle a succession of such terms can be accounted for but in practice mathematical difficulties have so far precluded application beyond the quadratic term. The inclusion of the quadratic term into the theory has been made by Verlet[6].

The quadratic term neglected in the expansion (5.32) is now included so that we are concerned with the functional term:

$$\frac{1}{2!} \int\int \left[g^{(2)}(\mathbf{r}_{13}) - 1\right]\left[g^{(2)}(\mathbf{r}_{14}) - 1\right]\frac{\delta^2\left[\ln\left\{\varrho^{(1)}(2\,|\,\chi)\exp\chi\right\}\right]}{\delta\varrho^{(2)}(3\,|\,\chi)\delta\varrho^{(1)}(4\,|\,\chi)}\bigg|_{\chi=0} d\mathbf{r}_3\, d\mathbf{r}\chi_4. \quad (5.35)$$

* Other known equations, such as the Kirkwood–Salsburg equation, can also be obtained this way. See L. Verlet, 1966, *Physica* **32**, 304.

The addition of this term to the Taylor expansion (5.32) has the effect of replacing the previous expression for $c(r)$, viz:

$$c(r) = h(r) - \ln y(r), \qquad (5.36)$$

which is equation (5.6), by the expression

$$c(r) = h(r) - \ln y(r) + \psi(r), \qquad (5.37a)$$

where

$$\psi(r) = \Phi(r) - \frac{1}{2} [h(r) - c(r)]^2, \qquad (5.37b)$$

and

$$\Phi(r) = \frac{1}{2} n^2 \int dr_3 \, dr_4 c(\mathbf{r}_{12}) c(\mathbf{r}_{13}) g^{(2)}(\mathbf{r}_{34}) [g^{(3)}(2, 3, 4) - \ln g^{(3)}(2, 3\ 4)$$

$$- h(2, 3) + \ln g^{(2)}(2, 3) - g^{(2)}(2, 3) + \ln g^{(2)}(2, 4)]. \qquad (5.37c)$$

This function Φ is not to be confused with the previously defined mean potential function: (5.37c) is not related to the mean potential. It is seen that the triplet function now appears in the function Φ and we have, as yet, no prescription for specifying the triplet function. For a self-contained theory, the triplet function must appear automatically. In the present case there is some choice open to us: Verlet in his paper suggests a possible first order theory for $g^{(3)}$ for insertion into (5.37c). The suggestion is that the linear theory for $g^{(2)}$ epitomised in the linear expansion (5.33) should be repeated again, but now with $[\ln \{\varrho^{(2)}(2, 3 \,|\, \chi) \times \exp \{\chi(1, 2) + \chi(1, 3)\}]$ treated as a linear functional of $[\varrho^{(1)}(4 \,|\, \chi)]$. The result is the equation for $g^{(3)}$, in an obvious notation:

$$\ln \left[\frac{g^{(3)}(1, 2, 3)}{g^{(2)}(2, 3)} \exp \{\chi(1, 2) + \chi(1, 3)\} \right] = n \int dr_4 \left[\frac{g^{(3)}(2, 3, 4)}{g^{(2)}(2, 3)} - 1 \right] c(1, 4). \qquad (5.38)$$

The set of equations (5.31), (5.37a), (5.37b), (5.37c) and (5.38) then allow the pair correlation function $g^{(2)}(r)$ to be computed for a given interparticle force potential. This set of equations is called by Verlet the second hypernetted chain equation, or HNC 2. The method could, in principle, be extended to include further terms in the Taylor expansion but the mathematical complications have so far prevented this programme from being carried through.

The first thing about this theory labelled HNC 2 is its complexity in application. Indeed, it has so far been applied only for the calculation of virial coefficients (i.e. for low fluid densities), but with some success. It will be found in Chapter 6 that it represents a definite improvement n calculated values over the linear theory, denoted by HNC 1. Application to liquid densities will present formidable problems of computation.

The same procedure was also applied by Verlet to the Percus–Yevick equation. The additional term to replace the HNC 2 term (5.35) is:

$$\frac{1}{!}\int\int [g^{(2)}(1, 3)-1][g^{(2)}(1, 4)-1]\frac{\delta^2[\varrho^{(1)}(2\mid\chi)\exp\chi]}{\delta\varrho^{(1)}(3\mid\chi)\delta\varrho^{(1)}(4\mid\chi)}\bigg|_{\chi=0}\,dr_3\,dr_4, \quad (5.39)$$

and this leads to the expression for the direct correlation in the quadratic approximation:

$$c(r) = \alpha(r)y(r)+\Phi(r), \quad (5.40)$$

where, again, Φ is given by the expression (5.37c). This replaces the linear expression:

$$c(r) = \alpha(r)\,y(r).$$

The triplet distribution in (5.37c) is now to be eliminated by using the equation for $g^{(3)}$ which results when $[\varrho^{(2)}(2, 3\mid\chi)\exp\{\chi(1, 2)+\chi(1, 3)\}]$ is treated as a linear functional of $[\varrho^{(1)}(4\mid\chi)]$. The result, for $g^{(3)}$, is the expression:

$$g^{(3)}(1, 2, 3)\exp\{\chi(1, 2)+\chi(1, 3)\}$$
$$= g^{(2)}(2, 3)+n\int c(1, 4)[g^{(3)}(2, 3, 4)-g^{(2)}(2, 3)]\,dr_4. \quad (5.41)$$

The set of equations (5.31), (5.40), (5.37c) and (5.41) are a prescription for calculating $g^{(2)}$, called, by Verlet, Percus–Yevick 2, or more simply, PY 2. As for HNC 2, PY 2 can be extended to higher approximations in principle, but has not yet been so extended in practice. It will be seen in chapter 6 that PY 2 allows for a numerical improvement in the calculation of virial coefficients, but has not so far been applied to studies involving liquid densities.

The theory has comment to make on the superposition approximation since equations (5.38) and (5.41) are integral relations between the pair and triplet distributions. Although in general they are not easy to arrange into a form which shows $g^{(3)}$ explicitly in terms of $g^{(2)}$, this is possible for low densities where a density expansion of the functions $g^{(3)}$, $g^{(2)}$, and c is legitimate. Both the expressions (5.38) and (5.41) then lead to the same expression for $g^{(3)}$ when only the linear term in n is included, but differ when terms of order n^2 and higher are introduced. The result is:

$$g^{(3)}(1, 2, 3) = \exp\{-\chi(1,2)-\chi(1, 3)-\chi(2, 3)\}$$
$$\times[1+ng_1^{(3)}(1, 2, 3)+0(n^2)], \quad (5.42)$$

where $g_1^{(3)}$ is now given by equation (4.40) but with h in that equation set equal to 3. The first order theory for $g^{(3)}$, therefore, is exact to the linear term of the density, but is inexact beyond this. The behaviour of the quad ratic and higher terms is not known. The expression (5.42) is a closur expression and is essentially a superposition approximation, but now de rived from a mathematical procedure rather than from a direct statemen of probabilities such as was resorted to in section 4.1. It is clearly superio to the Kirkwood formulation of the approximation (4.3) up to linea terms in the density, but no information can be deduced on this basis fo its value at liquid densities.*

5.4. SOME COMMENTS ON THE VARIOUS PROCEDURES

Several alternative theories have been reported in this chapter and th last one, for the calculation of the pair distribution, and some additiona comment might be useful before we pass on to a comparison betwee the deductions of these alternative approaches to the elucidation of liqui structure.

We have divided the discussion into two parts depending upon whethe a closure procedure (the superposition approximation) is to be invoke from outside for the solution of the set of exact equations, or not. Thi division is artificial in principle but expedient in practice for liquids at th present time. Each division has its advantages and deficiencies. The equa tions of Chapter 4 are derived simply and directly from the basic defini tions of the lower order distribution functions (such as equations (4.1) an (4.2)), and the equations are exact up to the point where the superpositio statement is introduced. Fisher's arguments (section 4.2(d)) allow a system atic correction of the approximation to be applied in principle. Th central problem of Chapter 4 is that of obtaining improved informatio about the triplet distribution for liquid densities.

The superposition approximation does not explicitly appear in th approach using the correlation equation (5.2), because the effect of third particle on a pair is accounted for by the introduction of the indirec correlation integral on physical grounds. The correlation equation fo particle triplets, analogous to equation (5.2), could act as a superpositio statement for an interaction potential which can be decomposed int particle pair contributions. The pair distribution is then involved and th result is an expression linking the triplet and doublet distributions. Suc an expression arises naturally from the technique of functional differentio (equation (5.38) or (5.41)), and is applicable to all densities. Although th method of functional differention leads to an equation involving $g^{(2)}$ an χ alone in the linear approximation, the function $g^{(3)}$ appears in the quac

* But see footnote, p. 106.

ratic approximation, and higher approximations will involve higher order functions. The hierarchical structure of the theory allows for closure at each stage, and so a self-contained theory at each stage, by using one approximation lower in the specification of the triplet and higher functions than is used in the deduction of the initial equation for $g^{(2)}$ itself. This is a definite mathematical improvement over the hierarchical use of the superposition approximation, although it is in some ways not unlike the technique of Fisher outlined in section 4.2 (d).

Application of the method of functional differentiation would seem to open up wide possibilities for the calculation of the equilibrium properties of fluids. But the method is still in its infancy. The present difficulty is that of selecting a suitable function to be treated as functional of some other selected function. We have in our arguments used four distinct sets of functions; three of them have provided the already known BGY, HNC, and PY equations, while the fourth has provided an equation, (5.34), whose value cannot be assessed without the calculation of thermodynamic functions. If the BGY, HNC, and PY had not been known before, it is almost certain that they would not have been discovered by the methods of functional differentiation. On the other hand, the new equations HNC 2 and PY 2 would not have been discovered on the basis of HNC and PY alone. But the ambiguity of equations is confusing. Some physical criterion would seem necessary for the selection of the appropriate function and functional, such as the condition that the entropy should be a maximum, although it may be rather more complicated than this.

A number of other questions remain to be answered. For instance, the linear approximation of the functional Taylor expansion need not be sufficient to provide information about $g^{(2)}$ for all densities. The value of further terms in the expansion in the description of fluids of increasing density requires investigation. Presumably, the information about fluid structure derived from the total PY series, the total HNC series, and the total BGY series (together with other appropriate series that could be formulated) will all coincide in the limit of a large number of terms. But this again has not yet been demonstrated. While the physical relationship between the physical interpretations of the various equations is clear at low densities (where cluster expansion techniques are valuable and generally wieldy if high accuracy is not required) this is not the case at liquid densities where diagram procedures lose their intuitive immediacy. At these densities, the numerical validity of approximations becomes very difficult to assess by comparison with experimental information on the basis of approximate formulae for the interparticle force.

There are, in fact, two uncertainties in the theoretical treatment of real matter. The first is the exact equation to be used in the calculation of the pair distribution for a specified interparticle force potential, together with the related problem of the stability of the solution against small changes in the potential. The other uncertainty is in the specification of the inter-particle force potential itself. The solution of these problems can be expected to be associated with a reconciliation between the approaches of Chapters 4 and 5.

Note added at page proof. Mr. A. Moreton and the author have deduced an improved superposition approximation for $g^{(3)}$ by treating $\varrho^{(1)}(3 \mid \chi_1 + \chi_2)$ $\{\exp [\chi(1, 3)] - 1\}$ as a functional of $\varrho^{(1)}(4 \mid \chi_1) \{\exp [\chi(1, 4)] - 1\}$. The expression (4.7) for $g^{(3)}$ is obtained, and the linear term in the functional Taylor expansion gives the Kirkwood approximation (4.3b), i.e. $S_3 = 1$. The inclusion of the quadratic term in the functional expansion gives the indirect correlation function

$$S_3(1,2,3) = 1 + n \int \alpha(1,4) y(1,4) \times$$
$$\times \left[\frac{g^{(3)}(2,3,4)}{g^{(2)}(2,3)} - g^{(2)}(2,4) - g^{(2)}(3,4) + 1 \right] \mathrm{dr}_4 \qquad (5.43)$$

This expression satisfies the normalisation condition (4.11a), and is supposed to apply to all densities including those appropriate to liquids. Further terms in the functional Taylor expansion have not been pursued. The integrand in (5.43) contains $g^{(3)}$; this is to be removed by iteration, starting with the Kirkwood approximation (4.3b). For low densities, where the expansion (4.42) is valid, (5.43) provides the exact coefficient of n in the density expansion of $g^{(3)}$. When used in conjunction with BGY equation (4.20) or the second order tensor equation (4.28), the expression (5.43) leads to exact data for the second, third and fourth virial coefficient, as does PY2 and HNC2. The function S_3 given by (5.43) can presumably be associated with the indirect correlation in the Fisher equations (Section 4.2(d)). The value of (5.43) at liquid densities is unknown. The selection of a closure expression for the equations considered in Chapter using the methods of functional differentiation could lead to a welding together of the various arguments for the calculation of the pair correlation. But a physical basis of the method is still awaited.

CHAPTER 6

SOME NUMERICAL CONSEQUENCES
OF THE EQUILIBRIUM THEORY

IN THE last three chapters, the statistical theory of equilibrium fluids has been developed to the point where numerical values can be deduced. The present chapter is devoted to some aspects of this study for the case of fluids of one component only, and where the constituent particles are spherically symmetric. Slightly more general circumstances are included in Appendix 6. Our aim here is not to be comprehensive, but rather to assess in broad terms the type of calculation that can be attempted at the present state of the theory. At the present time, numerical deductions from the theory must fall into two separate classes depending upon the form of the interparticle force potential used in the calculations.

The first class of calculation, and the one that will particularly interest us now, is concerned with the study of the equations of the theory for idealised potential functions. Comparisons here are between the calculated values of quantities (like the virial coefficients and other quantities) derived from the various equations of the theory, and those from exact expressions derived alternatively. By these means the nature of the equations can be evaluated and the importance of particular features of the interparticle potential highlighted. Clearly, although idealised potential forms are involved, these are chosen against a knowledge of more realistic forms. In this way, the relative importance of the repulsive and attractive regions of the potential can be assessed in determining the appearance of specific properties of macroscopic matter. This is the mathematical testing of the theory and is the task of understanding in physical terms the consequences and stability of the equations.

The second class of calculation is that involved in predicting numerical values for specific properties of macroscopic matter designed for detailed comparison with experimental data. This class of calculation must be based on a sufficiently realistic interparticle force potential to make the calculations physically significant. While the ultimate aim of the theory must be that of being capable of making such physically significant calculations, the theory is not yet at a stage where such calculations can be made for anything other than the most simple fluids. For our present purposes, therefore, this second class of calculation is of only secondary interest. But the use of idealised potential functions cannot be entirely discounted from a practical point of view. The features of an idealised potential form might be very broadly similar to those of a more realistic potential expression so that the broad features of the idealised calculation can, in this way, have certain similarity with corresponding measured data. In this way, even idealised calculations can have qualitative practical interest and can provide data for comparison with experiment, but of low accuracy.

Our present discussion will be divided into two parts, characterised by density: and each division itself will be divided between a study of the pair distribution and the calculation of idealised fluid thermodynamic functions. First, we shall consider low densities where the various thermodynamic functions can be adequately represented by an expansion in powers of the density. Second, we shall consider higher densities where such an expansion in powers of the density is not valuable.

6.1. THE PAIR DISTRIBUTION FOR A MODEL GAS OF SPHERICAL PARTICLES

At sufficiently low densities the pair distribution takes the expansion form (4.42), i.e.:

$$g^{(2)}(r) = \exp\left\{-\frac{\psi(r)}{kT}\right\} [1 + a_1(r)n + a_2(r)n^2 + a_3(r)n^3 + \ldots]. \quad (6.1)$$

The coefficients $a_j(r)$ depend not only upon the pair separation distance, but also upon the interparticle force potential ψ and the temperature. They are to be deduced by solving the several equations developed in the previous two chapters for various forms of ψ.

We set down the expressions for the first two coefficients a_1 and a_2 in the expansion (6.1) for the several equations derived so far, for the square-well potential, which also includes the hard-sphere potential as well. These are the most realistic forms of the ideal potentials.

(a) The Square-well Potential

The square-well potential function is that set down in Appendix 2.7, equation (A2.4). We particularise now the case where $g = 2$, so that

$$\begin{aligned} \psi(r) &= \infty \quad \text{for} \quad r < 1, \\ \psi(r) &= -\varepsilon, \quad \text{for} \quad 1 < r < 2, \\ \psi(r) &= 0 \quad \text{for} \quad r > 2, \end{aligned} \quad (6.2)$$

where the hard-sphere diameter is the unit of length. The spatial extent of the attractive region is the same as that of the repulsion. The associated parameter is α defined by

$$\alpha = \exp\left\{\frac{\varepsilon}{kT}\right\} - 1, \tag{6.3}$$

and is a constant for given potential depth ε and for given temperature. The square-well potential contains the hard-sphere potential as a special case, and there are two possibilities. For (6.2) reduces to the hard-sphere potential when $\varepsilon = 0$, i.e. $\alpha = 0$ then. It also reduces to the hard-sphere form if $\varepsilon = -\infty$ (i.e. if $\alpha = -1$), but with twice the radius of the former case. This can act as a check on the formulae derived from the theory.

We give now expressions for the coefficients a_1 and a_2 of the expansion (6.1) for $g^{(2)}$ for the hypernetted chain equation (5.7), the Percus–Yevick equation (5.10), the Born–Green–Yvon equation (4.22) under the Kirkwood superposition approximation (4.3), and the Kirkwood equation (4.25) under the same superposition approximation. These are obtained by inserting (6.1) into each equation in turn and comparing successively the coefficients linear and quadratic in the number density n in each equation separately. The square-well potential function is sufficiently realistic to make it worthwhile setting down here the expressions for $a_1(r)$ and $a_2(r)$.

(i) *The coefficient $a_1(r)$*

All the equations lead to the same expression for $a_1(r)$, which also is the expression (4.43) derived earlier in section 4.3. Explicitly,[1]

$$a_1(r) = a_{11}(r) + a_{12}(r)\alpha + a_{13}(r)\alpha^2, \tag{6.4a}$$

where

$$a_{11}(r) = \pi\left\{\frac{4}{3} - r + \frac{r^3}{12}\right\} \quad \text{for} \quad 0 \leqslant r \leqslant 2, \tag{6.4b}$$
$$= 0 \quad \text{for} \quad r \geqslant 2;$$

$$a_{12}(r) = \pi\left\{-2r + \frac{r^3}{6}\right\} \quad \text{for} \quad 0 \leqslant r \leqslant 1,$$
$$= \pi\left\{\frac{9}{2}\cdot\frac{1}{r} + 3r - \frac{28}{3}\right\} \quad \text{for} \quad 1 \leqslant r \leqslant 2, \tag{6.4c}$$
$$= \pi\left\{\frac{9}{2}\cdot\frac{1}{r} - 12 + 5r - \frac{r^3}{6}\right\} \quad \text{for} \quad 2 \leqslant r \leqslant 3,$$
$$= 0 \quad \text{for} \quad r \geqslant 3;$$

$$a_{13}(r) = \pi \left\{ \frac{28}{3} - 5r + \frac{r^3}{6} \right\} \quad \text{for} \quad 0 \leqslant r \leqslant 1,$$

$$= \pi \left\{ \frac{9}{2} \cdot \frac{1}{r} \right\} \quad \text{for} \quad 1 \leqslant r \leqslant 2,$$

$$= \pi \left\{ \frac{9}{2} \cdot \frac{1}{r} - \frac{4}{3} + r - \frac{r^3}{12} \right\} \quad \text{for} \quad 2 \leqslant r \leqslant 3, \qquad (6.4d)$$

$$= \pi \left\{ \frac{32}{3} - 4r + \frac{r^3}{12} \right\} \quad \text{for} \quad 3 \leqslant r \leqslant 4,$$

$$= 0 \quad \text{for} \quad r \geqslant 4.$$

It is seen that $a_1(r)$ is zero beyond four hard-core diameters. For the hard-sphere gas[2] of unit diameter only the term $a_{11}(r)$ remains in the expression (6.4a).

(ii) *The coefficient $a_2(r)$*

Each of the equations provide different expressions for this coefficient. Explicitly, it is found[3] that, in a standard notation: for the Born–Green–Yvon equation (4.22):

$$a_{2B}(r) = \frac{1}{2} \{a_1(r)\}^2 + c_3(r) + c_4(r) + c_5(r), \qquad (6.5a)$$

which follows from the expressions (4.48), (4.49), and (4.50) but with the coefficients Y_j set equal to zero; for the Kirkwood equation (4.25):

$$a_{2K}(r) = \frac{1}{2} \{a_1(r)\}^2 + c_3(r) + 2c_4(r) + \frac{1}{2} \{c_6(r) - c_4(r)\}; \qquad (6.5b)$$

for the hypernetted chain equation (5.7):

$$a_{2H}(r) = \frac{1}{2} \{a_1(r)\}^2 + c_3(r) + 2c_4(r); \qquad (6.5c)$$

and for the Percus–Yevick equation (5.10):

$$a_{2P}(r) = c_3(r) + 2c_4(r). \qquad (6.5d)$$

In these expressions, the various functions c_3, c_4, c_5 and c_6 are given a function of r and α by the following expressions[4]:

$$c_3(r) = c_{31}(r) + c_{32}(r)\alpha + c_{33}(r)\alpha^2 + c_{34}(r)\alpha^3, \qquad (6.6a)$$

where
$$c_{31}(r) = \pi^2\left\{-\frac{5}{6}+\frac{r^2}{2}-\frac{r^4}{10}+\frac{r^6}{630}\right\} \quad \text{for} \quad 0 \leqslant r \leqslant 1,$$

$$= \pi^2\left\{\frac{27}{70}\frac{1}{r}-\frac{9}{4}+\frac{9}{5}r-\frac{r^2}{4}-\frac{r^3}{6}+\frac{r^4}{20}-\frac{r^6}{1260}\right\} \quad \text{for} \quad 1 \leqslant r \leqslant 2,$$

$$= 0 \quad \text{for} \quad r > 2; \tag{6.6b}$$

$$c_{32}(r) = \pi^2\left\{\frac{17}{6}+\frac{3}{2}r^2-r^3+\frac{r^6}{420}\right\} \quad \text{for} \quad 0 \leqslant r \leqslant 1,$$

$$= \pi^2\left\{\frac{81}{70}\cdot\frac{1}{r}-\frac{17}{12}+\frac{27}{5}r-\frac{3}{4}r^2-\frac{3}{2}r^3+\frac{9}{20}r^4-\frac{r^6}{210}\right\} \quad \text{for} \quad 1 \leqslant r \leqslant 2,$$

$$= \pi^2\left\{-\frac{291}{14}\cdot\frac{1}{r}+\frac{431}{12}-\frac{69}{5}r-\frac{3}{4}r^2+\frac{7}{6}r^3-\frac{3}{20}r^4\right\} \quad \text{for} \quad 2 \leqslant r \leqslant 3,$$

$$= \pi^2\left\{-\frac{768}{35}\cdot\frac{1}{r}+\frac{128}{3}-\frac{96}{5}r+\frac{5}{3}r^3-\frac{3}{10}r^4+\frac{r^6}{420}\right\} \quad \text{for} \quad 3 \leqslant r \leqslant 4,$$

$$= 0 \quad \text{for} \quad r \geqslant 4; \tag{6.6c}$$

$$c_{33}(r) = \pi^2\left\{-\frac{68}{3}+9r^2-2r^3-\frac{3}{5}r^4+\frac{r^6}{210}\right\} \quad \text{for} \quad 0 \leqslant r \leqslant 1,$$

$$= \pi^2\left\{+\frac{303}{70}\cdot\frac{1}{r}-\frac{155}{4}+21r-\frac{3}{4}r^2-\frac{17}{6}r^3+\frac{3}{4}r^4-\frac{r^6}{140}\right\} \quad \text{for} \quad 1 \leqslant r \leqslant 2,$$

$$= \pi^2\left\{-\frac{2769}{70}\cdot\frac{1}{r}+\frac{3017}{84}-\frac{87}{5}r-\frac{3}{4}r^2+\frac{5}{2}r^3-\frac{9}{20}r^4+\frac{r^6}{420}\right\} \quad \text{for} \quad 2 \leqslant r \leqslant 3,$$

$$= \pi^2\left\{\frac{6303}{70}\cdot\frac{1}{r}-\frac{9457}{84}+\frac{183}{5}r-\frac{105}{28}r^2+\frac{r^3}{2}-\frac{21}{140}r^4+\frac{r^6}{420}\right\} \quad \text{for} \quad 3 \leqslant r \leqslant 4,$$

$$= \pi^2\left\{\frac{1875}{14}\cdot\frac{1}{r}-\frac{16625}{84}+75r-\frac{15}{4}r^2-\frac{119}{42}r^3+\frac{63}{140}r^4-\frac{r^6}{420}\right\} \quad \text{for} \quad 4 \leqslant r \leqslant 5,$$

$$= 0 \quad \text{for} \quad r \geqslant 5; \tag{6.6d}$$

$$c_{34}(r) = \pi^2\left\{27-r^3-\frac{3}{10}r^4+\frac{r^6}{420}\right\} \quad \text{for} \quad 0 \leqslant r \leqslant 1,$$

$$= \pi^2\left\{\frac{249}{70}\cdot\frac{1}{r}+\frac{55}{4}+\frac{87}{5}r-\frac{33}{4}r^2-\frac{3}{2}r^3+\frac{3}{4}r^4-\frac{r^6}{210}\right\} \quad \text{for} \quad 1 \leqslant r \leqslant 2,$$

$$= \pi^2\left\{\frac{4743}{70}\cdot\frac{1}{r}+\frac{567}{4}-\frac{297}{5}r+\frac{15}{4}r^2+\frac{5}{2}r^3-\frac{9}{20}r^4+\frac{r^6}{420}\right\} \quad \text{for} \quad 2 \leqslant r \leqslant 3,$$

$$= \pi^2\left\{\frac{13149}{210}\cdot\frac{1}{r}-\frac{45}{4}-\frac{9}{5}r+\frac{r^2}{4}+\frac{r^3}{6}-\frac{r^4}{20}+\frac{r^6}{1260}\right\} \quad \text{for} \quad 3 \leqslant r \leqslant 4,$$

$$= \pi^2\left\{\frac{5919}{70}\cdot\frac{1}{r}-\frac{647}{12}+\frac{174}{10}r+\frac{r^2}{4}-\frac{3}{2}r^3+\frac{r^4}{4}-\frac{r^6}{630}\right\} \quad \text{for} \quad 4 \leqslant r \leqslant 5,$$

$$= \pi^2 \left\{ -\frac{1728}{35} \cdot \frac{1}{r} + 144 - \frac{288}{5} r + 4r^2 + \frac{4}{3} r^3 - \frac{r^4}{5} + \frac{r^6}{1260} \right\} \quad \text{for} \quad 5 \leqslant r \leqslant 6,$$

$$= 0 \quad \text{for} \quad r \geqslant 6. \tag{6.6}$$

$$c_4(r) = c_{41}(r) + c_{42}(r)\alpha + c_{43}(r)\alpha^2 + c_{44}(r)\alpha^3 + c_{45}(r)\alpha^4, \tag{6.7}$$

where

$$c_{41}(r) = \pi^2 \left\{ -\frac{9}{35} \cdot \frac{1}{r} + \frac{16}{9} - \frac{97}{60} r + \frac{r^2}{4} + \frac{r^3}{6} - \frac{r^4}{20} + \frac{r^6}{1260} \right\} \quad \text{for} \quad 1 \leqslant r \leqslant 2,$$

$$= 0 \quad \text{for} \quad r > 2; \tag{6.7}$$

$$c_{42}(r) = \pi^2 \left\{ -\frac{31}{140} \cdot \frac{1}{r} - \frac{131}{60} r + \frac{|3}{4} r^2 + \frac{11}{18} r^3 - \frac{r^4}{4} + \frac{r^6}{315} \right\} \quad \text{for} \quad 1 \leqslant r \leqslant 2,$$

$$= \pi^2 \left\{ \frac{1137}{140} \cdot \frac{1}{r} - 16 + \frac{481}{60} r - \frac{r^2}{4} - \frac{13}{18} r^3 + \frac{3}{20} r^4 - \frac{r^6}{630} \right\} \quad \text{for} \quad 2 \leqslant r \leqslant 3,$$

$$= 0 \quad \text{for} \quad r > 3; \tag{6.7}$$

$$c_{43}(r) = \pi^2 \left\{ -\frac{1377}{140} \cdot \frac{1}{r} + \frac{601}{18} - 21r + 2r^2 + \frac{17}{9} r^3 - \frac{r^4}{2} + \frac{r^6}{210} \right\} \quad \text{for} \quad 1 \leqslant r \leqslant 2$$

$$= \pi^2 \left\{ \frac{11}{140} \cdot \frac{1}{r} + \frac{121}{18} - \frac{19}{20} r - \frac{|3}{4} r^2 - \frac{5}{18} r^3 + \frac{3}{20} r^4 + \frac{r^6}{420} \right\} \quad \text{for} \quad 2 \leqslant r \leqslant 3,$$

$$= \pi^2 \left\{ -\frac{256}{35} \cdot \frac{1}{r} + \frac{128}{9} - \frac{32}{5} r + \frac{5}{9} r^3 - \frac{r^4}{10} + \frac{r^6}{1260} \right\} \quad \text{for} \quad 3 \leqslant r \leqslant 4,$$

$$= 0 \quad \text{for} \quad r \geqslant 4; \tag{6.7}$$

$$c_{44}(r) = \pi^2 \left\{ \frac{127}{35} \cdot \frac{1}{r} - \frac{109}{6} - \frac{71}{10} r + \frac{11}{2} r^2 + r^3 - \frac{r^4}{2} + \frac{r^6}{315} \right\} \quad \text{for} \quad 1 \leqslant r \leqslant 2,$$

$$= \pi^2 \left\{ \frac{1133}{35} \cdot \frac{1}{r} - \frac{1639}{18} + \frac{709}{15} r - 6r^2 - \frac{8}{9} r^3 + \frac{r^4}{5} - \frac{r^6}{630} \right\} \quad \text{for} \quad 2 \leqslant r \leqslant 3,$$

$$= \pi^2 \left\{ \frac{368}{5} \cdot \frac{1}{r} - \frac{896}{9} + \frac{109}{3} r - \frac{5}{2} r^2 - \frac{7}{9} r^3 + \frac{r^4}{10} \right\} \quad \text{for} \quad 3 \leqslant r \leqslant 4,$$

$$= 0 \quad \text{for} \quad r \geqslant 4; \tag{6.7}$$

$$c_{45}(r) = \pi^2 \left\{ \frac{27}{2} \cdot \frac{1}{r} \right\} \quad \text{for} \quad 1 \leqslant r \leqslant 2,$$

$$= \pi^2 \left\{ \frac{15}{2} \cdot \frac{1}{r} + \frac{9}{2} r - \frac{|3}{2} r^2 \right\} \quad \text{for} \quad 2 \leqslant r \leqslant 3,$$

$$= \pi^2 \left\{ \frac{48}{r} - 9r + \frac{3}{2} r^2 \right\} \quad \text{for} \quad 3 \leqslant r \leqslant 4,$$

$$= 0 \quad \text{for} \quad r \geqslant 4. \tag{6.7}$$

$$c_5(r) = c_{51}(r) + c_{52}(r)\alpha + c_{53}(r)\alpha^2 + c_{54}(r)\alpha^3 + c_{55}(r)\alpha^4, \tag{6.8}$$

ere

$$c_{51}(r) = \pi^2 \left\{ \frac{5}{9} - \frac{5}{12}r + \frac{5}{144}r^3 \right\} \quad \text{for} \quad 1 \leqslant r \leqslant 2,$$

$$0 \quad \text{for} \quad r \geqslant 2; \tag{6.8b}$$

$$c_{52}(r) = \pi^2 \left\{ \frac{15}{16} \cdot \frac{1}{r} - \frac{23}{6} + \frac{49}{24}r - \frac{17}{144}r^3 \right\} \quad \text{for} \quad 1 \leqslant r \leqslant 2,$$

$$\pi^2 \left\{ \frac{15}{16} \cdot \frac{1}{r} - \frac{5}{2} + \frac{25}{24}r - \frac{5}{144}r^3 \right\} \quad \text{for} \quad 2 \leqslant r \leqslant 3,$$

$$0 \quad \text{for} \quad 3 \geqslant r; \tag{6.8c}$$

$$c_{53}(r) = \pi^2 \left\{ -\frac{45}{8} \cdot \frac{1}{r} + \frac{50}{3} - \frac{15}{2}r + \frac{5}{16}r^3 \right\} \quad \text{for} \quad 1 \leqslant r \leqslant 2,$$

$$\pi^2 \left\{ -\frac{45}{8} \cdot \frac{1}{r} + 15 - \frac{25}{4}r + \frac{5}{24}r^3 \right\} \quad \text{for} \quad 2 \leqslant r \leqslant 3,$$

$$0 \quad \text{for} \quad r \geqslant 3; \tag{6.8d}$$

$$c_{54}(r) = \pi^2 \left\{ \frac{69}{8} \cdot \frac{1}{r} - 25 + \frac{27}{4}r - \frac{3}{16}r^3 \right\} \quad \text{for} \quad 1 \leqslant r \leqslant 2,$$

$$\pi^2 \left\{ \frac{69}{8} \cdot \frac{1}{r} - \frac{311}{9} + \frac{167}{12}r - \frac{59}{144}r^3 \right\} \quad \text{for} \quad 2 \leqslant r \leqslant 3,$$

$$\pi^2 \left\{ -\frac{104}{9} + \frac{13}{3}r - \frac{13}{144}r^3 \right\} \quad \text{for} \quad 3 \leqslant r \leqslant 4,$$

$$0 \quad \text{for} \quad r \geqslant 4; \tag{6.8e}$$

$$c_{55}(r) = \pi^2 \left\{ \frac{243}{16} \cdot \frac{1}{r} - \frac{21}{2} + \frac{27}{8}r \right\} \quad \text{for} \quad 1 \leqslant r \leqslant 2,$$

$$\pi^2 \left\{ \frac{243}{16} \cdot \frac{1}{r} - \frac{33}{2} + \frac{63}{8}r - \frac{3}{8}r^3 \right\} \quad \text{for} \quad 2 \leqslant r \leqslant 3,$$

$$\pi^2 \left\{ 24 - 9r + \frac{3}{16}r^3 \right\} \quad \text{for} \quad 3 \leqslant r \leqslant 4,$$

$$0 \quad \text{for} \quad r \geqslant 4. \tag{6.8f}$$

d finally,

$$c_6(r) = c_{62}(r)\alpha + c_{63}(r)\alpha^2 + c_{64}(r)\alpha^3, \tag{6.9a}$$

ere

$$(r) = \pi^2 \left\{ \frac{27}{70} \cdot \frac{1}{r} - \frac{119}{252} + \frac{7}{15}r - \frac{r^2}{4} - \frac{r^3}{18} + \frac{r^4}{20} - \frac{r^6}{1260} \right\} \quad \text{for} \quad 1 \leqslant r \leqslant 2,$$

$$\pi^2 \left\{ \frac{27}{70} \cdot \frac{1}{r} - \frac{9}{4} + \frac{9}{5}r - \frac{r^2}{4} - \frac{r^3}{6} + \frac{r^4}{20} - \frac{r^6}{1260} \right\} \quad \text{for} \quad 2 \leqslant r \leqslant 3,$$

$$0 \quad \text{for} \quad r \geqslant 3; \tag{6.9b}$$

$$c_{63}(r) = \pi^2 \left\{ \frac{3}{r} - \frac{553}{36} + \frac{269}{20} r - \frac{7}{4} r^2 - \frac{25}{18} r^3 + \frac{7}{20} r^4 - \frac{r^6}{315} \right\} \quad \text{for} \quad 1 \leqslant r \leqslant 2,$$

$$= \pi^2 \left\{ \frac{2844}{315} \cdot \frac{1}{r} + \frac{503}{36} - \frac{163}{30} r - \frac{r^2}{2} + \frac{2}{3} r^3 - \frac{r^4}{10} \right\} \quad \text{for} \quad 2 \leqslant r \leqslant 3,$$

$$= \pi^2 \left\{ -\frac{256}{35} \cdot \frac{1}{r} + \frac{128}{9} - \frac{32}{5} r + \frac{5}{9} r^3 - \frac{r^4}{10} + \frac{r^6}{1260} \right\} \quad \text{for} \quad 3 \leqslant r \leqslant 4,$$

$$= 0 \quad \text{for} \quad r \geqslant 4; \tag{6.9c}$$

$$c_{64}(r) = \pi^2 \left\{ -\frac{3729}{420} \cdot \frac{1}{r} + \frac{14}{3} + \frac{58}{5} r - \frac{11}{2} r^2 - r^3 + \frac{r^4}{2} - \frac{r^6}{315} \right\} \quad \text{for} \quad 1 \leqslant r \leqslant 2$$

$$= \pi^2 \left\{ -\frac{1507}{28} \cdot \frac{1}{r} + \frac{866}{9} - \frac{2821}{60} r + \frac{15}{4} r^2 + \frac{37}{18} r^3 - \frac{7}{20} r^4 + \frac{r^6}{630} \right\} \quad \text{for} \quad 2 \leqslant r \leqslant$$

$$= \pi^2 \left\{ \frac{184}{5} \cdot \frac{1}{r} - \frac{448}{9} + \frac{109}{6} r - \frac{5}{4} r^2 - \frac{7}{18} r^3 + \frac{r^4}{20} \right\} \quad \text{for} \quad 3 \leqslant r \leqslant 4,$$

$$= 0 \quad \text{for} \quad r \geqslant 4. \tag{6.9d}$$

The functions allow the expressions for $a_2(r)$ for the various equations of the theory to be determined as function of α.

The exact expressions[5] for $a_2(r)$ are known in the present case, being obtained from the equations of section 4.3 of Chapter 4. Thus it is found that:

$$a_1(r) = \int \alpha(r_{13})\alpha(r_{23}) \, d\mathbf{r}_3, \tag{6.10a}$$

$$a_2(r) = \frac{1}{2} \{a_1(r)\}^2 + c_3(r) + 2c_4(r) + \frac{1}{2} c_7(r), \tag{6.10b}$$

where

$$c_3(r_{12}) = \int\int \alpha(r_{13}) \alpha(r_{24}) \alpha(r_{34}) \, d\mathbf{r}_3 \, d\mathbf{r}_4, \tag{6.10c}$$

$$c_4(r_{12}) = \int\int \alpha(r_{13}) \alpha(r_{24}) \alpha(r_{23}) \alpha(r_{34}) \, d\mathbf{r}_3 \, d\mathbf{r}_4, \tag{6.10d}$$

$$c_7(r_{12}) = \int\int \alpha(r_{13}) \alpha(r_{23}) \alpha(r_{24}) \alpha(r_{34}) \alpha(r_{14}) \, d\mathbf{r}_3 \, d\mathbf{r}_4. \tag{6.10e}$$

Comparison between the expressions (6.10) and the earlier expressions (6.5) show immediately the sources of the approximations introduced into the theory by the equations developed in the preceding chapters. To bring this out more clearly we form the difference between the exact expressions (6.10) and the several alternative expressions (6.5), denoted by Δa_2. We then have for:

ie Born–Green–Yvon equation:

$$\Delta a_{2B} \equiv a_2(r) - a_{2B}(r) = c_4(r) + \frac{1}{2} c_7(r) - c_5(r);$$

ie Kirkwood equation:

$$\Delta a_{2K} = \frac{1}{2} c_7(r) - \frac{1}{2} \left(c_6(r) - c_4(r) \right);$$

ie hypernetted chain equation:

$$\Delta a_{2H} = \frac{1}{2} c_7(r);$$

nd the Percus–Yevick equation:

$$\Delta a_{2P} = \frac{1}{2} \left\{ a_1(r) \right\}^2 + \frac{1}{2} c_7(r).$$

ach of the solutions (6.5) fails to account exactly for the integral $c_7(r$ iven by (6.10e).

The expansion (6.1) for the pair distribution is taken by these several ormulae as far as the quadratic term in n. No further terms have so far een reported in the literature.

) *The Hard-sphere Potential*

This potential is obtained from the square-well potential (6.2) by setting equal to zero. The resulting hard-sphere particle is taken as having unit iameter. The expressions (6.4)–(6.9) still apply but now with $\alpha = 0$. ecause α does not appear, all the formulae relating to the hard-sphere otential are independent of the temperature.

For the hard-sphere potential, therefore, equation (6.4a) becomes[6] $(r) = a_{11}(r)$, given by (6.4b), and the function $a_2(r)$ again has one of the orms (6.5) applying to a specific equation, but with: $c_3(r) = c_{31}(r)$, given y (6.6b); $c_4(r) = c_{41}(r)$, given by (6.7b); $c_5(r) = c_{51}(r)$, given by (6.8b); nd $c_6(r) = 0$. The exact expressions for a_2 calculated from the formulae .10) are also available.[7]

The further coefficient $a_3(r)$ in the expansion (6.1) is also known[8] for iis potential function for the Born–Green–Yvon equation (4.22) under ie Kirkwood superposition approximation. Explicitly, we have for $_3(r)$, the expression:

$$a_3(r) = a_1(r) a_{2B}(r) - \frac{1}{3} \left\{ a_1(r) \right\}^3 + a_{31}(r), \qquad (6.11a)$$

where

$$a_{31}(r) = \pi^2 \left\{ \frac{10829}{57600} \cdot \frac{1}{r} - \frac{26659}{45360} + \frac{9913}{16128} r - \frac{64}{315} r^2 \right.$$

$$- \frac{7951}{120960} r^3 + \frac{14}{225} r^4 - \frac{1}{90} r^5 - \frac{1}{945} r^6$$

$$\left. + \frac{1}{2520} r^7 - \frac{1}{453600} r^9 \right\} \quad \text{for} \quad 1 \leqslant r \leqslant 2,$$

$$= \pi^2 \left\{ \frac{80539}{403200} \cdot \frac{1}{r} - \frac{20963}{9072} + \frac{30331}{11520} r - \frac{3793}{5040} r^2 \right.$$

$$- \frac{749}{3456} r^3 + \frac{533}{3600} r^4 - \frac{31}{1920} r^5 - \frac{61}{15120} r^6$$

$$\left. + \frac{5}{5376} r^7 - \frac{1}{103680} r^9 \right\} \quad \text{for} \quad 2 \leqslant r \leqslant 3,$$

$$= \pi^2 \left\{ - \frac{2048}{1575} \cdot \frac{1}{r} + \frac{11264}{2835} - \frac{128}{45} r + \frac{128}{315} r^2 + \frac{8}{27} r^3 \right.$$

$$- \frac{28}{225} r^4 + \frac{1}{90} r^5 + \frac{2}{945} r^6 - \frac{1}{2520} r^7$$

$$\left. + \frac{1}{453600} r^9 \right\} \quad \text{for} \quad 3 \leqslant r \leqslant 4,$$

$$= 0 \quad \text{for} \quad r \geqslant 4. \tag{6.11b}$$

Further members a_j of the expansion (6.1) have not been reported in the literature.

The expressions for the hard-core potential have useful application to real gases at high temperatures.

(c) The Square-mound Potential

The coefficients $a_1(r)$ and $a_2(r)$ in the expansion (6.1) have been given by Cole[9] for this potential function, for the single case of the Born–Green–Yvon equation under the Kirkwood superposition approximation.

6.2. THE VIRIAL COEFFICIENTS FOR A MODEL GAS OF SPHERICAL PARTICLES

The virial coefficients are deduced from a knowledge of the pair distribution $g^{(2)}$ in the density expansion form (6.1) through either pressure equation (3.38) or (3.46). Alternatively, exact values of the coefficients are obtained by evaluating the integrals (4.44). A comparison between the expressions derived from (3.38) or (3.46) and the exact expressions, provides a method for checking the accuracy of the predictions of the statistical theory in the low density limit. It must be realised at once that such a test does not necessarily give direct information about the accuracy of the theory at liquid densities. And again, because idealised potential functions are involved it cannot be expected that data calculated with their use will have more than qualitative application to even restricted real situations. We consider now the various potential forms.

The insertion of the density expansion (6.1) for the pair distribution into the expression (3.38) for the pressure, leads to expressions for the virial coefficients distinguished by the subscript v to denote the virial origin:

$$B_v = \frac{2\pi}{3} \int_0^\infty r^3 \alpha'(r) \, dr, \tag{6.12a}$$

$$C_v = \frac{2\pi}{3} \int_0^\infty r^3 a_1(r) \, \alpha'(r) \, dr, \tag{6.12b}$$

$$D_v = \frac{2\pi}{3} \int_0^\infty r^3 a_2(r) \alpha'(r) \, dr, \tag{6.12c}$$

$$E_v = \frac{2\pi}{3} \int_0^\infty r^3 a_3(r) \alpha'(r) \, dr, \tag{6.12d}$$

and so on. Here, the function $\alpha(r)$ is defined by equation (3.49) and

$$\alpha'(r) = \frac{\partial \alpha(r)}{\partial r} = -\frac{\partial \chi(r)}{\partial r} \exp\{-\chi(r)\}. \tag{6.12e}$$

Alternatively, the insertion of (6.1) into the compressibility expression (3.46) also leads to a set of expressions for the virial coefficients, denoted now by a subscript c to denote their origin in fluctuation theory:

$$B_c = -2\pi \int_0^\infty \alpha(r) r^2 \, dr, \tag{6.13a}$$

$$C_c = \frac{4}{3} B_c^2 - \frac{4\pi}{3} \int_0^\infty a_1(r)[\alpha(r)+1] r^2 \, dr, \tag{6.13b}$$

$$D_c = 3B_c C_c - 2B_c^3 - \pi \int_0^\infty a_2(r)[\alpha(r)+1] r^2 \, dr, \tag{6.13c}$$

$$E_c = \frac{16}{5} B_c \left[D_c + B_c^3 - \frac{9}{4} B_c C_c \right] + \frac{9}{5} C_c^2 - \frac{4\pi}{5} \int_0^\infty a_3(r)[\alpha(r)+1] r^2 \, dr, \tag{6.13d}$$

and so on.

The corresponding members of the sets of equations (6.12) and (6.13) will be the same if exact information is available for the coefficients a_j. Approximate information about a_j will lead to different numerical values for the corresponding members of the sets (6.12) and (6.13) so that the theory will then show inconsistency. Comparison is to be made between numerical values deduced from the sets (6.12), (6.13), and the set (3.55). This is to be done for the various potential functions used so far.

(a) *The Square-well Potential*

We insert the expressions (6.4) and (6.5) into the set (6.12) and (6.13) to obtain the virial coefficients B, C, and D as function of the temperature through the parameter α defined by (6.3). We find[1] the following results.

For all the equations, $B_c = B_v = B$, and $C_c = C_v = C$, where

$$B(T) = b(1 - 7\alpha), \tag{6.14a}$$

and

$$C(T) = b^2 \left(\frac{5}{8} - \frac{17}{8}\alpha + 17\alpha^2 - \frac{81}{4}\alpha^3 \right). \tag{6.14b}$$

Here, $b = (16/3)\pi\sigma^3$, that is b is a volume equal to four times the volume of the particle hard-core repulsive region. Up to this point the calculations are both consistent and exact for the expressions (6.14a) and (6.14b) also follow respectively from the formulae (3.55a) and (3.55b). Consistency and exactness are lost beyond this point.

For the fourth virial coefficient D we have the following expressions.[1]

For the Born–Green–Yvon equation (4.22), a_{2B} is given by (6.5a) and from (6.12c) and (6.13c) we have:

$$4480D_v^B = b^3[1009 + 7453\alpha - 126658\alpha^2 + 287560\alpha^3$$
$$+ 198280\alpha^4 - 738990\alpha^5], \tag{6.15a}$$

and

$$26880D_c^B = b^3[9204 - 18492\alpha - 473298\alpha^2 + 350280\alpha^3$$
$$+ 1760460\alpha^4 - 3747870\alpha^5]. \tag{6.15b}$$

For the Kirkwood equation (4.25):

$$4480D_v^K = b^3[627 + 10991\alpha - 141200\alpha^2 + 313440\alpha^3$$
$$+ 37000\alpha^4 - 714420\alpha^5], \tag{6.15c}$$

and

$$26880D_c^K = b^3[11876 - 41020\alpha - 242955\alpha^2 - 404978\alpha^3$$
$$+ 2008050\alpha^4 - 3674160\alpha^5]. \tag{6.15d}$$

For the hypernetted chain equation (5.7):

$$44880D_v^H = b^3[1995 + 5231\alpha - 95900\alpha^2 + 203224\alpha^3$$
$$+ 405260\alpha^4 - 918540\alpha^5], \qquad (6.15e)$$

and

$$26880D_c^H = b^3[5623 + 58755\alpha - 759556\alpha^2 + 1813616\alpha^3$$
$$+ 912580\alpha^4 - 4592700\alpha^5]. \qquad (6.15f)$$

For the Percus–Yevick equation (5.10):

$$560D_v^P = b^3[140 + 1507\alpha - 15505\alpha^2 + 37233\alpha^3$$
$$+ 23725\alpha^4 - 102060\alpha^5], \qquad (6.15g)$$

and

$$6720D_c^P = b^3[1995 + 5231\alpha - 95900\alpha^2 + 203224\alpha^3$$
$$+ 405260\alpha^4 - 918540\alpha^5]. \qquad (6.15h)$$

The first thing to notice is that in each case D_v is not equal to D_c, so that the theory does not show internal consistency. This ambiguity is a present deficiency of the theory. The second point is that each form of D differs from the others, and it is not clear which is the better one. This can be tested only against alternative data known to be more accurate.

Alternative data is in fact available being derived from the expression (3.55c). Now the more general square-well potential can be used where the repulsive and attractive regions are not of equal extent, i.e. where (6.2) is replaced by the more general form:

$$\psi(r) = \infty \quad \text{for} \quad r < 1,$$
$$\psi(r) = -\varepsilon \quad \text{for} \quad 1 < r < g, \qquad (6.16)$$
$$\psi(r) = 0 \quad \text{for} \quad r > g,$$

where g is not necessarily equal to 2. Kihara[10] has given expressions for the second and third virial coefficients as follows:

$$B(T) = b[1 - (g^3 - 1)\alpha], \qquad (6.17a)$$

$$8C(T) = b^2[5 - (g^6 - 18g^4 + 32g^3 - 15)\alpha$$
$$- (2g^6 - 36g^4 + 32g^3 + 18g^2 - 16)\alpha^2 \qquad (6.17b)$$
$$- (6g^6 - 18g^4 + 18g^2 - 6)\alpha^3] \quad \text{for} \quad g \leqslant 2,$$

$$8C(T) = b^2[5 - 17\alpha - (-32g^2 + 18g^2 + 48)\alpha^2$$
$$- (5g^6 - 32g^3 + 18g^2 + 26)\alpha^3] \quad \text{for} \quad g \geqslant 2. \qquad (6.17c)$$

The expressions (6.17) reduce to those of (6.14) for the special case $g = 2$, when the potential (6.16) reduces to the earlier form (6.2).

Exact expressions for $D(T)$ are not available although expressions of good accuracy are for the case $g = 2$. The formula has been given by Katsura:

$$D(T) = b^3[0\cdot28642 + 1\cdot5397\alpha - 23\cdot554\alpha^2 + 53\cdot645\alpha^3$$
$$+ 69\cdot859\alpha^4 - 170\cdot01\alpha^5 - 14\cdot777\alpha^6]. \qquad (6.18)$$

This formula was derived using cluster arguments: two of the expressions in (3.55c) were evaluated analytically but the third integral was evaluated numerically. Improvements have been made by Katsura[10] and Barker and Monaghan[11]. Values of g and ε have been listed in Appendix 2.7 (iv), where it is seen that $g = 1\cdot8$ is a fair representation for the simpler molecules. For this case we have

$$B(T) = b[1 - 4\cdot83\alpha],$$
$$C(T) = b^2[0\cdot6250 - 2\cdot085\alpha + 10\cdot118\alpha^2 - 8\cdot430\alpha^3].$$

The expression (6.18) does not apply for $g = 1\cdot8$.

According to these formulae, there is a temperature for a given [well depth ε for which $B(T) = 0$, viz.:

$$(g^3 - 1)\alpha_B = 1.$$

This is the Boyle temperature T_B and the corresponding fluid pressure is given by:

$$p = nkT_B + 0(n^3).$$

At this temperature the gas behaves virtually as if it were ideal to order n^3. The existence of a Boyle temperature is seen to be linked with the attractive regions of the interparticle potential. For if there were no attraction, i.e. if $\varepsilon = 0$, then B would be a non-vanishing constant irrespective of the temperature. (See Fig. 7.)

(b) *The Hard-sphere Potential*

The formulae for the square-well reduce to those of the hard-sphere when $\alpha = 0$ (or when $\alpha = -1$ they become those for a hard-sphere of double radius). Values up to the sixth virial coefficient are available for this case, including values for HNC 2 and PY 2. These are as follows, [12,46] derived from the expressions (6.14) and (6.15).

$$B = b \qquad\qquad C = \frac{5}{8} b^2.$$

$$D_v^B = \frac{1009}{4480} b^3 = 0\cdot2252b^3; \qquad D_c^B = \frac{9204}{26880} b^3 = 0\cdot3424b^3.$$

$$D_v^K = \frac{627}{4480}\, b^3 = 0{\cdot}1400b^3; \qquad D_c^K = \frac{11876}{26880}\, b^3 = 0{\cdot}4418b^3.$$

$$D_v^H = \frac{57}{128}\, b^3 = 0{\cdot}4453b^3; \qquad D_c^H = \frac{5623}{26880}\, b^3 = 0{\cdot}2092b^3.$$

$$D_v^P = \frac{1}{4}\, b^3 = 0{\cdot}2500b^3; \qquad D_c^P = \frac{19}{64}\, b^3 = 0{\cdot}2969b^3.$$

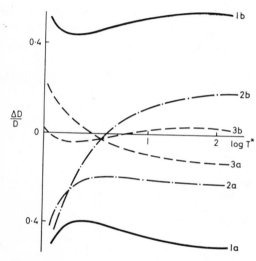

1 a : HNC I   (virial)
1 b : HNC I   (compressibility)

2 a : BGY   (virial)
2 b : BGY   (compressibility)

3 a : PY I   (virial)
3 b : PY I   (compressibility)

FIG. 7. Plot for the square-well potential gas of the relative difference between the various values of the fourth virial coefficient derived from the several equations of the theory and the best values for D, derived from equation (6.18) or from the expressions of Barker and Monoghan. The temperature is that relative to the Boyle temperature.

The corresponding exact values[13] derived from equations (3.55) are

$$B = b, \quad C = \frac{5}{8}\, b^2, \quad D = 0{\cdot}2869b^3.$$

We compare the various approximate values for the fourth virial coefficient D^j against the exact value D by forming the ratio:

$$\Delta D = \frac{D^j - D}{D},$$

and the results are collected in Table 3.

TABLE 3.

Equation	ΔD (virial)	ΔD (compress)
BGY	−0·2147	+0·1930
K	−0·5120	+0·5399
HNC 1	+0·5521	−0·2708
PY 1	−0·1287	+0·0349

It is seen that the PY 1 equation gives the more accurate data of the list but that the BGY values are not unacceptable.

The HNC 2 and PY 2 equations provide exact consistent information for D, as does the Fisher scheme outline in section 4.2(d).

Further values are also available. Thus, for the fifth virial coefficient we have Table 4.*

TABLE 4.

Equation	E_v/b^4	E_c/b^4	Source reference
BGY	0·0475	0·1335	8, 16
HNC 1	0·1447	0·0493	17
HNC 2	–	0·123	19
PY 1	0·0859	0·1211	18
PY 2	–	0·107	19

An exact value of E is not known[†] but Monte Carlo calculations have provided the value[15]

$$E = (0·115 \pm 0·005)b^4.$$

The inconsistency of the theory is quite marked where calculations are available, but no extensive information is yet available about the virial values for HNC 2 and PY 2. It is clear, however, that the PY 2 and HNC 2 values must represent a considerable improvement over the other values.

The sixth virial coefficient is known for HNC 1 and PY 1: thus,

$$F_v^H = 0·0382b^5; \qquad F_c^H = 0·0281b^5,$$
$$F_v^P = 0·0273b^5, \qquad F_c^P = 0·0449b^5.$$

Values are not yet available for other equations, including HNC 2 and PY 2.

It is seen that the equations of the theory developed in the last two chapters are able to provide reasonable values for the first six virial coefficients

* See also Appendix 6, p. 265.
† See also p. 265.

or a hard-sphere gas. Such values have some practical interest since a hard-phere potential is a reasonable approximation to that for real matter at igh temperatures.

c) *The Square-mound Potential*

The virial coefficients for this potential function, defined by equation A2.2) of Appendix 2, are also available for BGY. In this case it is found[9] hat:

$$B = bz, \qquad C = \frac{5}{8} b^2 z^3, \tag{6.19a}$$

$$D_v^B = \left[-\frac{34}{35} z^4 + \frac{5361}{4480} z^5 \right] b^3,$$

$$D_c^B = \left[-\frac{68}{105} z^3 + \frac{193}{256} z^4 + \frac{6347}{26880} z^5 \right] b^3. \tag{6.19b}$$

Hiroike[20] obtains, alternatively, the value:

$$D = \left[-\frac{34}{35} z^4 + \frac{6347}{4480} z^5 - 0 \cdot 1584 z^6 \right] b^3. \tag{6.19c}$$

In these formulae z is defined by equation (A6.1) of Appendix 6. There is here no finite Boyle temperature.

d) *Other Potential Forms*

Formulae for the virial coefficients for other potential forms have been given by a number of authors. The information is scant and concerns B and C. These are available for the inverse power-law potential and the Sutherland potential given respectively by the expressions (A2.3) and (A2.5) of Appendix 2.

Expressions are also available for B and C for the Lennard-Jones (12–6) potential and also for the (m–6) potential function. For details of the formulae, which are more useful for numerical predictions of real properties than as a direct test for the theory, the reader is referred to the original literature[21]. These expressions provide a surprisingly accurate representation of measured data for simple gases.[22, 14]

e) *Consistency Procedures*

Before leaving the study of the virial coefficients we must say a word about certain attempts that have been made to obtain internal consistency in the theory. Two sets of calculation will be considered here.

The first involves the superposition approximation in the form (4.7). According to the arguments of section 4.3 the function h_3 can, at low enough densities, be expanded in powers of the density as in equation (4.46). The first term in this expansion is given by equation (4.47). With the functions Y_j specified, the pair distribution (6.1) is determined on the basis of the Born–Green–Yvon equation (4.20) by evaluating the integrals (4.48), (4.49), and (4.50). If the functions Y_j are specified exactly, then this procedure is exact; approximate information for Y_j leads to only approximate information about the pair distribution.

Mathematically, the simplest case is when the Y_j are independent of the particle triplet separation distances. In this case,

$$\Xi_2(r) = Y_1 a_1(r), \tag{6.20a}$$

$$\Xi_3(r) = Y_1 \left[a_2^K(r) - \frac{1}{2} a_1^2(r) \right] + Y_2 a_2^K(r), \tag{6.20b}$$

and so on. The choice of the Y_j as being independent of the particle separation distances, although these coefficients will be a function of (ψ/kT), has the immediate consequence that normalisation of the triplet function $g^{(3)}$ is violated. We must, therefore, treat the function $g^{(3)}$ obtained by using the expressions (6.19) as simply a device for obtaining eventually significant information about the pair distribution, and not an expression of the physical characteristics of the triplet function itself. On this basis, Cole has used (6.19) for the calculation of virial coefficients, choosing the coefficients Y_j in such a way that consistency is obtained in the calculation with respect to the pressure equations (3.38) and (3.46). Reference to equations (6.12) and (6.13) shows that the coefficients B and C are independent of the coefficients Y_j, that D depends upon Y_1, E upon Y_1 and Y_2, and so on.

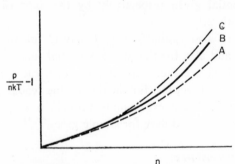

FIG. 8. Pressure as function of number density for hard-sphere gas. Curve A using Kirkwood superposition approximation and pressure arguments; curve C using this approximation and compressibility arguments; curve B using the modified superposition approximation and consistency arguments.

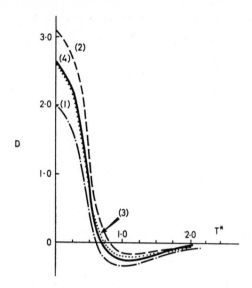

Fɪɢ. 9. Fourth virial coefficient for a square-mound potential gas, from equations (6.19) and (6.21). Comparison is made with the equation of Hiroike (6.19c). This figure is taken from G. H. A. Cole, 1962, *J. Chem. Phys.* **37**, No. 8, 1631–5

Y_1 is choosen such that $D_v = D_c = D^m$, and so on.[23] For a hard-sphere potential function, these conditions prevail if;

$$Y_1 = 0 \cdot 1014\, b, \quad \text{and} \quad Y_2 = -0 \cdot 0424\, b^2.$$

These lead to values:

$$D^m = 0 \cdot 2886\, b^3, \quad \text{and} \quad E^m = 0 \cdot 0240\, b^4. \tag{6.21}$$

While the value for D^m is highly satisfactory that for E^m is too low by a factor of about 5. The method may have value in the calculation of the fourth virial coefficient for gases. Usually, the pressure at low densities is well represented by a virial expansion that terminates at this term.

The method can be applied to the square-mound potential function: for D^m there follows the formula[23]:

$$\left[1 + \frac{5}{32}\, z \right] D^m = \left[-\frac{289}{210}\, z^4 + \frac{152191}{71680}\, z^5 - \frac{35555}{86016}\, z^6 \right] b^3. \tag{6.21}$$

This expression is to be compared with the previous expression (6.19c) due to Hiroike[20] (see Fig. 9).

For the square-well potential there results alternatively the expression:[23]

$$26880 \, [37 - 465\alpha + 1704\alpha^2 - 162\alpha^3]D^m$$
$$= b^3[286998 - 2638944\alpha - 26851050\alpha^2 + 40901162\alpha^3$$
$$- 1758651228\alpha^4 + 1386983676\alpha^5 + 4964391900\alpha^6$$
$$- 7744805280\alpha^7 + 273724920\alpha^8]. \tag{6.22}$$

The primary objection to these calculations is the fact that $g^{(3)}$ is not normalised in the way necessary for its interpretation as a distribution function.[25] This objection does not apply to an alternative approach due to Rowlinson.[24] The starting point is now the expression (5.2) for the total correlation between a representative particle pair, and involves a specification of the direct correlation $c(r)$. For known functions $g^{(2)}$ it is a fact that the difference $c_H - c_p$ given by (5.11) is numerically small, where c_H is the HNC 1 form (5.6) and c_p is the PY 1 form (5.8). Let us, therefore, define the direct correlation function $c_R(r)$ by:

$$c_R(r) = c_p(r) + \beta[y(r) - 1 - \ln y(r)], \tag{6.23}$$

where β is a simple numeric for a given ratio ψ/kT. β is, then, not a function of the pair separation. The parameter β is to be chosen so as to provide consistency between calculated values of the virial coefficients according to the same criteria as the functions Y_j considered above. In particular, β can be expanded in powers of the density for sufficiently low densities[45]. The method has been applied, so far,* only for the hard-sphere potential with the results:

$$D^R = 0 \cdot 2824 b^3,$$
$$E^R = 0 \cdot 1041 b^4, \tag{6.24}$$
$$F^R = 0 \cdot 0341 b^5.$$

These values are remarkably good although D^R is not in fact quite as close to the known exact value as D^m in (6.21). E^R is definitely superior to E^m. The method would seem well capable of providing accurate virial data for a range of interparticle force potential forms at least as far as the sixth virial coefficient. With the use of a realistic potential function[26], results of practical significance for simple molecules can be anticipated in the future.[43]

The case of non-spherical particles can be of wider practical interest but our present knowledge for these cases is less than for the spherical particle situations. References to the literature for non-spherical particles are collected in Appendix 6.27.

* See p. 266.

6.3. THE PAIR DISTRIBUTION FOR A MODEL LIQUID
OF SPHERICAL PARTICLES

At liquid densities the expansion of $g^{(2)}$ in powers of the density is ssentially a divergent series and so is not of physical interest. For liquid ensities, therefore, it is necessary to face the full problem of solving the quations of the theory in general terms applicable to any density.

) *Analytic Approach*

The most generally useful solution is one in analytic terms, but the equa- ons of the theory are not readily amenable to solution in analytic terms. ttempts have been made to deduce analytic solutions of the equations llowing the initial work of H. S. Green in connection with BGY.

Green[28] considered spherically symmetric particles and used BGY nder the Kirkwood superposition approximation, i.e. he considered quation (4.22). The equation (4.22) is non-linear, and one central mathe- atical procedure adopted by Green was that of linearising the equation. This has important consequences for the physical evaluation of the results, ince the physical consequences of the loss of the non-linearity are very ifficult to assess with any confidence. Indeed, it appears in the event that 1 linearising the BGY equation, no essential physical features are lost ut we cannot always be sure that this will be so.

In solving BGY equation (4.22) the pair distribution is written in the orm:

$$g^{(2)}(r) = \exp\left\{-\chi(r)\right\} \exp f(r),$$

nd $f(r)$ is some unknown function of the separation distance. The linear- sation procedure is introduced by assuming $f(r)$ to be sufficiently small or us to write:

$$\exp f(r) = 1 + f(r),$$

o that

$$g^{(2)}(r) = \exp\left\{-\chi(r)\right\}[1 + f(r)]. \tag{6.25}$$

The insertion of (6.25) into the non-linear BGY equation (4.22) provides, ecause $f(r)$ is small, a linear first order equation for $f(r)$.

Because the interparticle force is assumed to be short-ranged, both $\alpha(r)$, defined by equation (3.49), and the first space gradient $\alpha'(r)$ can be assumed egligibly small except at small values of r (less than say three particle iameters). If this is accepted, then Green proposes that in products in- volving $f(r)$ and either $\alpha(r)$ or $\alpha'(r)$, the unknown function $f(r)$ can be re- placed by some small mean value, written $\varepsilon-1$. Since $\varepsilon-1$ is assumed small, then ε is virtually unity. This means that, at small values of r, we are to insert into the appropriate terms of the equation for $f(r)$ a mean value of the expression $g^{(2)}(r) \, \alpha(r)$. This is rather a drastic assumption and its physical meaning is obscure.

Using these approximations, Green arrives at the explicit expression for $f(r)$:

$$f(r) = \frac{1}{\sqrt{2\pi}} \int_{-\infty}^{\infty} \left[\frac{s \varepsilon h(s)}{v - \varepsilon h(s)} \right] \frac{\sin (sr)}{sr} \, ds, \qquad (6.26a)$$

where, in Green's notation,

$$\sqrt{2\pi} \, sh(s) = \int r\alpha(r) \sin (sr) \, dr; \quad v = (2\pi^{3/2}n)^{-1}. \qquad (6.26b)$$

The insertion of these formulae into equation (6.25) gives an explicit expression for the pair distribution.

The details of $f(r)$ depend, according to the formulae, upon the details of the function $[v - \varepsilon h(s)]$. If v is sufficiently large (which means if the number density n is sufficiently small), then we can write:

$$[v - \varepsilon h(s)]^{-1} = \frac{1}{v} \left[1 + \frac{\varepsilon h(s)}{v} + \cdots \right]. \qquad (6.26c)$$

Accordingly, $f(r)$ can be expanded in powers of n which is appropriate for low gas densities. With $y(r)$ given the (12–6) potential, the formulae (6.25) and (6.26) provide numerical data for $g^{(2)}$ which agrees reasonably well with experimental data for monatomic gases.[29]

On the other hand, when the ratio $\left(\dfrac{\varepsilon h(s)}{v} \right)$ is not small, an expansion in powers of density is not valid so that this circumstance applies to liquid densities. The density for which $v = \varepsilon h(s)$ can be associated with the physical change from liquid to solid: it is less than that for particle close packing so that such a physical interpretation is legitimate. Analytical modifications[28] of Green's original procedure by McLellan and Rodriguez have failed to provide better than purely qualitative numerical data from the analytic theory.

Kirkwood and Boggs[30] have alternatively considered an analytic solution of the non-linear equation (4.25), under the Kirkwood superposition approximation, but in the linear approximation only. By making a number of mathematical approximations, an expression for $g^{(2)}$ is obtained for a hard-sphere fluid which has qualitatively many features of observed data.

Generally speaking, the analytic approach to the calculation of the pair distribution for general densities has proved disappointing.

(b) *Numerical Approach*

The worst difficulties of the analytic approach are avoided if numerical solutions are sought instead. In particular, non-linear effects can be accounted for.

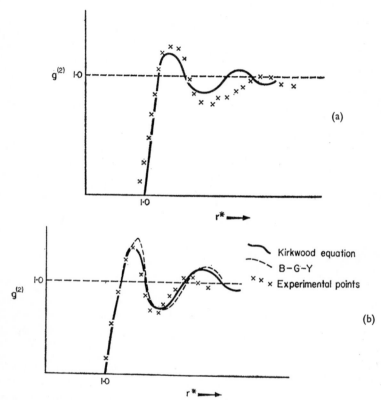

FIG. 10.(a) Comparison between approximate analytic expression for the pair distribution (solid line) using the approach of Kirkwood and Boggs, and experimental data (crosses) for liquid argon at 89° K. (b) Data for $g^{(2)}$ derived numerically for the Born–Green–Yvon and Kirkwood equations compared with experimental data for liquid argon at 89° K.

The first numerical solutions were given by Kirkwood and his collaborators in a series of papers.[31,44] Attractive features of an interparticle force potential modelled on the (12–6) potential were included, and numerical results obtained for $g^{(2)}$ which agree reasonably well with data measured for argon (see Fig. 10).

Numerical solutions of PY 1 and HNC 1 are also available, and particularly for the (12–6) potential (see Fig. 11) and also for the Guggenheim–McGlashan potential (see Appendix 2.6). Particularly important are some comprehensive numerical studies by Khan,[32] using interparticle force potentials specifically adapted to argon and krypton. The discussion given by Khan is too lengthy to report here, and the reader is referred to the original papers for details. We restrict ourselves to general comments on some of the conclusions drawn by Khan.

Apparently, it is necessary to link a particular form of potential with a particular equation, for Khan's calculation shows that when using PY 1 the Guggenheim–McGlashan potential gives better agreement with experimental X-ray data than does the (12–6) potential: but the situation is

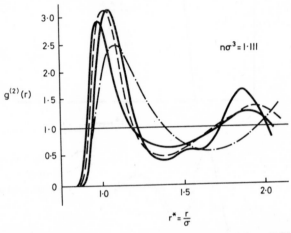

FIG. 11. Pair distribution for Lennard–Jones fluid derived from BGY (curve 1), HNC 1 (curve 3), and PY 1 (curve 2) theories. For comparison, machine calculations (MC) (curve 4) are also included. Sec. ref 6.36.
(From A.A. Broyles, Chung and Sahlin, 1962, *J. Chem. Phys.* **37**, 2462.)

reversed with HNC 1 where the (12–6) potential is to be preferred for comparison with experiment. The numerical studies also show that neither PY 1 nor HNC 1 can be expected to provide good data at high densities. The PY 2 and HNC 2 theories remain untested. Khan also finds that the Guggenheim–McGlashan potential is more realistic for argon at low temperatures than is the (12–6) potential. Interestingly, the PY 1 equation apparently agrees more closely with Monte-Carlo results for hard-spheres than does HNC 1 whereas the reverse is true if the attractive features of the potential are also included. One interesting conclusion drawn by Khan concerns the very fine detail found on the experimental $g^{(2)}$ curves. This is usually ascribed to inaccuracies introduced by the Fourier inversion process: Khan has given reasons for believing that not all are spurious but that some at least arise from fluid structural characteristics.

In summary, considerably more study of the solutions of the equation or $g^{(2)}$ is necessary than has been attempted so far at the lower temperatures. And not only is it necessary to improve on the equation for $g^{(2)}$: t appears increasingly important also to improve the specification of the nterparticle force potential itself.[33]

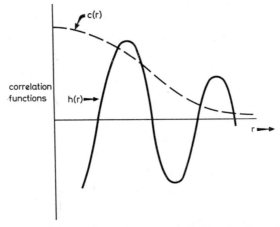

FIG. 12. The total and direct correlation functions for liquid argon, derived from neutron data (after Johnson, Hutchinson, and March[6.34]).

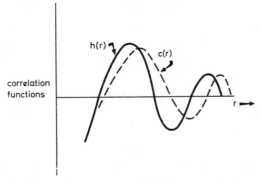

FIG. 13. The total and direct correlation functions for liquid rubidium, derived from neutron data (after Johnson, Hutchinson, and March[6.34]).

An interesting approach to the study of the interparticle potential funcion has been made by March[34] and his co-workers. The idea is to invert he usual procedure of assuming an expression for the interparticle force and from this calculating the pair distribution; instead, the equations of the heory are used to determine interparticle force potential data from experimental data for the pair distribution. Both X-ray and neutron diffraction

data have been used for this purpose (see Figs. 12 and 13), and both th
BGY and PY 1 equations were used in the calculations.

The pair potential for argon and liquid sodium are quite distinctivel
different. For argon the known features for $\psi(r)$ inferred[35] from solid an
gas studies are well reproduced, except for a few per cent numerical dis
screpancy at the potential minimum. The overall form is much like tha
prescribed by the (12–6) potential although this description is only qual
tative. For the liquid metals the curve is quite different, showing an oscilla
ing form of decreasing amplitude and three maxima were quite distinguish
able. The results can also be compared with those for the total correla
tion $h(r)$ and the direct correlation $c(r)$. Both for insulators and for liqui
metals $h(r)$ has the form of a succession of decreasing maxima and minim
about zero, with little distinction between the two cases. The curves fo
$c(r)$, however, are quite different. For argon, $c(r)$ is smooth and has a qua
itative similarity to one arm of a Gaussian distribution: for rubidiu
(representing the liquid metals) the $c(r)$ data is very close to the $h(r)$ dat
so that $c(r)$ is totally different as function of the separation distance for
liquid metal than for the typical rare element fluid argon. The very strik
ing difference between metals and non-metals may well be of cruci
importance in the later development of the theory.

6.4. THERMODYNAMIC DATA

The ultimate aim of the theory is the calculation of reliable thermodynam
ic data for fluids. This must rest upon an adequate representation of th
interparticle force and upon an adequate equation for the specification c
fluid (and especially liquid) structure. The direct comparison between ca
culated data, using a specific interparticle potential function, and exper.
mental data is not necessarily a test for the theory unless the potenti
function agrees closely with the real form. A more immediate test of th
theory is the comparison between its predicted values and alternative mor
exact calculated data. In this way, the equations of the theory based on th
distribution functions can be subjected to a quantitative test. The calcula
tions using simple potential forms may also reproduce experimental dat
qualitatively: the quantitative representation of measured data is then t
be approached by suitable modifications or replacements of specific fea
tures of the interparticle force potential data. In what follows we are cor
cerned principally with testing the theory against more accurate calculate
data, and not with a direct quantitative comparison with experiment.

The first requirement for us is to define our standard data against whic
those for the theory are to be measured. This we take to be numerica

tudies, involving electronic computation, in either the Monte-Carlo or he particle trajectory forms. In the Monte-Carlo method (MC) the nec-ssary configurational integrals are evaluated to prescribed accuracy by ntroducing specific probability concepts into the rigorous theory. In the particle trajectory approach, phase averages are derived on the basis of lynamical phase trajectories portrayed mathematically. The limit at the present time is the small number of particles that can be treated at the pres-nt time (not greater than about 10^3); it is not immediately clear whether he present number of particles is sufficiently large or not for quantitative tudies. These various "mathematical experiments" promise to play an mportant future role not only in the theory of fluids but also in the devel-pment of statistical physics generally. The reader is referred to the liter-ture[36] for details, and particularly to Chapter 8 of the book by Fisher[37]. 3y using these mathematical techniques, thermodynamic data are derived or a specific interparticle potential form such as the hard-core, with no ttraction, or the hard-core potential core with a Lennard-Jones potential orm at distances greater than σ. These data are to be regarded as the stand-rd against which results from the statistical theory involving the distri-ution functions are to be compared. To begin with, an analytic equation f state is known for a hard-sphere fluid.[38] The equation of state now has he general virial form:

$$\frac{p}{nkT} = 1 + 8bng^{(2)}(\sigma),$$

vhere $g^{(2)}(\sigma)$ is the value of the pair distribution at a particle diameter, nd b is four times the volume of each particle. The compressibility expres-ion for the equation of state will also involve values of σ for distances great-r that $\sigma = r$. Of particular interest is an analytic equation of state given or PY 1. Two forms are found, depending upon whether the virial pressure quation (3.36) or the compressibility equation (3.46) is used. These expres-ions are:

$$\left(\frac{p}{nkT}\right)_V = \frac{1+2x+3x^2}{(1-x)^2},$$

$$\left(\frac{p}{nkT}\right)_C = \frac{1+x+x^2}{(1-x)^3}, \tag{6.27}$$

vhere

$$x = \frac{1}{6}\pi\sigma^3 n.$$

These equations are the same as those obtained by Reiss, Frisch, and .ebowitz[39] using a different method. The interesting point about these

equations is that the denominator is zero when $x = 1$, i.e. when $\pi\sigma^3 n = 6$
This density n is associated with a phase transition. Unfortunately, the
fluid density associated with this condition is impossibly high, since the
close-packed array of hard spheres has a density of $x = 0.741$. It is on
these grounds concluded that a PY hard-sphere fluid does not show a

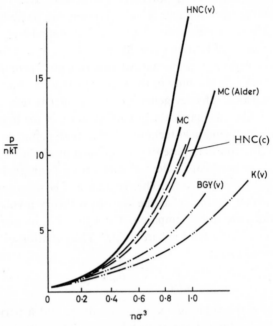

FIG. 14. Equation of state for a rigid sphere fluid as function of the density for
HNC 1, BGY, and K equations compared with the machine calculations (MC)
of Alder.
(From M. Klein, 1963, *J. Chem. Phys.* **39**, 1367.)

transition from liquid to solid. This contrasts with the BGY and K equations, and the computer experimental data, which all show a transition
region. For BGY the transition density is at $n/n_0 = 1/1.48$ and for K
it is at $n/n_0 = 1/1.24$ when $n_0\sigma^3 = \sqrt{2}$ gives the close-packed density. For
the computer model the density ratio is about 0.6. It seems that the BGY
and K equations are at least qualitatively correct in showing a phase transition for hard-sphere whereas the PY 1 and also the HNC 1 equations do
not. The point is not yet finally clear and Temperley[40] has recently suggested the possibility of PY 1 showing a transition. This important point
not clear and more work is awaited: the behaviour of PY 2 and HNC
in this connection is completely unknown. These comments refer to hard

spheres, but interest is also focused on interparticle potentials showing attractive features. Results here are virtually non-existent.

Thermodynamic data calculated from BGY, K, PY 1, and HNC 1 are compared against the mathematical model data in Figs. 14–17. Finally,

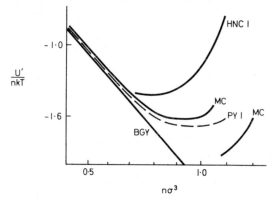

FIG. 15. Internal energy for a Lennard-Jones fluid calculated from the BGY, HNC 1, and PY 1 equations. For comparison, machine calculations (MC) are also included.
(From A. A. Broyles, Chung and Sahlin, 1962, *J. Chem. Phys.* **37**, 2462.)

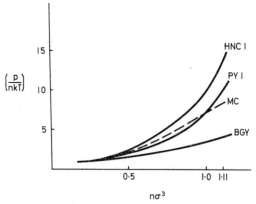

FIG. 16. Virial equation of state from BGY, HNC 1, and PY 1 theories for a hard-sphere gas as function of density. For comparison, machine calculations (MC) are included.

we should mention that the critical ratio pV/RT has been calculated using the various theories. The value using BGY is 0·359, and this value is typical. The experimental value of this critical ratio for argon is 0·291. Generally speaking, the predicted values calculated from the theory are in error by some 25–30 per cent.

6.5. A TEST OF THE SUPERPOSITION APPROXIMATION

Although the arguments of Chapter 4 can be used to test the validity of the Kirkwood superposition approximation at low gas densities, any analytic test at liquid densities is not yet possible. Numerical tests using molecular dynamics have, however, been reported. For a hard-sphere gas, Alder[41] has provided numerical data for the function S defined by equation (4.45) as function of the separation distance for a hard-sphere fluid for the density $n/n_0 = 1/1\cdot60$ (i.e. just below the transition density). He finds that

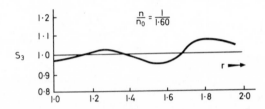

Fig. 17. Comparison between deduced triplet and pair distribution functions for dense hard-sphere fluid, as function of the pair separation distance. The ordinate line ($S_3 = 1$) corresponds to the exact validity of the Kirkwood superposition approximation.

S has the value unity to better than 10 per cent (see Fig. 17). Alternatively, Rahman[42] has considered a dense fluid with (12–6) interaction beyond a rigid core with parameters adapted to argon and has obtained the same general result, although the accuracy is now probably not so great. The tentative conclusion can be drawn that the superposition approximation is more reliable at high liquid densities than might be expected on the basis of studies at low density. The superposition approximation can be looked upon as including contributions from particle clusters at all densities: the improved accuracy at high, as opposed to low, fluid densities is presumably the result of considerable cancellation of contributions in the high density case. This is yet one more example of the limited value of the results of density expansions of functions, valid at low densities, in the elucidation of fluid properties at liquid densities.

6.6. SOME CONCLUSIONS

It will probably be helpful to end this chapter with a short summary of some of the conclusions and implications of the results that we have collected together.

We have available exact expressions for the fluid thermodynamic functions in terms of the lower order distribution functions. For those fluids where the total particle interaction can be adequately represented as the sum of the separate contributions between pairs of particles, the exact thermodynamic functions take on a form involving explicitly the pair distribution. Uncertainties in the thermodynamic functions calculated on the basis of these equations arise entirely from an inadequate specification of the pair distribution. A number of equations have been presented from which certain information can be deduced about the pair distribution. This information is not exact because of the mathematical difficulties associated with accounting for the non-linear indirect interaction between the many particles in continuous interaction. We divide our discussion into two related parts.

The first part involves exact relations between distribution functions of consequentive order: thus $g^{(2)}$ is related exactly to $g^{(3)}$ and possibly also $g^{(4)}$ and higher order functions. A hierarchy of equations results which is closed by making an assumption about the form of the distribution functions of order higher than the second, viz. some form of superposition mathematical approximation. The Kirkwood form is the most simple to use: it is exact in the limit of indefinitely low density but is not very accurate at normal gas densities. It is, however, apparently more reliable at liquid densities, and its reliability can be improved further by some corrective procedure, such as that proposed by Fisher (see section 4.2(d)). According to this approach, future work is to centre around the problem of improving the superposition approximation.

The second part of the discussion hinges on the relation (5.2) between the total and direct correlation function, and in particular involves the detailed specification of the direct correlation function. This specification is open to some arbitrary assertions and the future development of the method must centre upon the proper choice of the direct correlation function for liquid densities. The methods of functional differentiation offer particularly bright prospects in this connection, but their full application would seem, at the present time, to need the use of a physical principle that so far has not been applied. The PY 1 equation would seem the most reliable equation for the study of gases at the present time, although PY 2 and HNC 2 ultimately must become serious contenders in this connection. The value of these several equations at liquid densities is still open to question. The interesting thing, perhaps, is the fact that BGY is still not out-dated at liquid densities.

We can conclude that the calculation of the thermodynamic properties of equilibrium fluids is still far from its final state even though better than qualitative procedures are now available for simple liquids. Future work will be associated with the further improvement of the mathematical approximations at present necessary in the practical utilisation of the theory.

CHAPTER 7

IRREVERSIBILITY

ANY macroscopic bulk physical system which is not in equilibrium, and which is unrestrained by external agencies, is found experimentally to move irreversibly in time towards an equilibrium state. Expressed alternatively, non-uniformities in bulk matter tend to disappear and consequently require for their maintenance the presence of external energy sources. The movement to equilibrium is not instantaneous, and can be characterised by a time (the relaxation time) which is required by the particular system to relax into the appropriate condition of equilibrium. The movement to equilibrium can be described in terms of the action of dissipative processes which work to destroy any initial non-equilibrium state. In macroscopic terms, these processes are specified by a set of empirical transport coefficients which for simple systems are the coefficients of viscosity (fluid velocity gradient), thermal conductivity (temperature gradient), diffusion (particle concentration gradient), and so on. Usually conditions are not simple and more than one transport process is involved at any given time.[1] In macroscopic terms the transport processes must ultimately be related to the collective behaviour of the interacting particles contained in the volume V which represents theoretically the actual physical system. In particular, the transport coefficients describe the elimination of non-uniformaties in bulk matter by the internal transfer of momentum, energy, mass, and so on, from local regions of excess to local regions of deficiency. For equilibrium there are no non-uniformities in the mean, in the absence of external forces.

The actual details of transfer depend upon the microscopic structural features of the non-equilibrium physical systems under investigation: in what follows we are concerned only with simple, non-polar fluid systems obeying the laws of classical physics. Up to the present time, theories of non-equilibrium fluid systems have been restricted to either steady, or only slowly varying, small non-uniformities of macroscopic flow, temperature, or possibly the concentration.

7.1. NON-EQUILIBRIUM DISTRIBUTION FUNCTIONS

It is assumed that the same molecular properties control the irreversible approach to equilibrium as determine the equilibrium condition itself. The interparticle force, therefore, plays potentially as important a role in the calculation of the transport coefficients for a non-uniform fluid as it has been found in previous chapters to do in the calculation of the thermodynamic functions describing the uniform state.

The characteristic of the physical state of a non-equilibrium dilute gas is a spatially, highly disordered array of only weakly coupled particles, the disorder being less complete than for equilibrium conditions due to the constraints imposed by the initial non-uniformities. The degree of disorder increases with time to become ultimately the random equilibrium disorder. For a dense fluid the characteristic of the physical state is short-range particle spatial ordering specified by an appropriate pair distribution function which, however, is different from the corresponding equilibrium pair distribution. If deviations from equilibrium are small (as will always be assumed to be the case in what follows), the difference between the equilibrium and non-equilibrium pair distributions is itself small. This small difference is, however, vital to the discussion of non-equilibrium situations since it depends explicitly on the details of the fluid non-uniformities. Calculated non-uniform properties are critically affected by the distortion of the pair distribution. For equilibrium conditions, where the distortion is absent, there is no flow of momentum, energy particle number density, and so on, so that the transport coefficients are irrelevant. Consequently, even the smallest deviation from equilibrium, although it may be indefinitely small, has far reaching effects from a theoretical point of view.[†] When departures from equilibrium are small the corresponding equilibrium and non-equilibrium distributions can be assumed to be related in a simple manner.

In principle at least, the non-equilibrium pair distribution is open to experimental determination although in practice the difficulties of perform-

[†] Conditions are nowhere near as severe experimentally. In order to demonstrate the existence of macroscopic equilibrium conditions, it is necessary to show that the relations of the previous section 3.3. are valid *within the limits of accuracy of the experiment*. There is, on this prescription, no exact equilibrium arrangement but only equilibrium to given accuracy. This has, for instance, the consequence of allowing for the practical discussion of non-isothermal fluid flow, based on equations derivable in terms of thermodynamic functions. The deviation of the entropy from its equilibrium value is of a smaller magnitude than that for other quantities, and it is this fact that is used in the usual derivations of the energy (temperature) equation of hydrodynamics. The rate of production of entropy must be small for this approach to be useful.

ng the experiments to acceptable accuracy and interpreting the resulting xperimental data have so far precluded this possibility. Consequently, the heoretical calculation of the distortion of the equilibrium pair distribuion for specific fluid non-uniformities is one of the central problems of the tatistical theory of fluid non-equilibria. This distortion will be angularlependent even for simple fluids composed of spherical particles in a way lictated by the spatial distribution of the non-uniformity within the fluid.

The statistical microscopic spatial distribution of particles of the fluid s described by the specific phase and configurational distribution functions previously introduced in section 2.5 or the generic distributions of secions 3.1 and 3.2. If the non-uniformities initially set up are not maintained by some external agency (source of energy such as a pump or heat reseroir), then the distribution functions will depend upon the time. Because t is known experimentally that any initial fluid non-uniformities must ultimately disappear, we know that the theoretical distribution function or the total system must approach the canonical form (3.11) asymptotially with time. It is not necessarily the case, however, that the time is to be allowed to increase without limit[2]. If, on the other hand, the initial luid non-uniformities are maintained steady in time then the distribution unctions are time-independent. In this case the system is strictly conserrative with known Hamiltonian although the total phase distribution till differs from the canonical form.

The non-equilibrium total phase distribution $f^{(N)}$ describing the evoluion of the physical system in time from the non-canonical to the canonical orms is a solution of the time-dependent Liouville equation (2.23).

Other theoretically possible time-dependent solutions of (2.23) that either lo not approach the canonical form or alternatively move away from it, nust be rejected on physical grounds. The Liouville equation, it will be emembered, expresses the conservation of the probability function $f^{(N)}$ as he system of interacting particles moves, according to classical particle nechanics set down in section 2.5. For steady non-equilibria the left hand side of (2.23) is zero. By integrating the Liouville equation over selected egions of phase, momenta, or configuration, an equation involving reluced distribution functions results. For instance, an equation introducing he configurational pair distribution results when (2.23) is averaged over all the momenta and the configuration of the $(N-2)$ unwanted particles. Solutions relating to steady non-equilibria can be derived as time-independent forms of acceptable time-dependent solutions.

So far we have considered implicitly functions which change monotonically with the time, these solutions complying immediately with the primitive requirement of irreversibility provided that the direction of change is towards the canonical form. It is possible, however, that quasi-periodic solutions of (2.23) will exist. Such solutions must be considered carefully before rejection since, over chosen restricted time intervals, they also show a monotonic time-dependence; this is considered further in section 7.3.

It will be realised, by now, that there is an apparent contradiction between some of the physically acceptable non-canonical solutions of the Liouville equation (which are characterised by an irreversible time evolution at constant energy towards a final canonical form independent of the exact details of the initial situation) and the underlying microscopic particle mechanics which are always strictly reversible (i.e. if one particle trajectory can occur with initial phase A and final phase B, then the reverse trajectory is also possible with initial phase B and final phase A). The resolution of this apparent paradox is a central problem of the theory of non-equilibria and will concern us here in its application to fluid non-equilibria. Its general resolution requires the enunciation of a physical principle (or possibly a set of physical principles) which must specify in detail, within the statistical structure of the theory, the mechanism whereby equilibrium is established. This problem will be considered further in section 7.3.

A formal solution of the Liouville equation (2.23) is readily obtained and is useful in showing concisely the theoretical problem of non-equilibria. Let us define the quantity L according to:

$$L = i \sum_{j=1}^{N} \left[\left(\frac{\partial \mathcal{H}}{\partial \mathbf{r}_j} \cdot \frac{\partial}{\partial \mathbf{p}_j} \right) - \left(\frac{\partial \mathcal{H}}{\partial \mathbf{p}_j} \cdot \frac{\partial}{\partial \mathbf{r}_j} \right) \right], \qquad (7.1)$$

where $i = \sqrt{-1}$. L is, in fact, an operator since it acts upon, and changes, any phase function which follows it. The Liouville equation (2.23) now has the compact form:

$$i \frac{\partial f^{(N)}}{\partial t} = L f^{(N)}. \qquad (7.2)$$

Because L is not an explicit function of the time, this equation can be formally solved to give the operator solution:

$$f^{(N)}(t) = \exp\{-itL\} f^{(N)}(0), \qquad (7.3)$$

where $f^{(N)}(0)$ is the initial value of $f^{(N)}$ when $t = 0$. The evolution of $f^{(N)}$ in time is then known if the function $\exp\{-itL\}$ is known as function of the time.[3] It is required, naturally, that $f^{(N)}$ should have canonical form for large values of t. It will be seen from (7.3) that L is to be associated with some inverse time, τ say, which determines the rate at which equi-rium is reached. τ is linked indirectly with the strength of the dissipative nctions controlling the system, i.e. with the appropriate transport coeffi- nts. If $\exp\{-itL\}$ is known, then the transport coefficients themselves e essentially also defined in terms of microscopic particle data.

The problem of finding the function $\exp\{-it\,L\}$ (which is in fact the oblem of solving the Liouville equation itself according to (7.3)), or of ding acceptable approximations to it for given non-equilibrium con- tions, is one of the major concerns of the modern theoretical work on atistical irreversibility. For equilibrium, where there is no time change $f^{(N)}(0)$, we have $\exp\{-itL\} = 1$. For non-equilibrium, a much dis- ssed method of determining $\exp\{-itL\}$ is very much like that for deter- ining the equilibrium structure, viz, by starting with the fully uncoupled rticle (free particle) approximation, and successively correcting this to clude the interparticle coupling.[4] For this purpose, the Liouville operator written in the form:

$$L = L_0 + \lambda \delta L,$$

here λ is a coupling parameter continuous in the unit range: $0 \leqslant \lambda \leqslant 1$. ere:

$$L_0 = -i \sum_{j=i}^{N} \left(\frac{p_j}{m_j} \cdot \frac{\partial}{\partial \mathbf{r}_j} \right),$$

nd

$$\delta L = i \sum_{j<n} \left(\frac{\partial \psi_{jn}}{\partial \mathbf{r}_j} \cdot \left(\frac{\partial}{\partial \mathbf{p}_j} - \frac{\partial}{\partial \mathbf{p}_n} \right) \right).$$

he completely uncoupled case is when $\lambda = 0$: coupling can be introduced radually by increasing λ.

7.2. THE PROBLEM OF THE ENTROPY

The movement of a macroscopic system to equilibrium is expressed ermodynamically by the continual increase of entropy until the maximum quilibrium value is reached. Thermodynamically, the entropy is defined s being the phase average of the logarithm of the specific total distribu- on $f^{(N)}$ according to (3.18). The canonical form (3.11) is in fact that orm of $f^{(N)}$ which gives the entropy, S, its maximum value for a given nergy. According to (3.19), for a given U and T, when S has its maximum alue then F has its minimum value. For non-equilibrium conditions the ppropriate macroscopic mean values will be calculated using the phase veraging of microscopic functions defined by (2.29) of section (2.6). In particular, the entropy is again defined by the expression (3.18). It will t realised that the calculated values are essentially ensemble averages.[5]

The usefulness of definitions such as (2.29) and (3.18) for non-equilil rium situations can be gauged only by making a comparison betwee calculated values and the corresponding experimental data. It is foun in practice that these formulae can be used for fluid non-equilibria, but onl if the total distribution function for the system of N interacting particl is defined in a special way. This is seen by the following arguments initia ed by J. W. Gibbs.[6]

Consider the quantity $H \equiv -S/k$, the so-called H-function of Gibb defined by:

$$H = -\frac{S}{k} = \int \int f^{(N)}(\mathbf{p}^N, \mathbf{r}^N) \log f^{(N)}_{\underline{}}(\mathbf{p}^N, \mathbf{r}^N) \, d\mathbf{p}^N \, d\mathbf{r}^N. \qquad [(7.4]$$

Thus the H-function is the phase average of the quantity $\log f^{(N)}$. Fe equilibrium this expression is known to give the entropy according t (3.18), H having its minimum value then. For an arbitrary non-equilibriur situation which has the same value of the internal energy as the corresponc ing equilibrium situation, Gibbs[6] showed that the value of the H-functio is larger than that for equilibrium. In terms of (7.4) this means that th entropy of the non-equilibrium system is less than that for the equilibriur system of equal internal energy. There is not yet the possibility of equatin this calculated entropy with the physical entropy. According to the Liou ville equation, of which $f^{(N)}$ is a solution, $df^{(N)}/dt$ is zero during th phase motion, i.e. $f^{(N)}$ is a constant of the motion in γ-space. But s is any function of $f^{(N)}$ such as $\log f^{(N)}$ and this result holds goo whether $f^{(N)}$ describes equilibrium or non-equilibrium. Consequently H is constant of the phase motion if $f^{(N)}$ is the phase distribution defined i section 2.5. Even though H for non-equilibrium is larger than H for equi librium, for the same internal energy, the non-equilibrium value of H doe not decrease towards the equilibrium value as time proceeds, and S i (7.4) calculated in this way cannot be identified with the physical entropy

The situation can be described geometrically in γ-space. Liouville' theorem expresses the incompressibility of the flow of the phase fluid even for elementary volumes. For non-equilibrium conditions, the phas points are distributed non-uniformly in the space between two neighbour ing energy surfaces whereas for equilibrium the distribution is uniform[†]

---

† We are using here the concept of the micro-canonical ensemble which is essentiall; equivalent to the canonical ensemble for our present purposes. For details see, e.g R. C. Tolman, *Principles of Statistical Mechanics*, p. 56.

ecause the phase fluid is incompressible (a result derived directly from
e equations of particle motion), the magnitude of any elementary fluid
olume must remain constant as the mechanical system evolves, although
e shape will change with time. As a consequence, any volume element
ontaining many phase points at some initial time will contain the same
umber of phase points at some later time, while another volume element
ontaining fewer points will remain relatively deficient at a later time.
nce the number of particles in contiguous elementary phase volumes
ust remain fixed, the change in *shape* of the contiguous elements with
ne is the only variable which can transform the initial non-uniform phase
oint distribution into a uniform distribution. The movement of a non-
iform system to equilibrium is, in this way, pictured as a mixing process
which an initial gross microscopic mozaic of phase volumes, containing
fferent numbers of phase points in γ-space, changes in time into a finer
icroscopic mozaic. This final finer mozaic of elementary phase volumes
s the *appearance* of a uniform distribution of phase points between the
o neighbouring energy surfaces only if we agree to limit the fineness in
ase with which it is examined. We say, then, that there is a coarseness
phase which must be recognised such that any description of phase can
ply only to a small but finite phase volume. This picture, which is in
cord with the impossibility of any practical exact specification of the
ase and is in the spirit of the statistical approach upon which our work
based, was given a mathematical formulation by Ehrenfest[7] who defined
oarse-grained probability phase distribution, written $\bar{\bar{f}}^{(N)}$, according to:

$$\bar{\bar{f}}^{(N)}(\mathbf{p}^N, \mathbf{r}^N)\delta\mathbf{p}^N\delta\mathbf{r}^N = \int\int_{\Delta\omega} f^{(N)}(\mathbf{p}^N, \mathbf{r}^N)\, d\mathbf{p}^N\, d\mathbf{r}^N. \qquad (7.5)$$

ere $\delta\mathbf{p}^N\delta\mathbf{r}^N$ is a small though finite phase volume, which forms the in-
gration limit $\Delta\omega$ for the integral on the right hand side. With this defi-
tion of $\bar{\bar{f}}^{(N)}$, the H function is defined by:

$$H = \int\int \bar{\bar{f}}^{(N)} \log \bar{\bar{f}}^{(N)}\, d\mathbf{p}^N\, d\mathbf{r}^N, \qquad (7.6)$$

 here the integration now is to be made over all the phase available to
e system. In order to distinguish the coarse-grained distribution $\bar{\bar{f}}^{(N)}$
om the distribution $f^{(N)}$ defined in section 2.5 the latter is often referred
as the fine-grained distribution since there is, in principle, no limit to
e fineness in phase with which such functions can be associated. Study
H defined by (7.6) shows that this function is greater for a non-uniform

system than for a uniform system having the same energy, and further th
it decreases in time to approach the value appropriate to the unifor
system. The arguments here have concerned the micro-canonical ensemb
rather than the canonical ensemble itself, and this is a deficiency. Howeve
results derived from the canonical ensemble cannot be significantly differe
from those for the micro-canonical ensemble under the conditions usua
envisaged for non-equilibria (where deviations from equilibrium are smal
and the physical entropy for this case can to good approximation be re
resented by (3.18) with $f^{(N)}$ replaced by $\bar{f}^{(N)}$ defined by (7.5).

Attempts have been made to treat non-equilibria without recourse e
plicitly to the H-theorem; no explicit reference is then made to entrop
An important procedure which will be used in the two remaining chapte
is that due to Kirkwood,[9] and does not explicitly involve the H-functi
of Gibbs. According to Kirkwood, for a time-dependent non-equilibriu
system the experimentally measured functions are to be represented in t
theory by the ensemble average of the corresponding time smooth
(i.e. time averaged) phase functions, the time smoothing being defined
in (2.15). The phase averages are now to be given by equation (2.29)
section (2.6) but with $f^{(N)}$ replaced by $\bar{f}^{(N)}$, where

$$\bar{f}^{(N)}(\mathbf{p}^N, \mathbf{r}^N, t) = \frac{1}{\tau} \int_0^\tau f^{(N)}(\mathbf{p}^N, \mathbf{r}^N, t+s) \, \mathrm{d}s. \qquad (7.$$

In the integration, τ is a time interval which is long enough for the force
each particle due to neighbours to become effectively random and y
short enough to be small in comparison with the macroscopic relaxati
time for the system. In this approach the concept of irreversibility is i
troduced into the theory by restricting the discussion to the lower ord
distribution functions, such as the singlet and the doublet, which are
be derived from the Liouville equation (2.23) by averaging over the pha
of the remaining particles. The procedure, then, is first to phase avera
(2.23) over the appropriate particle phase of the system, and then to tir
smooth the equation so derived. Although the phase and time averagir
procedures can be interchangeable if all the phase for the total system of
particles is involved, they are never interchangeable (i.e. do not commut
if the phase for a small number of particles is excluded from the integr
tion. It is this non-commutibility that is connected, according to the theor
with the observed irreversible approach to equilibrium. This approach
the problem will be developed in the next two chapters.

It remains to determine the size of a mechanical system which can sho
non-equilibrium features. The statistical arguments used above assun

he distribution of phase points in γ-space to be virtually a continuous unction of the phase and this implies an indefinitely large number of phase points. On the other hand, if the known physical non-uniformities are to be accounted for statistically, deviations from mean values must also be insignificant. This means that the number of particles of the mechanical system must be large in comparison with the number of parameters necessary to specify fully the non-uniformities of the actual physical system. The conclusion must be drawn that a system showing true irreversible behaviour according to our present notions must have a very large number (more properly an indefinitely large number) of relevant degrees of freedom; this means for simple particles that the mechanical system must contain an indefinitely large number of interacting particles to exhibit completely irreversible behaviour.[9] We shall, in fact, be concerned now with the situation $N \to \infty$, $V \to \infty$, $n = N/V = $ constant, which was also previously assumed for equilibrium conditions.

7.3. STATISTICAL PARTICLE INTERACTIONS

In the movement to equilibrium the macroscopic structure of the system becomes progressively less complex as the details of the initial non-uniformities blur to become ultimately the featureless equilibrium uniformity (for instance, any velocity or temperature gradients disappear). This smoothing out process which characterises irreversibility is brought about by the interaction between the constituent particles, which must be considered in statistical terms. The problem then arises of specifying the interaction process in such a way as to ensure the required irreversible behaviour of the macroscopic system.

The equilibrium state is a degenerate state in the sense that it is the ultimate state of (almost) any initial non-equilibrium state of the same macroscopic energy, provided the initial non-uniformities are not too large. It follows that the movement to equilibrium involves a continuous obliteration of detail. The initial non-uniformities then become more simple and ultimately are lost; conditions are now completely uniform and equilibrium is established. This irreversible movement can, for convenience in broad discussion, be given a pseudo-physiological pictorial description by saying that the physical system has an imperfect *memory* and as time proceeds *forgets* information which it cannot subsequently recover. As it evolves, the system then gradually and permanently loses detail until finally there is no more detail to lose, i.e. uniformity has been reached. This is in agreement with the general solution of the Liouville equation

(2.23) being that function $f^{(N)}$ which approaches the canonical form wit time.

No phase information can be lost in fact during the period of interactio between any two particles since the process can be fully described by th well-defined laws of physics which are laid down beforehand. Any los of information can arise only because the interaction laws are not full applied, such as when statistical arguments are invoked.

There is, as yet, no agreed general way in which information of the phas of a system of particles not in equilibrium is to be systematically discarde (i.e. lost) as the system evolves in time due to particle interactions, an which is applicable to all non-equilibrium situations. Procedures for re stricted situations are, however, available that would appear reliable These procedures involve a coarse graining of the distribution functions especially over the time.[†] This is achieved either by an actual time-smooth ing operation where the time interval is suitably chosen,[9] or else by makin certain restrictive assumptions about the relative form of the lower orde distributions at some time in the past.[10] It would seem that the statistica description of the irreversible movement to equilibrium of a system o interacting particles cannot be developed, at least on present ideas, with out some phase or time averaging of the relevant distribution functions

7.4. RECURRENCE OF INITIAL PHASES

Before proceeding further it is necessary to consider a periodicity prop erty of a system of interacting particles first considered by Poincaré an later by Boltzmann.

Poincaré showed[11] that for a closed conservative dynamical system o interacting particles, where the force on each particle depends only on th relative configuration of the particles, any given initial phase must recui to any arbitrarily specified degree of accuracy an indefinitely large numbei of times. The trajectories representing the system of N interacting particle

---

[†] The elementary phase volume to be used in the coarse-graining of phase distribu tions defined by (7.5) is not theoretically defined but must be found empirically. The same is also true of the time interval τ to be used in the time-smoothing operation defined by (7.7). It is found in the theory, however, that the time-smoothing operation can be used without the detailed specification of τ; it is possible to set wide limits on τ in terms of the time interval involved for individual particle interactions on the one side, and the Poincaré recurrence time of the total system on the other (see section 7.4). There are no analogous natural limits of the elementary phase volume in the classica theory, although a natural choice for the magnitude of this volume results from the quantum theory. This quantum limit, essentially the cube power of Planck's constant, is nevertheless itself far too small to act as the coarse-graining limit for quantum systems.

contained in a finite space volume V then, according to Poincaré, must have a quasi-periodic structure. Any initial phase will reappear again if we are prepared, or able, to wait long enough. The time taken for this to happen is often called the Poincaré time period, τ_p, and the whole repetitive process is the Poincaré cycle. The existence of such a cycle would seem, at first sight, to be contrary to the whole experimental concept of irreversibility; this apparent contradiction forms Zermelo's paradox.[12] The exact value of τ_p to be expected for any system of particles is somewhat vague because it depends upon how nearly we require the initial phase to be repeated; the more stringent our requirements the greater is τ_p. There is, however, some limit set by the dimensions of the elementary phase volume defined by any coarse-graining procedure.

The existence of a Poincaré cycle for a closed system depends upon two properties of the phase of the total system of particles plotted in γ-space, viz.: first, that the trajectories of the particles remain unique in phase, neither crossing each other nor themselves; and second that the phase fluid is incompressible. We indicate here the form of the argument establishing the Poincaré cycle; for detailed discussion the interested reader is referred to the references.[11] As time proceeds the initial phase of the system evolves, at constant phase volume but not at constant phase shape, to a future phase. Because the particle trajectories are unique, the future phase is exactly specified by the initial phase. Conversely, if the future phase is exactly specified, then the initial phase is essentially also known. The phases of the system before and after those found at some time t each form a domain of phase points whose volume would be expected to increase with the time were it not for Liouville's theorem. Further, because we are considering a closed system of particles having a finite phase volume then the domain of phase points must itself occupy a finite phase volume. It follows that as time increases the initial phase changes to include all the phase available to the system, including also the initial phase. Consequently, the initial phase can be expected to recur after a sufficient (possibly extremely large) time interval has elapsed. The argument can be reversed since the initial state can itself, on these arguments, be supposed to be the recurrence of an earlier initial state. In this way the cyclic (periodic) property of the system follows. Boltzmann[13] has attempted to estimate the recurrence time, i.e. the time period of the cycle, of an abnormal state of a unit volume of gas containing 10^{18} particles, where all the particles have exactly the same speed of 500 m/sec and not the Maxwell–Boltzmann distribution. This initial state of equal particle velocity will be accepted as having recurred if the final particle positions within the gaseous volume are the same as the initial positions to within 10 per cent of the average interparticle distance, and if the velocities agree to within 1 part in 500, i.e. to 1 m/sec. On this basis the recurrence time is estimated as being orders of magnitude greater than the age of the Universe. We can then say that the initial state, characterised by the particles all having the same velocity, will disappear never to return. There is, then, an irreversible movement away from the initial state which is strictly irreversible within the confines of experimental possibilities even though it is analytically not irreversible. In this way, experimental irreversibility is seen not to be in contradiction (at least in this case, but in fact more generally) with the inherent reversibility of the underlying particle dynamics.

These arguments, where the recurrence time of a specific phase is calculated, have been treated in detail by von Smoluchowski in his theory of probability after-effects[14] (*Wahrscheinlichkeitsnachwirkung*). When applied to the study of colloidal particle statistics this theory has received convincing experimental support. The theory places the recurrence of states firmly within the theory of fluctuations, and a continuous spectrum of particle fluctuation events can be encounted from those of very firmly microscopic scale (which have short recurrence times and are within the limits of error of macroscopic measurements confirming equilibrium through the validity of the formulae of section (3.3)) to those of definitely macroscopic scale which are associated with macroscopic irreversibility.

As an example, let a macroscopic volume element V_1 enclosed by a surface of area σ contain on the average ν_1 particles each of mass m, but $n \neq \nu_1$ such particles at some specific time. If the total macroscopic fluid of which the elementary volume V_1 is a part is at an equilibrium temperature T, then Smoluchowski's theory provides the following expressions for the mean life of the state with n particles in V_1, written $\tau_L(n)$, and the average time of recurrence of this state by $\tau_R(n)$. Explicitly, when n and ν_1 are both large numbers:

$$\tau_L(n) = \frac{V_1}{\sigma} \left(\frac{2\pi m}{kT}\right)^{\frac{1}{2}} \frac{1}{(n+\nu_1)}, \qquad (7.8)$$

$$\tau_R(n) = \frac{\pi V_1}{\sigma} \left(\frac{m}{kT}\right)^{\frac{1}{2}} \nu_1^{-\frac{1}{2}} \exp\left[\frac{(n-\nu_1)^2}{2\nu_1}\right]. \qquad (7.9)$$

The most probable states of the system are those for which τ_L is largest and τ_R is smallest. According to (7.8), τ_R is not particularly sensitive to changes in n and ν_1. Thus if $n = 2\nu_1$, $\tau_L\alpha(3\nu_1)^{-1}$, while if $n = \frac{1}{2}\nu_1$, $\tau_L\alpha(\frac{3}{2}\nu_1)^{-1}$: by multiplying n by a factor 4, τ_L decreases only by a factor 2. More drasti cally, if n is changed from $100\nu_1$ to $1/100\ \nu_1$, i.e. by a factor 10^4, τ_L is increased only by a factor 10^2. The mean life of various states is, then, broadly similar for an appreciable range of fluctuating states. Things are quite different for the average time of recurrence of the state where, according to (7.9), the value of τ_R is controlled by the exponential function with exponent proportional to $(n-\nu_1)^2$. Enormous changes in τ_R will result from relatively small changes in n for constant ν_1. Smoluchowski gave values for τ_R for an elementary sphere of gas of variable radius R for the fluctuation in which the molecular concentration will differ from the mean by 1 per cent. The uniform temperature of the total gas volume containing the elementary volume is taken as $T = 300°K$. We have here an essentially indefinitely large volume of gas and we consider the fluctuations of particle number in an elementary volume of the gas $V_1 = (4\pi/3)n^3$. Taking $\nu = 3\times10^{19}$ particles per unit volume, then for the elementary spherical volume V_1, $\nu_1 = \nu V_1 = 3\times10^{19}\ V_1$. This is the value of ν_1 to be inserted into (7.9). For the purposes of our present inquiry we assert that n may differ from this value by 1 per cent. Smoluchowski found that if this spherical volume has a radius of 1 cm, the corresponding value of the recurrence time τ_R has the staggering value of $\sim 10^{145}$ years (the age of the Universe $\sim 10^{10}$ years); if $R_1 = 5\times10^{-5}$ cm, then $\tau_R \sim 10^{10}$ years; if $R_1 = 3\times10^{-5}$ cm, $\tau_R \sim 1$ month; if $R_1 = 2\cdot5\times10^{-5}$ cm then $\tau_R \sim 1$ sec; while if $R_1 = 1\times10^{-5}$ cm, $\tau_R \sim 10^{-11}$ sec. The very strong dependence of τ_R on scale is clearly evident. It seems that for volumes which we would normally regard as macroscopic the recurrence times of the 1 per cent deviation from the mean particle number are enormous, but these times become themselves very small for microscopic volumes. Recurrence times for deviations of more than 1 per cent are correspondingly greater than these values (the effect being greatly magnified by the exponential factor in 7.9), while deviations of less than 1 per cent have correspondingly shorter recurrence times. This example is rather specialised and simple but the overall conclusion to be drawn for general systems is clear. States near to the uniform state have short recurrence times, while those far from uniformity have long recurrence times. Smoluchowski concluded that the change from an initial state to a final state is a change from a less probable to a more probable state and is described as reversible or irreversible according as to whether the time of recurrence of the initial state τ_R is very small or very large in comparison with the time interval for which the system is subjected to observation.

The apparent contradiction between macroscopic irreversibility and the inherent reversibility of particle dynamics is now fully resolved in a satisfying way. It is not, however, resolved in a manner which is useful for calculating the transport coefficients in terms of molecular data. From the experimental point of view the movement to equilibrium is irreversible and the process is not cyclic. It is in rejecting the possibility even in principle of the recurrence of the initial non-uniform state that the formal difficulties considered in section 7.2 have their roots. The concepts of the coarse-graining and time smoothing of distribution functions would seem to be necessary because the cyclic features of the time evolution of the system are in this way suppressed, and the idea of the system having a bad *memory* precludes the system ever returning to the initial state that it has *forgotten*.

7.5. THEORIES OF RESTRICTED VALIDITY

Special solutions of the problem of irreversibility in macroscopic matter are available even though the general solution is not yet known. These restricted theories are important in indicating the type of theory that is able to account for irreversibility. We mention briefly three of these theories now.

(a) *The Dilute Gas*

The next chapter is devoted to the treatment of gaseous non-equilibria but it is convenient to forestall the discussion to some extent by making a brief reference to it here. It is possibly the best known and most generally successful branch of non-equilibrium statistical theory[15].

In a dilute gas, the uniform motion of each molecule is interrupted by a succession of *binary* elastic collisions with other molecules, characterised by the fact that the duration of an actual collision is very small in comparison with the time between collisions. It is plausible to assume that successive collisions are essentially statistically independent events, so that the trajectory of each particle of the gas is a stochastic sequence of events in time. This assumption is closely connected with the hypothesis of molecular chaos according to which there is no statistical correlation between the position of a molecule in the gas and its momentum when the gas is either in equilibrium or near to equilibrium. It is the inclusion of these concepts into the arguments that ensures their applicability to non-equilibrium situations.

On these assumptions Maxwell and Boltzmann obtained the integro-differential equation which carries their name, and which has as its solution the probability distribution of particle velocities as function of the position and the time. This equation is derived in the next chapter using the full statistical theory of non-equilibria. When the distribution functions appropriate to a given macroscopic velocity or temperature distribution are known, the coefficients of viscosity or thermal conductivity can be calculated. It is assumed in these calculations that the total flow of momentum and energy in the gas, which is associated respectively with viscosity and thermal conduction, is due to the contribution of single molecules carrying momentum and kinetic energy along the paths between successive collisions. Momentum and energy are transferred from one particle to another during collisions, the hypothesis of molecular chaos ensuring that equilibrium is either maintained or else is reached irreversibly in time. The classical theory of Maxwell and Boltzmann is intimately connected with the concept of binary collisions and does not easily admit generalisation to higher densities. Certainly it cannot be applied to the study of liquids where the concept of an actual collision has virtually no meaning. The specification of the irreversible dynamics of a system of particles not in weak interaction must face implicitly if not explicitly the problem of defining a proper statistical entropy function.

(b) *The Brownian Movement*

For determining the phase distribution functions appropriate to liquid (and incidentally also solid) non-equilibria, use has been made of partial differential equations similar to those used in the semi-macroscopic theory of the Brownian motion.[16] The Brownian movement is the continuous erratic movement which is observed to be executed by small grains or solid particles of semi-macroscopic colloidal size (i.e. particles which are macroscopically small) when they are suspended in a fluid with which they have no chemical interaction. This continual movement arises from collisions between the Brownian particle and the smaller molecules of the fluid. For a liquid there are of the order of 10^{21} such collisions per unit time (and for a gas at standard temperature and pressure the number is down only by a factor 10^2 or 10^3) so that the observed path of the Brownian particle will be a coarse mean of a highly complex actual path. This example of translational Brownian motion which will be considered here is only one of a large number of such random processes showing irreversibility; for instance, rotational Brownian motion is important in the problem of refining measurements involving suspended torsional instruments.

The classical theory of the translational Brownian movement of a solid particle suspended in a liquid at temperature T, has been developed almost entirely by Smoluchowski, Langevin, Einstein, Fokker, and Planck.[16] An excellent review has been given by Chandrasekhar.[14] The theory is based on arguments of probability rather than on any special molecular model or the principles of particle dynamics. It is assumed that during a small but finite interval τ (to be specified more precisely later) the momentum of the suspended particle suffers an increment, say $\Delta\mathbf{p}$, which results from the competition between a fluctuating acceleration due to molecular agitation and a systematic deceleration resulting from dynamic internal friction (i.e. viscosity). The probability for the occurrence of possible increments, usually called the transition probability, is assumed to satisfy various restrictive conditions. In particular, it is assumed to be a function of both the initial momentum, $\mathbf{p}$, and the increment of momentum $\Delta\mathbf{p}$ during τ. The mean increment of the momentum, $\langle\Delta\mathbf{p}\rangle$, is assumed to have the form $\langle\Delta\mathbf{p}\rangle = -\beta\mathbf{p}\tau$, where β is a friction constant which is to be obtained from classical hydrodynamics (Stokes' law of friction). In terms of the shear viscosity η of the fluid in which the particle (now assumed of spherical shape) is suspended, we write:

$$\beta = \frac{6\pi\eta a}{m},$$

where a and m are respectively the radius and mass of the particle. Moreover, it is assumed that the mean square increment of momentum, $\langle\Delta\mathbf{p}^2\rangle$, is given by $\langle\Delta\mathbf{p}^2\rangle = 2mkT\beta\tau$, where m is the mass of the suspended particle. It is important to notice that the assumption $\langle\Delta\mathbf{p}^2\rangle \propto \tau$ leads to results in agreement with experiment whereas the apparently more reasonable assumption $\langle\Delta\mathbf{p}^2\rangle \propto \tau^2$ does not. These proposed values for $\langle\Delta\mathbf{p}\rangle$ and $\langle\Delta\mathbf{p}^2\rangle$ are not to be imposed for all values of τ but only for those values which are neither very large nor very small as compared with the magnitude of β^{-1}. More specifically, the upper value of τ must be such as to allow for the validity of the condition $\beta\tau \ll 1$. For motion in three dimensions the mean cross products of the increments of different momentum components, and all mean powers of increments higher than the second, are assumed to be negligibly small. The most general application of these assumptions leads to a second order partial differential equation, usually called the Fokker–Planck equation, which determines the distribution of single particles in the phase and the time, in the phase space of six dimensions. The singlet distribution $f^{(1)}(\mathbf{p}, \mathbf{r}; t)$ then satisfies the equation:

$$\frac{\partial f^{(1)}}{\partial t} + \left(\frac{\mathbf{p}}{m}\cdot\frac{\partial f^{(1)}}{\partial \mathbf{r}}\right) + \left(\mathbf{F}\cdot\frac{\partial f^{(1)}}{\partial \mathbf{p}}\right) = \beta[\mathrm{div}_\mathbf{p}\,(f^{(1)}\mathbf{p}) + mkT\nabla_\mathbf{p}^2 f^{(1)}], \quad (7.10)$$

where the possibility of the presence of an external field of force **F** acting on the particle has also been included. It will be realised that the right hand side of (7.10) can be written alternatively in terms of the mean and mean square increments of momentum to become:

$$-\left(\frac{\partial}{\partial \mathbf{p}} \cdot \left(\frac{\langle \Delta \mathbf{p}\rangle}{\tau}\right)\right) + \frac{1}{2}\frac{\partial}{\partial \mathbf{p}} : \frac{\partial}{\partial \mathbf{p}}\left(\frac{\langle \Delta \mathbf{p}\cdot\Delta \mathbf{p}\rangle}{\tau}\right).$$

It has been assumed here that β, τ, and m are independent of particle momentum.

The theory may be generalised in various ways. Thus it may be extended to describe the Brownian movement of two or more particles, or (as stated above) it may be applied to more general systems, and to variables other than the positions and momenta.

The theory of the Brownian movement is greatly simplified for systems where β is sufficiently large. In this case it is sufficient in many calculations to consider a distribution function in coordinates alone, $g(\mathbf{r}, t)$, and Kramers has shown that this distribution function may be derived from the equation:

$$\frac{\partial g}{\partial t} = \mathrm{div}_r\left(\frac{kT}{\beta m}\,\mathrm{grad}_r\,g - \frac{\mathbf{F}}{m}\frac{1}{\beta}g\right). \tag{7.11}$$

where the presence of an external field of force **F** has also been accounted for. Equation (7.11) is usually called the Smoluchowski equation and is widely used in the description of diffusion processes. In the absence of a force, (7.11) becomes:

$$\frac{\partial g}{\partial t} = \frac{kT}{\beta m}\nabla_r^2 g, \tag{7.12}$$

where $kT/\beta m$ has been assumed independent of the position **r**. Introducing the quantity D by:

$$D = \frac{kT}{\beta m}, \tag{7.13}$$

(7.12) becomes alternatively

$$\frac{\partial g}{\partial t} = D\nabla_r^2 g. \tag{7.14}$$

This is a form of the diffusion equation when D is interpreted as a diffusion coefficient: (7.14), then, is essentially an expression for the rate of particle diffusion in terms of the particle concentration gradient. The Smoluchowski equation may be generalised so as to include the Brownian motion of two or more particles: particle interaction forces can also be included into the discussion. Equations of the type (7.10) and (7.11) will be encountered again in Chapter 9 devoted to liquid non-equilibrium.

(c) *Thermal Conductivity for Crystals*

The Fokker–Planck equation was used by Peierls for studying the exchange of energy between the vibrational modes of a non-metallic crystal lattice as a step in the calculation of the thermal conductivity.[17] The mean increments of the first and second order of the energies are obtained from the lattice dynamics for a restricted time interval and no resort is made to macro-physics. The theory provides the known result that the thermal conductivity is inversely proportional to the temperature at high temperatures, but the theory cannot at present provide an absolute value of the conductivity. The quantitative theory of the thermal conduction in crystals has, in the meantime, developed more firmly along other lines, but it is beyond our present aims to consider this work here.

(d) *Common Features of the Theories*

The three special theories outlined briefly above have three general features in common. First, they each use the concept of probability to describe the particular system at time t, the previous history of the system being irrelevant. The arguments involve the concept of chance and so are stochastic theories. Systems where the explicit history is not used to describe the present state are said to be Markov systems: the three special irreversible restricted theories of the present section are therefore of the Markov stochastic type[18].

The second common feature is that each theory uses a time interval which cannot be either indefinitely small or indefinitely large. And the third feature is that the mean square increments of variables during this time interval are strictly proportional to the time interval itself and not to the square or any other power. Further, higher mean powers of the variables, and mean component products, beyond the second are assumed negligibly small.

It can be expected that these three characteristics of restricted theories of irreversibility, or some equivalent statements of them, will appear also in more general theories: more especially they might be expected in the theory of liquid irreversible behaviour considered in Chapter 9.

It can be noticed here that these common features for non-equilibria are also found in the time-dependent perturbation theory of quantum physics.

his analogy has been developed by Prigogine and his co-workers in the ffort to apply the already well-established mathematical techniques for he solution of the Schrödinger wave equation to the solution of the iouville equation. It should be stressed that the Liouville equation can be onsidered in either classical or quantal form: the link with the Schrödin- er equation is through the mathematical structure rather than the exact etails of the physical content of the theories.

The Liouville equation is a partial differential equation including the ime, and so describes a continuous field, i.e. the probability in phase. he Schrödinger equation has the same mathematical form, describing the 1ore abstract probability state function. The solution of the Liouville quation is known to be entirely equivalent to the result of integrating the anonical equations of motion. The importance of the Liouville equation is very pronounced for a system of many degrees of freedom since the ingle equation describes the behaviour of the total system.

The mathematically significant feature of the Liouville equation in the orm (7.2) is that the operator L is Hermitian. It is to ensure this property hat the imaginary unit is introduced in (7.1). There is, then, a striking imilarity between the Liouville equation (7.2) and the time-dependent ichrödinger equation:

$$\hat{H}\psi = \frac{ih}{2\pi} \frac{\partial \psi}{\partial t}, \tag{7.2a}$$

vhere $\hat{H}$ is the Hamiltonian operator and ψ is the quantum probability vave function. The approach of Prigogine exploits the mathematical simi- irities between the equation (7.2a) above and the previous equation (7.2).

Action-angle variables are particularly valuable in this comparison, and he development centres upon the expansion of the phase distribution unction in a Fourier series using these variables. This expansion proce- lure is, it appears, equivalent to a development of the Liouville operator n eigen functions. The coefficients of this expansion express interparticle orrelations for the system and the evolution of the physical system is epresented by an evolution of the various correlations dictated by the roperties of the Liouville operator. On this approach, the existence of rreversibility is directly related to the limit where the volume of the physi- al system becomes indefinitely large, the number density remaining onstant. This limit is necessary in order that a firm distinction be made etween advanced and retarded solutions of the Liouville equation. Irre- ersibility arises from a successive widening of the number of degrees of reedom included in the correlations. This correlation flow is properly recognised only for times of the order of that describing the duration of a interaction. The process is most clear where the interaction forces are of short range and of short duration: long-range forces (like gravitation present special practical problems associated with that of isolating for mally a single interaction process. The irreversible approach of a system to equilibrium is then described by a succession of interaction processes in which the range of correlation is successively widened until ultimately the whole physical system is spanned by a multiplicity of incoherent corre lations. The movement to this ultimate state is described causally throug retarded solutions of the mechanical equations of particle motion. Such solutions are also general solutions of the equations of motion because the number of degrees of freedom of the system is indefinitely large: an recurrence time is so large as to be irrelevant, so that advanced solution play no final part in the arguments.

One interesting feature of the theory is that the equations describing the future evolution of the system from some chosen time depend not only on the chosen time itself but also in the general case on the history of the system as well.

Such systems are designated non-Markovian, and the associated mathe matical discussion can be most complicated. Fortunately, the situation can be simplified legitimately for simple systems. The non-Markovian character of the theory appears through certain time averages, which link the state of the distribution function at a given time to values of the func tion over a past time interval. This time interval can be pictorially describ ed as the memory of the system: for short-range forces with shor duration times, this memory also is short compared to the macroscopic times of appreciable change for the physical system. Such long time therefore, which mark the time behaviour of the macroscopic propertie of matter allow for a special simplification of the theory. If the time of interaction is, in comparison, short enough, the time average associate with the non-Markovian character of the describing equations can, wit negligible error, be replaced by a mean value referring to a single time The history of the system is then collapsed into the specification of the state at a chosen time and the equations of the theory are of the mor simple Markov type. This is the case when interest centres on processe where the long time behaviour alone is significant and where the individua particle interaction processes are virtually instantaneous events. One im portant example of this study is that of the approach of a system of interacting particles to the equilibrium state envisaged as the asymptot state for indefinitely large time.

The approach of Prigogine very briefly touched upon here would appear to offer wide possibilities for the future: but it has not yet developed beyond its early states. In particular, it is not yet clear that it is able, in its present form, to apply to dense fluids. It does provide a basis for the known Boltzmann equation (to be considered in Chapter 8) and the Fokker–Planck equation (to be treated in Chapter 9). Its use in the construction of more general equations is beyond our present scope and we refer the reader to the literature[21] for more details.

7.6. THE COEFFICIENTS OF VISCOSITY AND THERMAL CONDUCTIVITY

From the macroscopic point of view, the coefficients of viscosity and thermal conductivity describe the irreversible flows of the molecular momentum and energy respectively within the fluid. The macroscopic transport coefficients are defined in terms of mean macroscopic flows measured experimentally and related to the measured stresses according to known empirical laws such as those of Stokes (viscosity) and Fourier (thermal conductivity). According to the arguments of the statistical theory of fluids, the mean macroscopic flows are to be calculated from molecular data by performing appropriate phase averages of the pertinent phase functions using phase distribution functions relating to the particular fluid non-uniformities of interest. By comparing the calculated and empirically defined mean flows, expressions for the macroscopic transport coefficients can be constructed in terms of molecular data. The irreversible features of the flow appear, in this approach, in connection with the phase distribution functions to be used in the calculations.

For the macroscopic flow of momentum, the associated pressure stress, p_{ij}, for isothermal viscous flow with fluid velocity $\mathbf{v}$ is related to the fluid macroscopic velocity gradients and the phenomenological shear and bulk viscosity coefficients, written respectively η and ζ, according to Stokes' law.[19] If p_{ij} is the pressure stress in the direction of the i-axis across unit surface area in the fluid which is itself perpendicular to the j-axis, then it is known that the following symmetric relation holds:

$$-p_{ij} = p\,\delta_{ij} - \eta\left(\frac{\partial v_i}{\partial x_j} + \frac{\partial v_j}{\partial x_i}\right) + \left(\frac{2}{3}\eta - \zeta\right)\delta_{ij}\frac{\partial v_l}{\partial x_l}, \qquad (7.15)$$

where $\partial v_l / \partial x_l$ denotes the divergence of the velocity $\mathbf{v}$, i.e.

$$\frac{\partial v_l}{\partial x_l} = \frac{\partial v_x}{\partial x} + \frac{\partial v_y}{\partial y} + \frac{\partial v_z}{\partial z}. \qquad (7.16)$$

In (7.15) the usual component notation is used, with (i, j) each taking any of the Cartesian forms (x, y, z) and where in terms of the Cartesian axes, $x_1 \equiv x$, $x_2 \equiv y$, $x_3 \equiv z$. Also, δ_{ij} is the Kronecker delta symbol defined such that

$$\delta_{ij} = 1 \quad \text{if} \quad i = j$$
$$= 0 \quad \text{if} \quad i \neq j. \tag{7.17}$$

If the velocity vanishes, (7.15) reduces to the simple hydrostatic form appropriate to equilibrium $p_{ij} = p\delta_{ij}$. This corresponds to a simple hydrostatic pressure p, the same in all directions, because

$$-\frac{1}{3}(p_{xx} + p_{yy} + p_{zz}) = p; \quad p_{xy} = \ldots = p_{yz} = 0. \tag{7.18}$$

Examples of the forms of (7.15) using Cartesian coordinates for a fluid in motion are:

$$-p_{xx} = p - 2\eta \frac{\partial v_x}{\partial x} + \left(\frac{2}{3}\eta - \zeta\right)\left(\frac{\partial v_x}{\partial x} + \frac{\partial v_y}{\partial y} + \frac{\partial v_z}{\partial z}\right), \tag{7.19a}$$

i.e.

$$-p_{xx} = p - \left(\frac{4}{3}\eta + \zeta\right)\frac{\partial v_x}{\partial x} + \left(\frac{2}{3}\eta - \zeta\right)\frac{\partial v_y}{\partial y} + \left(\frac{2}{3}\eta - \zeta\right)\frac{\partial v_z}{\partial z}, \tag{7.19b}$$

and

$$p_{xy} = \eta\left(\frac{\partial v_x}{\partial y} + \frac{\partial v_y}{\partial x}\right), \tag{7.19c}$$

and so on.

For the case of simple laminar flow, it is convenient to choose the Cartesian frame in such a manner that the fluid velocity is directed along the positive direction of the x-axis, with the velocity gradient being in the direction of the y-axis. In this case τ has the single component v_x and grad $\mathbf{v}$ the single component $\partial v_x/\partial y$. The formulae for p_{ij} then simplify to become:

$$p_{xx} = p_{yy} = p_{zz} = p, \tag{7.20a}$$

$$p_{xy} = p_{yx} = -\eta \frac{\partial v_x}{\partial y}: \tag{7.20b}$$

and all other components vanish. The function p_{ij} can then be expressed in the simple matrix array for this particular flow situation:

$$-p_{ij} = \begin{pmatrix} p & -\eta\alpha & 0 \\ -\eta\alpha & p & 0 \\ 0 & 0 & p \end{pmatrix}, \tag{7.20c}$$

here α is the time rate of shear and for a Newtonian fluid considered here equal to the velocity gradient, i.e.

$$\alpha = \frac{\partial v_x}{\partial y}. \tag{7.20d}$$

1 more complex flows α itself has components which differ in the different irections and should be written $\alpha_i (i = x, y, z)$.

If conditions are not isothermal the heat (energy) flows within the uid along the (negative) temperature gradient. The simplest case is when ae fluid is at rest and in this case the local heat flux vector $\mathbf{q}$, which acts reversibly towards temperature uniformity, is related to the local temperature space gradient, $\text{grad}_r\, T$, according to the simple empirical rule f Fourier:

$$\mathbf{q} = -\lambda\, \text{grad}_r\, T. \tag{7.21}$$

Iere λ is the thermal conductivity, assumed independent of the location vithin the fluid. The expression (7.21) applies in the locality of some specific space location $\mathbf{r}$.

From the viewpoint of statistical theory the mean flux of particle momentum and energy is to be derived[20] by an application of the arguments f section 2.6. In particular, we use the phase average relation (2.29). For ae flow of momentum we assume the time-independent phase function Q o be given by

$$Q(\mathbf{p}, \mathbf{r}) = \sum_{j=1}^{N} (\mathbf{p}_j, \mathbf{r}_j), \tag{7.22}$$

There the summation is over all the particles of the system. The form (1.40) s immediately recovered: interpreting the potential function V as referring o the action of the containing vessel, and using the arguments associated vith equation (3.38), which are now to apply to a non-uniform situation, ve obtain first that:

$$\left\langle \sum_j \left(\mathbf{r}_j \cdot \frac{\partial \mathcal{H}}{\partial \mathbf{r}_j} \right) \right\rangle = \mathbf{P}V,$$

vhere $\mathbf{P}$ is the stress tensor, and then that

$$\mathbf{P} = \frac{N}{V} \cdot \frac{1}{m} \langle \mathbf{p}_j \mathbf{p}_j \rangle - \frac{n^2}{2V} \left\langle (\mathbf{r}_j - \mathbf{r}_k) \frac{\partial \psi}{\partial \mathbf{r}_j} \right\rangle. \tag{7.23}$$

The subscripts here refer to a representative particle pair. For equilibrium, vhere the non-diagonal components of the general expression (7.23) are dentically zero, the isotropic pressure is obtained as one-third of the diagonal sum (i.e. the trace) of the expression (7.23). The result is the exactly the previous equation (3.38) referring to equilibrium condition: The expression (7.23) is more general and applies to non-equilibrium flui flow. The link between macro- and micro-physics is to be made by com paring the non-diagonal terms in (7.23) with the corresponding terms i (7.15). The result is an expression for the shear viscosity in terms of th non-equilibrium fluid structure and the interparticle force, and corre sponding expression for the bulk viscosities (respectively equations (9.69a and (9.69b) to follow). In this way, the calculation of the shear and bul viscosities is brought within the sphere of the statistical theory. Th appearance of an explicit expression for the bulk viscosity is an importar aspect of the theory. This coefficient is hardly open to discussion in term of the standard arguments of hydrodynamics and is very difficult to meas ure accurately experimentally.

The averages in (7.23) are over the total phase. The first term on the righ hand side refers to one particle, whereas the second term involves tw particles through the interparticle force potential. Consequently, the firs term can be reduced to a phase integration over the partial phase of on particle, and this involves a knowledge of the singlet distribution $f^{(1)}$. Th second term involves two particles and so will involve the doublet functio $f^{(2)}$. The first term, therefore, applies specifically to a dilute gas where th interparticle force potential is negligible. The second term, involving th interparticle force potential, applies to a dense gas or a liquid. The tw terms taken together, along with (7.15), allow for the calculation of th shear and bulk viscosities for the whole range of densities from that of th dilute gas right up to that of a liquid.

The derivation of (7.23) just presented is rather formal: the direc physical significance of its form can, in fact, be derived from elementar considerations. For this purpose we revert to the special case of Cartesia coordinates, with the x-axis parallel to the direction of the mean macro scopic laminar flow direction of the fluid. The momentum flux in the flui is along the y-direction. Let the origin of coordinates be located on representative fluid molecule. A second molecule nearby at the point (x, y) which is in interaction with the origin particle, contributes to the flow o momentum in two distinct ways. First it carries its x-component o momentum p_x in its trajectory: if its component of velocity in the y direction is p_y/m then this translational motion contributes an amoun $(p_x p_y/m)$ to the total momentum flow in the y-direction due to all th molecules. But the second molecule is in interaction with the first origi molecule through the interparticle force, and this interaction will affec ie trajectory of the second molecule. This contribution to the momentum equal to the product of the x-component of the interparticle force (which ierefore affects p_x) and the distance y (being the relevant component :paration distance between the particles). The contribution to the x-ɔmponent of the momentum in the y-direction is then to be written:

$$\left(-\frac{\partial \psi}{\partial x} y\right).$$

'he final contribution to the x-component of the momentum flow in the -direction for the particle at (x, y) is then the sum of these two contribu-ons. To obtain the total contribution for all the particles it is necessary ɔ sum all those contributions for all fluid particles. The first translational ontribution (sometimes called the kinetic term) is to be averaged over all ie N particles in volume V. The second contribution involves the inter-ction force and is to be summed over all particle pairs. If the brackets $\rangle$ denote an average over the appropriate distribution function we have he expression for the y-component of the momentum flux in the x-irection:

$$p_{xy} = n \left\langle \frac{p_x p_y}{m} \right\rangle - \frac{n^2}{2V} \left\langle \frac{\partial \psi}{\partial x} y \right\rangle. \qquad (7.23a)$$

\n expression for the shear viscosity then follows, for given flow velocity radient in the y-direction, by the direct comparison between equations 7.23a) and (7.20b). The expression (7.23a) represents one component orm of the general flux expression (7.23). It will be clear from our deduc-ion of (7.23a) that a knowledge of the single particle momenta is adequate or the calculation of the viscosity of a dilute gas since then only the first erm in (7.23a) is relevant. But a knowledge of the relative configuration ɔf a particle pair is necessary for the evaluation of the second term in 7.23a), which refers to conditions pertaining to a liquid.

The microscopic expression for the heat flux vector $\mathbf{q}$ is derived from the ɔhase average relation (2.29) by assuming for the system of N interacting ɔarticles:

$$Q(\mathbf{p}, \mathbf{r}) = \frac{1}{4m} \sum_{j=1}^{N} \left[p_j^2 \mathbf{r}_j - \sum_{k \neq j} (\mathbf{r}_j + \mathbf{r}_k) \psi(j, k) \right]. \qquad (7.24)$$

\gain we interpret the potential in (2.4) as being due to the action of the :ontaining wall. The energy flux supplied through the surface to the fluid ɔer unit time must equal exactly the heat flux $\mathbf{q}$, because conditions are supposed steady in time, and this must equal numerically the work done

on the particles by the wall in maintaining the constant fluid volume V
Consequently we can write:

$$\frac{1}{m}\sum_{j=1}^{N}\left\langle \mathbf{r}_j\frac{\partial V}{\partial \mathbf{r}_j}\mathbf{p}_j\right\rangle = \int_{\text{surface}}(\mathbf{r}\cdot\mathbf{q})\,\mathrm{d}\sigma = \mathbf{q}V,\qquad(7.25)$$

analogously to (4.28). Using (7.25), (7.24), and (1.39) we obtain, afte
simple rearrangement of the ensuing expression:

$$\mathbf{q} = \frac{1}{V}\sum_{j=1}^{N}\left[\frac{1}{2m^2}\langle p_j^2\mathbf{p}_j\rangle+\frac{1}{4m}\sum_{i\neq j}\mathrm{B}(j,\,i)\right],\qquad(7.26a$$

where

$$\mathrm{B}(j,\,i) = \left\langle\left(\psi(i,j)\tilde{\mathbf{I}}_{ij}-(\mathbf{r}_j-\mathbf{r}_i)\frac{\partial\psi(i,j)}{\partial\mathbf{r}_j}\right)\cdot(\mathbf{p}_j+\mathbf{p}_i)\right\rangle,\qquad(7.26b$$

where $\tilde{\mathbf{I}}$ is the unit tensor. The thermal conductivity is expressed in mole
cular terms when the expressions (7.26) are equated to (7.21). It will b
seen that the first term on the right hand side of (7.26a) refers to singl
particles, whereas the second term involving $\mathrm{B}\,(j,\,i)$ includes the inter
particle force between a particle pair. Thus $f^{(1)}$ is involved in the phas
evaluation of the first term whereas $f^{(2)}$ is involved in the phase integratio
for the second term. The first term therefore applies to dilute gases wherea
the second term applies to dense gases and liquids. Two contributions ar
involved in $\mathrm{B}\,(j,\,i)$. The first, involving ψ, refers to the motion of the singl
particle j in the field of force of the neighbour i; the second contributio
arises from the relative motion of the particle pair $(i,\,j)$.

Further transport properties can be studied in the same way, for in
stance mass diffusion, by coupling the macroscopic Ficks' law with th
microscopic expression for the particle mass flow.

The evaluation of these expressions for fluid viscosity and thermal con
ductivity can be made only when the appropriate non-equilibrium single
and doublet distributions are known. The central problem of fluid non
equilibria is in this way reduced to the problem of determining the lowe
order distribution functions for non-equilibrium conditions. It is to thi
problem that we now turn.

CHAPTER 8

NON-EQUILIBRIUM GASES

THE theoretical description of a dilute gas which is not in equilibrium has been widely studied by many authors, and with considerable success. Agreement between theory and experiment has been established over many aspects of the subject and there is now a wide literature.[1] It was seen in the last chapter (section 7.6) that the viscosity and thermal conductivity of a dilute gas can be calculated once the singlet phase distribution is known. The integro-differential equation by means of which this is to be done has been known for many years; it is the well-known Maxwell–Boltzmann equation. This equation was derived originally by the so-called kinetic arguments,[2] and not from statistical arguments based on the Liouville equation. It was only in 1946–7 that Kirkwood and Bogoliubov independently showed[3] how the Maxwell–Boltzmann equation can be derived from the Liouville equation using statistical arguments, and even more recently that the theory has been finally clarified.[4] It is the purpose of the present chapter to derive the Maxwell–Boltzmann equation from the Liouville equation,[5] and we shall use the approach given by Kirkwood. This is not simply an academic exercise. By basing the theory of dilute gases on statistical arguments, where the required equation is known already, valuable experience is gained for the problem of deriving the equivalent equation for dense gases and liquids which is still essentially being constructed. Of course, once the Maxwell–Boltzmann equation is derived from statistical arguments, the many successful results already obtained from it can be claimed as also supporting the statistical approach.

8.1. KINETIC DERIVATION OF THE MAXWELL-BOLTZMANN EQUATION

Before beginning the statistical theory, it is convenient to derive the Maxwell–Boltzmann equation, from here onwards referred to simply as MB, using elementary arguments which have been known for a long time and which do not appeal directly to the Liouville equations. These arguments involve the so-called kinetic distribution function, which differs in some respects from the specific and generic distributions introduced previously.

(a) The Kinetic Distribution Function

The gas is composed of N particles without internal degrees of freedom contained in the volume V, and its instantaneous state is defined by speci fying the number of particles contained in the phase element $d\mathbf{p}_i\,d\mathbf{r}_i$ abou the phase point $\mathbf{p}_i\mathbf{r}_i$. This is the μ-space representation where the 6-di mensional phase space is divided up into elementary small, though finite phase elements. The number of particles of the gas in any of the phase elements (say $d\mathbf{p}_i\,d\mathbf{r}_i$ about $\mathbf{p}_i\mathbf{r}_i$) will vary with the time; it is proper, there fore, that this number of particles be specified as the average number ove some small macroscopic time interval δt about the instantaneous time t It is necessary to specify the space and time elements $\delta\mathbf{r}_i$ and δt more care fully. Explicitly, we will require that $\delta\mathbf{r}_i$ shall be microscopically large enough to contain a very large number of particles and yet macroscopically small enough for the various macroscopic properties such as density, tem perature, or fluid velocity, to remain virtually constant across its extent For the time element δt we assume that it must be large in comparison with the time taken for the particle located at $\mathbf{r}_i$ to cross the elementary dis tance $\delta\mathbf{r}_i$, and yet be very small in comparison with the time interval neces sary for the macroscopical fluid properties to change appreciably.

With this introduction we now define the kinetic distribution function $f(\mathbf{p}, \mathbf{r}, t)$ by stating that the number of particles in the phase element $\delta\mathbf{p}_i\,\delta\mathbf{r}_i$ about the phase point $\mathbf{p}_i\,\mathbf{r}_i$ at the time t will be denoted by:

$$f(\mathbf{p}_i, \mathbf{r}_i, t)\,\delta\mathbf{p}_i\,\delta\mathbf{r}_i. \tag{8.1}$$

In this notation the kinetic distribution carries no superscript and so i distinguished from the generic distribution introduced in Chapter 3 which always carried a superscript. Because the total number of particles in the gas is N, then if f is a continuous function of the phase, it will satisfy the normalisation condition:

$$\int\int f(\mathbf{p}, \mathbf{r}, t)\,\delta\mathbf{p},\,\delta\mathbf{r} = N, \tag{8.2}$$

where the integration is over the total phase available to the system. The integral is independent of the time if N is constant. In those cases where the kinetic distribution is independent of the location it follows from (8.2

that:

$$\int f(\mathbf{p}, t)\, d\mathbf{p} = \frac{N}{V} = n, \qquad (8.2a)$$

so that f (**p**) d**p** is then the number of particles per unit volume having momentum in the range d**p** about **p**.

(b) *The Time Change of f*

Consider the phase volume $\delta\mathbf{p}\,\delta\mathbf{r}$ about the phase point **pr**. The number of particles contained in this volume changes with the time, due to three distinct causes. First, the molecules are in motion and the number of particles initially in the volume which move out during the time interval δt is to first order of small quantities:

$$-\left(\frac{\mathbf{p}}{m}\cdot\frac{\partial f}{\partial r}\right)\delta\mathbf{p}\,\delta\mathbf{r}\,\delta t.$$

Second, if the particles are acted on by a force **F** of external origin, the number of particles moving out of the phase volume during δt due to the action of the force is, again, to first order of small quantities:

$$-\left(\frac{\mathbf{F}}{m}\cdot\frac{\partial f}{\partial \mathbf{p}}\right)\delta\mathbf{p}\,\delta\mathbf{r}\,\delta t.$$

In each case the negative sign refers to particles lost to the phase volume.

The third mechanism causing changes in the number of particles in $\delta\mathbf{p}\,\delta\mathbf{r}$ is that involving the interaction between pair of particles. Due to the particle interactions some particles originally contained in $\delta\mathbf{p}\,\delta\mathbf{r}$ will move out during δt, but also some particles originally outside the volume will move in during δt. Let us, for the moment, denote the total resultant change in the number of particles in $\delta\mathbf{p}\,\delta\mathbf{r}$ during δt which arises from particle interactions by the symbolic notation:

$$\left(\frac{\delta f}{\delta r}\right)\delta\mathbf{p}\,\delta\mathbf{r}\,\delta t.$$

Those three contributions taken together must be equal, by definition, to the change in f during δt, i.e. to:

$$\frac{\partial f}{\partial t}\,\delta\mathbf{p}\,\delta\mathbf{r}\,\delta t.$$

We are led immediately to the expression to be satisfied by f,

$$\frac{\partial f}{\partial t} = -\left(\frac{\mathbf{p}}{m}\cdot\frac{\partial f}{\partial \mathbf{r}}\right) - \left(\frac{\mathbf{F}}{m}\cdot\frac{\partial f}{\partial \mathbf{p}}\right) + \left(\frac{\delta f}{\delta t}\right)_I,$$

i.e.

$$\frac{\partial f}{\partial t} + \left(\frac{\mathbf{p}}{m}\cdot\frac{\partial f}{\partial \mathbf{r}}\right) + \left(\frac{\mathbf{F}}{m}\cdot\frac{\partial f}{\partial \mathbf{p}}\right) = \left(\frac{\delta f}{\delta t}\right)_I. \tag{8.3}$$

This expression is nothing more than a statement of the conservation of f, i.e. of the number of particles of the gas. It has, as it stands, essentially no physical content; this is introduced explicitly by specifying the interaction contribution on the right hand side, viz. $(\delta f/\delta t)_I$, in detail in terms of the particle interaction mechanism. When this interaction is that of direct binary particle elastic collisions, the right hand side of (8.3) takes on the special form to be set down in a moment and the total equation is then called the Maxwell–Boltzmann equation.

(c) *The Collision Term*

Physical content is introduced into (8.3) by specifying $(\delta f/\delta t)_I$ in detail. For a dilute gas it is assumed that the particles of the gas are not in constant interaction but instead make binary encounters of such a form that the time of duration of a collision is very small in comparison with the time between collisions. In constructing an expression for $(\delta f/\delta t)_I$ it must be remembered that f must either move irreversibly towards its equilibrium form corresponding to phase uniformity, or else retain always this equilibrium form. It is assumed explicitly that the simultaneous encounter between more than two particles is sufficiently rare an event to be neglected entirely.[6]

There are two opposing effects in connection with the collision term of (8.3). To begin with, two particles which initially occupy the phase volumes $\delta\mathbf{p}'\,\delta\mathbf{r}'$ and $\delta\mathbf{p}_1'\,\delta\mathbf{r}_1'$, respectively, may collide with each other during the time interval δt with the distinguishing result that one of the two particles moves into the phase volume $\delta\mathbf{p}\,\delta\mathbf{r}$ referred to by (8.3) On the other hand, one particle initially inside the phase element $\delta\mathbf{p}\,\delta\mathbf{r}$ may collide during the interval δt with a particle that was originally within the different phase element $\delta\mathbf{p}_1\,\delta\mathbf{r}_1$, with the result that neither particle is ultimately to be found in $\delta\mathbf{p}\,\delta\mathbf{r}$. The resultant change in the number of particles to be found in $\delta\mathbf{p}\,\delta\mathbf{r}$ due to collisions which occur during the time δt is thus the algebraic sum of these two contributions, one of which is positive (corresponding to the addition of particles to the phase volume) and the other which is negative (corresponding to the loss of particles to the volume).

It is easy to represent this situation mathematically, using also certain physical assumptions. For particles whose interaction force is not long range (thus charged particles are excluded) the time for the interaction between two particles is macroscopically indefinitely small, and the distance apart of two phase volumes each containing a particle which will collide with the other during the interval δt is also macroscopically negligible, unless the gas pressure is very low.[15] It is plausible to assert that the distribution of momenta within each of the two phase volumes is independent of the presence of the remaining volume, i.e. that at least locally microscopically in collisional terms, the form of the phase distribution is the same for each of the neighbouring phase elements $(\delta p \ \delta r)$, $(\delta p_1 \ \delta r_1)$, $(\delta p' \ \delta r')$, $(\delta p_1' \ \delta r_1')$. This assumption is the hypothesis of molecular chaos.[7] It allows us to write the following expression for the time change in f during the interval δt due to collisions as:

$$\delta t \left[\delta p' \ \delta r' \ \delta p_1' \ \delta p_1' \ f(p', r') \ f(p_1', r_1') - \delta p \ \delta r \ \delta p_1 \ \delta r_1 f(p, r) \ f(p_1, r_1) \right], \quad (8.4)$$

referring to the specific phase volumes referred to above. The phase variables appearing in (8.4) are, it must be remembered, not any variables but only those associated with a binary encounter occurring during the time interval δt. This situation will be accounted for explicitly later (in equation (8.9)) through the integration of (8.4) over the possible particle configurations. In order to obtain the total contribution of the collision terms including all the possible phase elements, (8.4) must be summed over the phase volumes $(\delta p', \ \delta r')$, $(\delta p_1', \ \delta r_1')$, and $(\delta p_1, \ \delta r_1)$: for the case of continuous phase conditions always assumed to be the case here, this summation can be written as an integration procedure. A simplification comes about, however, because of the validity of Liouville's theorem: because this theorem applies now we have (neglecting three body interactions):

$$\delta p \ \delta r \ \delta p_1 \ \delta r_1 = \delta p' \ \delta r' \ \delta p_1' \ \delta r_1', \quad (8.5)$$

so that the collision term itself becomes:

$$\left(\frac{\delta f}{\delta t} \right)_I = \int \int \left[f(p', r') \ f(p_1', r_1') - f(p, r) f(p_1, r_1) \right] dp_1 \ dr_1. \quad (8.6)$$

The insertion of (8.6) into (8.3) then gives the MB equation in the general integro–differential form:

$$\frac{\partial f}{\partial t} + \left(\frac{p}{m} \cdot \frac{\partial f}{\partial r} \right) + \left(\frac{F}{m} \cdot \frac{\partial f}{\partial p} \right)$$

$$= \int \int \left[f(p', r') \ f(p_1', r_1') - f(p, r) \ f(p_1, r_1) \right] dp_1 \ dr_1, \quad (8.7)$$

each term referring to the same time t, and the full equation covering a unit time interval. The right hand side of this equation can be related to the parameters of the collision processes by rewriting the space integration over r_1. The integration in (8.7) is to be made formally over all the phase available to the system but in practice contributions arise only from those regions involved in a binary collision. A binary collision will occur only if two chosen particles approach each other to within a specified vector distance b, called the collision parameter. Whether they will in fact approach to within this distance during unit time interval depends upon their relative velocities both as regards magnitude and direction. The collisions augmenting the number of particles in the phase volume ($\delta p \; \delta r$) have relative velocity $1/m \, |p' - p_1'|$; those depleting the volume have relative velocity $1/m \, |p - p_1|$. The Liouville theorem (8.5) is a formal way of asserting the validity of the laws of particle dynamics. For interparticle potential functions which are spherically symmetric, the energy conservation law leads to the result that the magnitude of the relative velocity g_0 for the two particles is unaffected by the collision, i.e. that:

$$\frac{1}{m} \, |p' - p_1'| = \frac{1}{m} \, |p - p'| = |g_0| = g_0. \qquad [(8.8)$$

A collision will occur between the two particles after unit time if the initial particles have the relative speed (8.8) and also if the direction is such that their trajectories actually cross to within the collision parameter. It occurs any time during a unit time interval if the trajectories cross at any instant during the time interval. Any particle contained in the cylinder of base area πb^2 about one particle and with height g_0 perpendicular to the base plane can cause an impact with the first particle during unit time. If (b, φ) are the polar coordinates of any point on the base plane, and l is the coordinate parallel to the relative velocity vector g_0 then we can make the substitution in connection with the integral (8.6):

$$\int_V dr_1 = \int_0^B b \; db \int_0^{2\pi} d\varphi,$$

where B is the effective range of the interaction force. Then (8.6) becomes alternatively:

$$\left(\frac{\delta f}{\delta t}\right)_I = \int dp_1 \int b \; db \int d\psi \, [f(p', r') f(p_1', r_1') - f(p, r) f(p_1, r_1)] g_0.$$

This integral shows explicitly the binary collision mechanism. It is difficult to evaluate except in simple cases (for example for a hard-sphere gas or for particles showing a point repulsion force). For other cases it is ιecessary to employ numerical procedures. The MB equation then takes he form:

$$\frac{\partial f}{\partial t} + \left(\frac{\mathbf{p}}{m} \cdot \frac{\partial f}{\partial \mathbf{r}}\right) + \left(\frac{\mathbf{F}}{m} \cdot \frac{\partial f}{\partial \mathbf{p}}\right)$$
$$= \int \int \int \left[f(\mathbf{p}', \mathbf{r}') f(\mathbf{p}_1', \mathbf{r}_1') - f(\mathbf{p}, \mathbf{r}) f(\mathbf{p}_1, \mathbf{r}_1)\right] g_0 b \, db \, d\varphi \, d\mathbf{p}_1. \quad (8.9)$$

n equation (8.9) the dependence of f on $\mathbf{r}$ is to be assumed sufficiently weak for all terms to be regarded as applying to the same location in space. This is the final form of the MB equation applied to direct binary colli-.ions, each term is to be evaluated at the same time instant t. (8.9) is, in a .ense, an approximate equation in that the left hand side represents the leading terms in a Taylor series expansion; additionally, the time interval δt appearing in its derivation is not exactly defined. The methods now ιvailable for solving this equation, and the irreversible nature of the solu-ions so obtained, will be considered in later sections of the present chapter.

8.2. STATISTICAL DERIVATION OF THE MB EQUATION

In order to possess a statistical theory of gases it is necessary to relate he equation (8.7) to the Liouville equation (2.23) by direct arguments ιnd well-defined assumptions, applicable to dilute gases where binary en-:ounters are the only significant particle interaction. We follow here the ιpproach proposed by Kirkwood.

To begin with, it is necessary to define a statistical distribution function ιnalogous to the kinetic distribution of the last section. It will be remem-bered that the kinetic distribution is defined as an average over some small :ime interval δt. Kirkwood[3] proposed that the analogous statistical distri-bution should be the time smoothed singlet distribution. The Nth order :ime smoothed function is defined in the previous equation (7.7). The sin-glet distribution, $\bar{f}^{(1)}$, is to be derived from $\bar{f}^{(N)}$ by using the Liouville equa-tion (1.33b) integrated over all the phase except for that relating to the particle of interest.

The time smoothed singlet distribution referring to the time instant t will be defined as:

$$\bar{f}^{(1)}(\mathbf{p}_1, \mathbf{r}_1, t) = \frac{1}{\tau} \int_0^\tau f^{(1)}(\mathbf{p}_1, \mathbf{r}_1, t+s) \, ds, \quad (8.10)$$

where s is a later time, and τ is a time interval to be defined carefully later. The time smoothed singlet distribution (8.10) is to be interpreted later as the kinetic distribution of the previous section divided by the number of particles. For the moment we require only that τ will be microscopically

large, although macroscopically it must be small, certainly in comparison
with the Poincaré time of the system and more restrictively in comparison
with the relaxation time. The Liouville equation for the system of N interacting particles can be written:

$$\frac{\partial f^{(N)}}{\partial t} + \sum_{j=1}^{N} \left\{ \left(\frac{\mathbf{p}_j}{m} \cdot \frac{\partial f^{(N)}}{\partial \mathbf{r}_j} \right) + \left(\frac{\mathbf{X}_j}{m} \cdot \frac{\partial f^{(N)}}{\partial \mathbf{p}_j} \right) \right\} = - \sum_{j=1}^{N} \left(\mathbf{F}_j \cdot \frac{\partial f^{(N)}}{\partial \mathbf{p}_j} \right). \qquad (8.11)$$

Here $\mathbf{F}_j$ is the resultant force on the jth particle due to interparticle action,
while $\mathbf{X}_j$ is the force on the jth particle due to external sources. $\mathbf{F}_j$ is taken
as being the sum of pair interaction forces. If the force between particles 1
and 2 is typical, then $\mathbf{F}_j$ is the sum of $\frac{1}{2}N(N-1)$ terms of the form $\mathbf{F}_{12}$.
The expression (8.11) is applicable to any time instant; suppose now that
it applies to the instant $(t+s)$.

The first order distribution function is of interest in connection with
gases. This is derived from (8.11) by integrating over the phase of the
remaining $(N-1)$ particles. Considering the phase distribution of the particle at the space location $\mathbf{r}_1$ we have from (8.11):

$$\frac{\partial f^{(1)}}{\partial t} + \left(\frac{\mathbf{p}_1}{m} \cdot \frac{\partial f^{(1)}}{\partial \mathbf{r}_1} \right) + \left(\frac{\mathbf{X}_1}{m} \cdot \frac{\partial f^{(1)}}{\partial \mathbf{p}_1} \right)$$

$$= - \int \int \sum_{j=1}^{N} \left(\mathbf{F}_j \cdot \frac{\partial f^{(N)}}{\partial \mathbf{p}_j} \right) \prod_{k=2}^{N} \mathrm{d}\mathbf{p}_k \, \mathrm{d}\mathbf{r}_k, \qquad (8.12)$$

where we have used the fact that $f^{(N)}$ vanishes if any particle momentum
is infinite, or if any particle coordinate lies outside the volume V available
to the gas. The right hand side of this expression can be rewritten. The
force acting on the particle can be written:

$$\mathbf{F}_j = \frac{\mathrm{d}\mathbf{p}_j}{\mathrm{d}t}, \qquad (8.13)$$

where $\mathbf{p}_j$ is the instantaneous value of the momentum, so that:

$$\left(\mathbf{F}_j \cdot \frac{\partial f^{(N)}}{\partial \mathbf{p}_j} \right) = \left(\frac{\mathrm{d}\mathbf{p}_j}{\mathrm{d}t} \cdot \frac{\partial f^{(N)}}{\partial \mathbf{p}_j} \right). \qquad (8.13a)$$

Then (8.12) becomes, referring to the time $(t+s)$,

$$\frac{\partial f^{(1)}}{\partial t} + \left(\frac{\mathbf{p}_1}{m} \cdot \frac{\partial f^{(1)}}{\partial \mathbf{r}_1} \right) + \left(\frac{\mathbf{X}_1}{m} \cdot \frac{\partial f^{(1)}}{\partial \mathbf{p}_1} \right) = -N \int \int \left(\frac{\mathrm{d}\mathbf{p}_j}{\mathrm{d}t} \cdot \frac{\partial f^{(2)}}{\partial \mathbf{p}_j} \right) \mathrm{d}\mathbf{p}_2 \, \mathrm{d}\mathbf{r}_2, \qquad (8.14)$$

where in integrating the right hand side of (8.12) account has been taken
of the doublet nature of the interparticle force, and the subscript j can
take the values 1 and 2.

Let us now time average (8.14) according to (8.10). To achieve this end, we first integrate each term in (8.14) between the time limits 0 and τ, and divide the resulting equation throughout by τ. The left hand side of (8.14) is converted immediately into the expression involving the time smoothed distribution, i.e.:

$$\frac{\partial \bar{f}^{(1)}}{\partial t} + \left(\frac{\mathbf{p}_1}{m} \cdot \frac{\partial \bar{f}^{(1)}}{\partial \mathbf{r}_1}\right) + \left(\frac{\mathbf{X}_1}{m} \cdot \frac{\partial \bar{f}^{(1)}}{\partial \mathbf{p}_1}\right), \qquad (8.15)$$

referring to the time t. The right hand side of (8.14) becomes:

$$-\frac{N}{\tau} \int_0^\tau \int \int \left(\frac{d\mathbf{p}_j}{dt} \cdot \frac{\partial f^{(2)}}{\partial \mathbf{p}_j}\right) d\mathbf{p}_2 \, d\mathbf{r}_2 \, ds = -\frac{N}{\tau} \int \int d\mathbf{p}_2 \, d\mathbf{r}_2 [f^{(2)}(\tau) - f^{(2)}(0)].$$

$$= \frac{N}{\tau} \int \int d\mathbf{p}_2 \, d\mathbf{r}_2 [f^{(2)}(t) - f^{(2)}(t+\tau)] = \frac{N}{\tau} \int \int d\mathbf{p}_2 \, d\mathbf{r}_2 [f^{(2)}(t-\tau) - f^{(2)}(t)].$$

The last expression is obtained from the previous expression by employing a canonical transformation and using Liouville's theorem for the particles. The equation (8.15), therefore, becomes:

$$\frac{\partial \bar{f}^{(1)}}{\partial t} + \left(\frac{\mathbf{p}_1}{m} \cdot \frac{\partial \bar{f}^{(1)}}{\partial \mathbf{r}_1}\right) + \left(\frac{\mathbf{X}_1}{m} \cdot \frac{\partial \bar{f}^{(1)}}{\partial \mathbf{p}_1}\right) = \frac{N}{\tau} \int \int [f^{(2)}(t-\tau) - f^{(2)}(t)] \, d\mathbf{p}_2 \, d\mathbf{r}_2.$$

$$(8.16)$$

We must now introduce some physical criteria in order to reduce this expression to the conventional form of MB equation (8.9).

To begin with, we make the assumption that the doublet distribution $f^{(2)}$ can be written as the product of the separate singlet distributions, i.e. in the symmetric form:

$$f^{(2)}(\mathbf{p}_1, \mathbf{r}_1, \mathbf{p}_2, \mathbf{r}_2) = f^{(1)}(\mathbf{p}_1, \mathbf{r}_1) f^{(1)}(\mathbf{p}_2, \mathbf{r}_2). \qquad (8.17)$$

The choice of the two singlet functions in (8.17) as having the same form is in a sense a statement of the hypothesis of molecular chaos.

This relation is true only if the particles 1 and 2 are completely independent at the time t, and the particles must be independent at every instant during the time interval τ if (8.17) is to apply rigorously throughout this period. This cannot, however, actually be the case since we have already postulated that the particles must collide in pairs. But we assume that the time interval between any two successive collisions between one particle and *any* other is very large in comparison with the time of duration of a collision. During the time interval τ appearing in (8.16), if the total time interval during which the particles are involved in a collision is τ_c while the total time interval during which they are entirely free is τ_f we can write

$$\tau = \tau_f + \tau_c = \tau_f \left(1 + \frac{\tau_c}{\tau_f}\right) \sim \tau_f,$$

since $\tau_c/\tau_f \ll 1$. Consequently, if τ is assumed to be large in comparison with the time taken for a single binary encounter we can regard (8.17) as applying for the total time interval τ to good first approximation, and this assumption will be made now.[8] In this way the right hand side of (8.16) is reduced to involve the product of singlet functions in place of the doublet function itself.

The singlet functions in (8.17) are the unsmoothed distributions but in order that (8.16) shall be comparable to the MB equation (8.9) it is necessary, we will later assert, that the time-smoothed distribution be interpreted as the kinetic distribution. The right hand side of (8.16) must be arranged to involve $\bar{f}^{(1)}$ and not $f^{(1)}$.

According to (8.10) we can write:

$$\bar{f}^{(1)}(t) = \frac{1}{\tau} \int_0^\tau f^{(1)}(t+s)\, ds = f^{(1)}(t) + \frac{\tau}{2}\, \frac{\partial f^{(1)}(t)}{\partial t} + \frac{\tau^2}{6}\, \frac{\partial^2 f^{(1)}(t)}{\partial t^2} + \cdots.$$
$$(8.18)$$

It is now asserted that for a time-dependent distribution, the time interval τ will be chosen to have the maximum value that is compatible with the second and subsequent terms on the right hand side of (8.18) being negligibly small in comparison with the first term. Thus we choose τ such that it is a sufficient approximation to equate $\bar{f}^{(1)}(t)$ to $f^{(1)}(t)$, and this is to apply at all values of t. This will be the case if the time dependence of $f^{(1)}$ is not too strong, such as when the deviation from equilibrium is small. On this understanding then, using (8.17) and (8.18), the right hand side of (8.16) becomes:

$$\frac{N}{\tau} \int \int \left[\bar{f}_1^{(1)}(t-\tau)\bar{f}_2^{(1)}(t-\tau) - \bar{f}_1^{(1)}(t)\bar{f}_2^{(1)}(t)\right] d\mathbf{p}_2\, d\mathbf{r}_2, \qquad (8.19)$$

where we have used the obvious shorthand notation:

$$\bar{f}_1^{(1)}(t-\tau) = \bar{f}^{(1)}(\mathbf{p}_1, \mathbf{r}_1, t-\tau),$$
$$\bar{f}_2^{(1)}(t-\tau) = \bar{f}^{(1)}(\mathbf{p}_2, \mathbf{r}_2, t-\tau), \qquad (8.19a)$$

and so on.

Up to this point no explicit mechanism has been ascribed to the binary particle interaction except, according to (8.17), that the time of interaction is very small in comparison with τ. The statement that the interaction is a binary elastic collision is included into (8.19) by making the appropriate

hysical interpretation of the time smoothed distributions and by making
ιe integration over the position vector in a proper way (see the previous
ɛmarks following the expression (8.4)).

To begin with it must be realised that, according to the definition for
ιme smoothing (8.10), the form of the time-smoothed singlet distribution
t time t depends also on the trajectory during the *subsequent*[9] time τ. Thus
$^{1)}$ is an average value of the function $f^{(1)}$ taken over some time interval τ,
ut assigned in the time hierarchy to the beginning of the interval τ rather
ιan to its midpoint (i.e. time $t+\tau/2$), or to the end (i.e. time $t+\tau$).
onsequently $\bar{f}^{(1)}(t-\tau)$ refers in fact to the phase trajectory during the
ιme interval τ between the times $(t-\tau)$ and t, while $\bar{f}^{(1)}(t)$ refers to the
ιme interval τ between the times t and $(t+\tau)$. In evaluating the configura-
on integral in (8.19) it is, then, asserted that the product of the functions
$^{1)}(t-\tau)\bar{f}_2^{(1)}(t-\tau)$ is to be interpreted as referring to two particles which
ιffer a direct collision during the time interval τ with the consequence that
ιe particle 1 enters the phase element $\delta\mathbf{p}_1\,\delta\mathbf{r}_1$ associated with the left hand
ide of (8.16). On the other hand, the product $\bar{f}_1^{(1)}(t)\bar{f}_2^{(1)}(t)$ is to refer to
collision between particles 1 and 2 during the later time interval τ with
he result that the particle 1 which was originally inside $\delta\mathbf{p}_1\,\delta\mathbf{r}_1$ will leave
. With this interpretation an equivalence can be asserted between the
ɔtal function

$$[f(\mathbf{p}',\mathbf{r}')\,f(\mathbf{p}_1',\mathbf{r}_1')-f(\mathbf{p},\mathbf{r})\,f(\mathbf{p}_1,\mathbf{r}_1)]$$

f equation (8.7) and the total function

$$[\bar{f}_1^{(1)}(t-\tau)\,\bar{f}_2^{(1)}(t-\tau)-\bar{f}_1^{(1)}(t)\,\bar{f}_2^{(1)}(t)]$$

ɔf (8.19). The integration over $\mathbf{r}_1$ is to be made according to the require-
nents of the conservation laws applying to binary encounters during the
ime interval τ. By making exactly the same analysis as that used previously
n passing from (8.7) to (8.9), the relative velocity between the particles 1
nd 2 is introduced and the integral in (8.19) is proportional to τ. The total
xpression on the right hand side of (8.16) is, then, independent of τ, and
ιas the same form as the right hand side of (8.9). There is, however, one
urther thing to do, and that is to relate the time-smoothed singlet distribuion $\bar{f}^{(1)}$ to the kinetic distribution f of the last section.

The equation (8.16) with the right hand side replaced by (8.19) derived
ɔy statistical arguments can be written:

$$N\frac{\partial \bar{f}^{(1)}}{\partial t}+N\left(\frac{\mathbf{p}_1}{m}\cdot\frac{\partial \bar{f}^{(1)}}{\partial \mathbf{r}_1}\right)+N\left(\frac{\mathbf{X}_1}{m}\cdot\frac{\partial \bar{f}^{(1)}}{\partial \mathbf{p}_1}\right)$$
$$=N^2\int\int[\bar{f}_1^{(1)}(t-\tau)\,\bar{f}_2^{(1)}(t-\tau)-\bar{f}_1^{(1)}(t)\,\bar{f}_2^{(1)}(t)]\,\mathrm{d}\mathbf{p}_2\,\frac{\mathrm{d}\mathbf{r}_1}{\tau}. \qquad (8.20)$$

This is to be compared with the previous kinetic equation (8.7). Remembering the agreed method of evaluating the integral on the right hand side of (8.20) to account for binary elastic collisions, (8.20) and (8.7) become identical if the kinetic distribution f is related to the time-smoothed single distribution by

$$f(\mathbf{p}, \mathbf{r}, t) = \frac{N}{\tau} \int_0^\tau f^{(1)}(\mathbf{p}, \mathbf{r}, t+s) \, ds = N\bar{f}^{(1)}(t). \tag{8.21}$$

With this substitution the equation (8.20) can then be put into the form (8.9), and the statistical arguments have reconciled the MB equation to the Liouville equation. Four main assumptions have been made in the statistical derivation, viz.: the kinetic distribution of section 8.1 is interpreted statistically in terms of the time-smoothed specific singlet distribution; deviations from equilibrium are assumed small, and the time changes in the singlet specific distribution are small; the particle interaction in the gas is entirely by binary elastic collisions: and finally the time interval used in the time-smoothing operation is to be larger than the time for a binary encounter and yet small enough to allow the specific singlet distribution to be replaced in the collision term by the corresponding time smoothed function. Although we have in this section used the statistical arguments to derive the known MB equation, there is more potential strength to the arguments than this. It would seem possible to use them to deduce a more general equation than (8.9) referring to binary encounters which will apply to extended interactions or to the simultaneous encounter of more than two particles. One such equation will be considered in the next chapter, section 9.1, but the broad potentialities of the approach would seem to remain largely unexplored.

8.3. THE MOVEMENT TO EQUILIBRIUM

It is necessary to demonstrate that the MB equation (8.9) has solutions which move irreversibly towards equilibrium. To show this we study the entropy per unit gas volume and invoke the H-function of Gibbs defined in (7.4), and use the kinetic distribution function. Let us simplify the discussion by making the inessential assumption that the kinetic distribution is independent of the position in the gas, and that no external forces are present. Thus in (8.9) we set

$$f(\mathbf{p}, \mathbf{r}, t) = f(\mathbf{p}, t), \quad \frac{f}{\partial \mathbf{r}} = 0, \quad \mathbf{X} = 0,$$

so that

$$\frac{\partial f}{\partial t} = \int \int \int [f(\mathbf{p}', t) \, f(\mathbf{p}_1', t) - f(\mathbf{p}, t) \, f(\mathbf{p}_1, t)] g_0 b \, db \, d\varphi \, d\mathbf{p}_1 \quad (8.22)$$

is the MB equation for this case. The kinetic distribution now relates to the particle momentum only, referring to unit fluid volume.

The H-function of Boltzmann is defined by:

$$H = \int f \log f \, d\mathbf{p} \quad (8.23)$$

per volume unit of the fluid. The time rate of change of H is relevant in the discussion of the movement to equilibrium, and from (8.23) we have

$$\frac{\partial H}{\partial t} = \int \frac{\partial}{\partial t} (f \log f) \, d\mathbf{p} = \int \frac{\partial f}{\partial t} (1 + \log f) \, d\mathbf{p}. \quad (8.24)$$

Let us insert (8.22), i.e. the MB equation, into the last expression of (8.24). As a result we obtain:

$$\frac{\partial H}{\partial t} = \int \int \int (1 + \log f)[f'f_1' - ff_1] \, d\mathbf{k} \, d\mathbf{p}_1 \, d\mathbf{p}, \quad (8.25)$$

where we have used the obvious shorthand of writing all the parameters of the binary encounter in the elemental form $d\mathbf{k}$ and have used the notation:

$$f_1' = f(\mathbf{p}_1', t), \quad \text{and so on.}$$

The expression (8.25) applies to all collisions in the gas, and necessarily remains true if we interchange the roles of the colliding particles. More specifically, the integral in (8.25) remains unaltered if $\mathbf{p}_1$ is replaced by $\mathbf{p}$, $-\mathbf{p}_1'$, or $-\mathbf{p}'$, in each case the result being a variant of a single expression. If these substitutions are in fact made, and the three resulting expressions added together and to (8.25), we obtain the result:

$$4\frac{\partial H}{\partial t} = \int \int \log \left[\frac{f(\mathbf{p}) \, f(\mathbf{p}_1)}{f(\mathbf{p}') \, f(\mathbf{p}_1')} \right] [f(\mathbf{p}') \, f(\mathbf{p}_1') - f(\mathbf{p}) \, f(\mathbf{p}_1)] \, d\mathbf{k} \, d\mathbf{p}_1 \, d\mathbf{p}. \quad (8.26)$$

Now

$$\log \left[\frac{f(\mathbf{p}) \, f(\mathbf{p}_1)}{f(\mathbf{p}') \, f(\mathbf{p}_1')} \right]$$

is positive or negative according as to whether $f(\mathbf{p}) \, f(\mathbf{p}_1)$ is greater than or less than $f(\mathbf{p}') \, f(\mathbf{p}_1')$. This means that the product

$$\log \left[\frac{f(\mathbf{p}) \, f(\mathbf{p}_1)}{f(\mathbf{p}') \, f(\mathbf{p}_1')} \right] [f(\mathbf{p}') \, f(\mathbf{p}_1') - f(\mathbf{p}) \, f(\mathbf{p}_1)]$$

is either negative or zero, but not positive. This result means, using (8.26)
that

$$\frac{\partial H}{\partial t} < 0,$$

so that H decreases in time and the entropy density increases. In the limit
$\frac{\partial H}{\partial t} = 0$, the steady state

$$f(\mathbf{p}') \, f(\mathbf{p}_1') = f(\mathbf{p}) \, f(\mathbf{p}_1) \tag{8.27}$$

is reached, and from there on no further change in H occurs. In this way
it is seen that the system moves towards equilibrium, and once there does
not move away. The MB equation, upon which this argument is based,
then has solutions which describe the irreversible movement to equilibrium
and is able to describe non-equilibrium conditions met with in real dilute
gases.

8.4. THE STEADY STATE

The gas is in a steady state when the condition (8.27) applies; written
logarithmically, the steady state condition is:

$$\log f(\mathbf{p}') + \log f(\mathbf{p}_1') = \log f(\mathbf{p}) + \log f(\mathbf{p}_1). \tag{8.28}$$

This expression must not violate the conservation requirements applying
to the binary elastic encounter to which it refers. This means that (8.28)
is to be used in conjunction with the conservation of particle mass, momentum, and kinetic energy. The general solution of (8.28) can, therefore,
be written:

$$\log f(\mathbf{p}) = \frac{\alpha_1}{m}(\mathbf{p} \cdot \mathbf{p}) + (\boldsymbol{\alpha}_2 \cdot m\mathbf{v}) + \alpha_3, \tag{8.29}$$

where α_1, and α_3 are simple constants, and $\boldsymbol{\alpha}_2$ is a constant vector with
three components, i.e. one for each of the momentum components with
which it is associated. There are, then, five simple constants in (8.29) which
remain to be defined in terms of the physical state of the gas. The con-
stants $(\alpha_1, \boldsymbol{\alpha}_2, \alpha_3)$ can be replaced by three other constants $(A, \text{h}, \mathbf{p}_0)$ and
(8.29) written in the alternative non-logarithmic form:

$$f(\mathbf{p}) = A \exp\left[-\frac{\text{h}}{m}(\mathbf{p} - \mathbf{p}_0)^2 \right]. \tag{8.30}$$

Because $f(\mathbf{p})$ is the distribution for unit volume (see section 8.1) then A must
have the dimensions (volume) $^{-1}$. The meaning of the constant $\mathbf{p}_0$ is easily

ascertained. The exponential in (8.30) has its maximum value when $\mathbf{p} = \mathbf{p}_0$ so that $\mathbf{p}_0$ is the velocity of most frequent occurrence in this case, i.e. the velocity of centre of gravity of the whole gas. Expressed alternatively, $\mathbf{p}_0$ is the mean velocity of the gas treated macroscopically. When the mean fluid velocity is zero ($\mathbf{p}_0 = 0$), conditions are those of equilibrium so that

$$h = \frac{1}{2kT}, \tag{8.31}$$

where T is the temperature. This identification remains valid also when $\mathbf{p}_0$ does not vanish.

The constant A is derived from the normalisation condition (8.2a) which in the present case is:

$$A \int \exp\left[-\frac{(\mathbf{p} - \mathbf{p}_0)^2}{2mkT} \right] d\mathbf{p} = n,$$

where n is the number density. Thus,

$$A = n \left(\frac{1}{2\pi mkT} \right)^{\frac{3}{2}},$$

so that the solution of (8.28) is

$$f_0(\mathbf{p}) = n \left(\frac{1}{2\pi mkT} \right)^{\frac{3}{2}} \exp\left[-\frac{(\mathbf{p} - \mathbf{p}_0)^2}{2mkT} \right]. \tag{8.32}$$

The subscript $_0$ in (8.32) is introduced to designate that (8.32) is the solution of the steady state equation (8.28). From the method used here to derive (8.32) it is not certain that other solutions of (8.28) do not exist; no other solutions are, however, known and there is no evidence that they do in fact exist.

The relation (8.28) is often quoted as an expression of the principle of detailed balancing according to which, during a specified time interval, in a gas in the steady state, as many collisions occur which remove particles from a given phase volume as cause particles to enter it.

For a gas in thermodynamical equilibrium, $\mathbf{p}_0 = 0$ and (8.32) becomes:

$$f_0(\mathbf{p}) = n \left(\frac{1}{2\pi mkT} \right)^{\frac{3}{2}} \exp\left[-\frac{p^2}{2mkT} \right]. \tag{8.33}$$

This is the well-known Maxwell distribution[2] and is itself also a solution of (8.28). It follows that the relation (8.28) is a necessary condition for the existence of thermodynamic equilibrium in the gas (i.e. for (8.33) to be a solution) but is not a sufficient condition (because (8.32) is also a solution of (8.28)).

8.5. REMARKS ON THE SOLUTION
OF THE MAXWELL–BOLTZMANN EQUATION

For non-steady distributions the momentum distribution has not the simple form (8.32), but must be derived by solving the full transport equation (8.9). The way in which this can be achieved was first suggested by Enskog.[10] In recounting this procedure it is useful, for avoiding unnecessary writing out of complicated formulae, to rewrite the initial equation (8.9) in a slightly different way.

The binary collision term forming the right hand side of (8.9) concerns the particles that leave and enter the elementary phase volume $\delta p \, \delta r$ in the time interval δt. Let us agree on a precise notation to describe the process by explicitly recognising formally two classes of particles, implicitly involved in the previous arguments. The first class i (say) is defined as containing any particle which moves into or out of the elementary phase volume in time δt due to binary collisions: the other particle in the binary encounter (which is not a member of class i) will be regarded as being a member of the second class j. This division into two classes of particles is, of course, somewhat formal since each particle can still be regarded as physically identical with all the others in regard to mass and interparticle force potential. The extension to mixtures of gases is readily made, as will be seen later in the chapter. The distribution functions for particles of classes i and j are, of course, indistinguishable according to the hypothesis of molecular chaos and the conservation laws of particle collision. Consider the distribution in phase of the particles of class i. This distribution is a solution of (8.9) which is now written:

$$\frac{\partial f_i}{\partial t} + \left(\frac{p}{m} \cdot \frac{\partial f_i}{\partial r} \right) + \left(\frac{X}{m} \cdot \frac{\partial f_i}{\partial p} \right) = J(f_i, f_j), \qquad (8.34a)$$

where

$$J(f_i, f_j) = \int \int \int (f_i' f_j' - f_i f_j) g_0 b \, db \, d\varphi \, dp_j. \qquad (8.34b)$$

The collision term is therefore denoted by the symbol J.

According to the method proposed by Enskog, the equation (8.34) is to be solved by introducing a parameter ε defined so that $(1/\varepsilon)$ is a measure of the frequency of collisions between particles. If ε is small, so that $(1/\varepsilon)$ is very large, the particle collisions occur with very small time intervals between them: in this case local equilibrium is very rapidly set up and then maintained. Larger values of ε then correspond to less frequent collisions, and so to a slower approach to equilibrium. If the distribution f_i appearing in (8.34) represents a gas in which deviations from local equilibrium are small, it is plausible[16] to expand f_i in powers of the inverse collision frequency ε, i.e. to write for $f(\mathbf{p}_i, \mathbf{r}, t)$:

$$f = f_0 + \varepsilon f_1 + \varepsilon^2 f_2 + \varepsilon^3 f_3 + \cdots = \sum_{k=0}^{\infty} \varepsilon^k f_k. \tag{8.35}$$

Here f_0 can be expected to be the steady state distribution (8.32) and $f_1, f_2, \ldots$ successively the first, second, ... order deviations from uniformity. The expansion (8.35) can be usefully inserted into (8.34) only if this equation shows ε explicitly. Enskog proposed that the right hand side of (8.34a) should be replaced by $(1/\varepsilon)J$, so that the actual equation (8.34) is replaced by the hypothetical equation:

$$\frac{\partial f_i}{\partial t} + \left(\frac{\mathbf{p}}{m} \cdot \frac{\partial f_i}{\partial \mathbf{r}}\right) + \left(\frac{\mathbf{X}}{m} \cdot \frac{\partial f_i}{\partial \mathbf{p}}\right) = \frac{1}{\varepsilon} J(f_i, f_j). \tag{8.36}$$

(8.36) becomes identical with (8.34a) when we set $\varepsilon = 1$. The functions f_k in (8.35) are to be obtained by inserting (8.35) into (8.36), and then equating the coefficients of ε successively to zero in the resulting equation.

As a result, (8.36) is replaced by the scheme of component equations:

$$0 = J(f_{i0}, f_{j0}), \tag{8.37a}$$

$$\frac{\partial f_{i0}}{\partial t} + \left(\frac{\mathbf{p}}{m} \cdot \frac{\partial f_{i0}}{\partial \mathbf{r}}\right) + \left(\frac{\mathbf{X}}{m} \cdot \frac{\partial f_{i0}}{\partial \mathbf{p}}\right) = J(f_{i0}, f_{j1}) + J(f_{i1}, f_{j0}), \tag{8.37b}$$

$$\frac{\partial f_{i1}}{\partial t} + \left(\frac{\mathbf{p}}{m} \cdot \frac{\partial f_{i1}}{\partial \mathbf{r}}\right) + \left(\frac{\mathbf{X}}{m} \cdot \frac{\partial f_{i1}}{\partial \mathbf{p}}\right) = J(f_{i0}, f_{j2}) + J(f_{i1}, f_{j1}) + J(f_{i2}, f_{j0}), \tag{8.37c}$$

and so on. The first equation (8.37a) involves the unknown function f_0; the second involves the two functions f_0 and f_1, the third equation involves the three functions f_0, f_1, f_2, and so on. A solution procedure can then be followed in principle where the knowledge of the solutions of the equations previous to any given equation allows this latter equation to be reduced to involve a single unknown function. Thus, where f_0 is determined from (8.37a), (8.37b) becomes an equation in the single unknown function f_1. Knowledge of f_0 and f_1 allows (8.37c) to be reduced to a form involving the single unknown function f_2, and so on.

The most general solution of (8.37a) is known from the discussion of the steady state in section 8.4, viz. f_0 is given by (8.32). The trio of functions n, $\mathbf{p}_0$, and T appearing in (8.32) are arbitrary at this stage. In order that these quantities shall be interpreted in the usual way in terms of the local fluid conditions it is necessary that the complete distribution f shall satisfy the following expressions for the particle number density, the mean fluid momentum, and the mean kinetic energy:

$$\int f \, d\mathbf{r} = n,$$

$$\int \mathbf{p} f \, d\mathbf{p} = \mathbf{p}_0,$$

(8.38

$$\int \frac{1}{2} \frac{(\mathbf{p}-\mathbf{p}_0)^2}{m} \, f \, d\mathbf{p} = \frac{3}{2} \, nkT.$$

If these conditions hold, then n, $\mathbf{p}_0$, and T have the required physical loca
meanings. It is permissible in the analysis (the reasons will not be persue
here) that functions appearing in (8.37b), (8.37c), and so on, satisfy th
subsidiary conditions (where $k = 1, 2, 3, \ldots$):

$$\int f_k \, d\mathbf{p} = 0,$$

$$\int \mathbf{p} f_k \, d\mathbf{p} = 0,$$

(8.39

$$\int (\mathbf{p}-\mathbf{p}_0)^2 f_k \, d\mathbf{p} = 0,$$

and specify the set of functions f_k uniquely. According to the relation
(8.38) and (8.39) the steady state function f_0 can be inserted in (8.38) i
place of f, since the three functions n, $\mathbf{p}_0$, and T refer to local equilibrium
The set of functions defined in this way also satisfy (8.38), and so can b
taken to be a physically acceptable solution of the Maxwell–Boltzmani
equation.

It is unfortunate that, with the leading member f_0 of the set (8.35) known
the remaining functions f_k cannot be readily determined; for finding thos
remaining it is necessary in each case to solve an integral equation, witl
the unknown function appearing in the integrand. For determining f_1 le
us introduce a perturbation function ϕ according to:

$$f_1(\mathbf{p}, \mathbf{r}, t) = f_0(\mathbf{p}, \mathbf{r}, t) \, \phi(\mathbf{p}, \mathbf{r}, t),$$

(8.40

so that we assume for general functions:

$$f = f_0[1+\phi].$$

(8.40a

ϕ is here a small function, representing the local deviation from equilib
rium, the values of n, $\mathbf{p}_0$, and T varying only slightly from point to point i
the gas. This situation is relevant in the study of gaseous transport proces
ses, such as viscosity and thermal conductivity. The insertion of (8.40a

into (8.37b) leaves the left hand side unaffected, but the right hand side becomes, to the first approximation in the small quantity ϕ,

$$\int \int \int f_{i0} f_{j0} [\phi_i' + \phi_j' - \phi_i - \phi_j] g_0 b \, db \, d\varphi \, d\mathbf{p}_j. \tag{8.41}$$

The subsidiary conditions (8.39) apply with f_k replaced by $f_0 \phi$. Any solution ϕ of the equation, resulting when (8.41) replaces the right hand side of (8.37b), must conform to the requirements of mass, momentum, and energy conservation. Consequently, a solution of (8.37b) still remains a solution when

$$\mathbf{Z} = A_1 + (\mathbf{A}_2 \cdot \mathbf{p}) + A_3 p^2 \tag{8.42}$$

is added to it, provided the five scalar constants $(A_1, \mathbf{A}_2, A_3)$ conform to the five conditions (8.39). On the other hand, the derived solution of the MB equation has physical validity only if it is fully specified by the space gradients of n, $\mathbf{p}_0$, and T. This follows from the experimental knowledge that these quantities are sufficient for specifying the state of the gas at each point.

It is possible on physical grounds, therefore, to assume for $f_0 \phi$ the general form:

$$f_0 \phi = \left(\mathbf{B}_1 \cdot \frac{\partial \log T}{\partial \mathbf{r}} \right) + \left(\mathbf{B}_2 \cdot \frac{\partial \mathbf{p}_0}{\partial \mathbf{r}} \right) + B_3 n + \mathbf{Z}, \tag{8.43}$$

where $\mathbf{Z}$ is given by (8.42). The constants $\mathbf{B}$ and $\mathbf{A}$ are to be determined such that (8.40a) is to be a solution of (8.37b), under the auxiliary conditions (8.39). The determination of the constants in (8.43) involves the evaluation of the collision integral (8.41) for a specific form of interaction between the pairs of colliding particles. This evaluation can proceed in analytic terms at the present time only for a gas of hard-sphere particles where the interaction potential is given by (1.4), or for the point repulsion potential (1.6) in the special case where m $= 5$ (Maxwell particle). In other cases numerical procedures must be employed and these turn out to be very complicated.[11]

The problem of determining the next number f_2 of the series (8.35) is more complicated than that for determining f_1 which we have just briefly outlined, and has not been seriously tackled up till now. It is usually claimed that the series (8.35) converges rapidly, and that a knowledge of the first two terms is sufficient for representing the non-uniform states of a gas that are ordinarily met with in laboratory experiments. In particular, excepting possibly at low pressures,

$$f = f_0 + f_1 \tag{8.44}$$

is a sufficient approximation to f for the determination of the transport coefficients of a gas. It is remembered that for the practical use of the expansion (8.35) it is necessary to set $\varepsilon = 1$.

8.6. VISCOSITY AND THERMAL CONDUCTIVITY

When the kinetic distribution is once determined in the approximation (8.44) this function can be used in the formulae of section 7.6 for the determination of the shear viscosity η and thermal conductivity λ of the gas. η follows from (7.15) and (7.23), while λ follows from (7.21) and (7.26). For a gas only the first terms in (7.26) and (7.23), where the interparticle force does not explicitly appear, are relevant. The details of the interparticle force are not irrelevant since they define the exact form of the collision integral J in the MB equation, and so affect the calculated distribution f of (8.44). It is found ultimately,[12] to the first approximation associated with (8.44), that η and λ are given by:

$$\eta(T) = \frac{RT}{\beta(T)}, \quad \text{and} \quad \lambda(T) = \frac{15}{4} R\eta, \tag{8.45}$$

where the parameter $\beta(T)$ has the explicit form:

$$\beta(T) = \frac{2}{5} \frac{\sqrt{(2\pi)}}{m} \int_0^\infty r^6 e^{-r^2/2} \left\{ \int b \sin^2 \varphi \cos^2 d\varphi \right\} dr. \tag{8.46}$$

In (8.46), b is the collision parameter and φ is the angle specifying the collision trajectories of the particles. b is in general a function of the relative particle momentum g_0, and so of the temperature, and of the trajectory azimuthal angle φ. In this way $\beta(T)$ is an implicit function of the temperature.

The calculation of the function $\beta(T)$ is difficult, and in general can be conducted only in numerical terms. For Maxwell particles (where there is only a repulsion region of the potential inversely proportional to the fifth power of the separation distance) b is a function of φ alone and $\beta(T)$ can then be evaluated analytically. For a hard-sphere gas the distribution has been evaluated in terms of polynomial expansion, and $\beta(T)$ ultimately evaluated.[13]

One important general result, valid to the first approximation involved in (8.44), follows from (8.45) without any calculation. For we have

$$\frac{\lambda}{\eta} = \frac{15}{4} R,$$

and remembering that, for a gas[†] the specific heat at constant volume C_V is given classically by:

$$C_V = \frac{3}{2} R,$$

then

$$\frac{\lambda}{\eta} = \frac{5}{2} C_V. \tag{8.47}$$

This relation has obtained experimental support. η and λ are found to behave roughly in the same way with temperature change, and further it is known that for a gas C_V is only weakly dependent upon the temperature, so that the ratio λ/η is not a sensitive function of the temperature. In addition, η and λ themselves both increase only weakly with increasing temperature. In this respect a gas is quite unlike a liquid, as will be seen in the next chapter. In a liquid the shear viscosity[14] *decreases* strongly with temperature, whereas the thermal conductivity increases weakly. It is to the credit of the statistical theory that it is able to account for this marked difference in the transport properties of a gas and a liquid in a consistent and natural way, as will be seen in the next chapter.

Finally, it should be noticed that the theory is able to include mixtures of gases without any essential rearrangement. The Maxwell–Boltzmann equation (8.9) now contains additional collision terms referring to unlike particles, and there is an equation of the type (8.9) applying to each particle species. The arguments developed for simple gases then apply to mixtures, and lead to expressions for the transport coefficients which agree with experiment whenever the formidable computational problems make a comparison possible.

8.7. FURTHER COMMENTS

The rather brief discussion of the kinetic theory of dilute gases given in the present chapter was designed to show an application of the statistical method based on Liouville's equation in one case where an alternative theory is already well established. Before leaving the subject, however, we should point out that the MB equation itself has its limitations and is open to improvement.

The MB transport equation is based upon the concept of molecular chaos, and applies to a dilute gas on those occasions when this concept applies. Unfortunately, molecular collisions can cause conditions of molec-

---

[†] We refer here to a monatomic gas without internal particle degrees of freedom.

ular chaos to be violated: the MB equation is useful only when conditions of molecular chaos apply for most of the time. In this way, the MB equation is to be accepted as a true representation of the non-equilibrium condition of a dilute gas only in statistical terms. It describes the movement to equilibrium in some average sense, and is coupled with an H-function which is a mean value compatible with an associated fine fluctuating dependence on the time. It is by these means that the time reversibility of molecular dynamics is destroyed in the deduction of the MB equation which is not left invariant when the time variable is reversed. The MB equation refers to μ-space. A more general discussion of the approach of a system to equilibrium can be expected from equations in γ-space, and this is attempted through the so-called master equations. It is beyond our present purposes to consider this matter here.

The Chapman–Enskog solution procedure is also capable of generalisation. It is based on the recognition of conditions of local thermodynamic equilibrium in the non-uniform gas.

It is asserted that the flux vectors in the fluid are adequately specified by a knowledge of the three macroscopic quantities, density, average mass velocity, and the fluid temperature, together with their space gradients. The first derivatives of the macroscopic quantities have been seen to be involved in the calculation of the first approximation to the distribution function. Higher approximations will involve higher derivatives together with powers of lower derivatives. The three macroscopic quantities are used to define the first three velocity moments of the distribution function and these can then be specified for all points in space at some particular time. The Enskog solution procedure amounts to a description of the time evolution of the fluid, starting at some chosen time from a knowledge of the first three velocity moments alone. The series that results does not represent the most general solution of MB, but relates to a particular class of distribution function that is asserted to be adequate for the calculation of macroscopic properties. The comparison between theory and experiment supports this assertion at least as far as the first order approximation to the distribution function. The problem of the convergence of the Enskog series is not touched upon.

Two questions arise, one of a general nature and the other more specialised. First, the specialised question: we may ask about the form of the Enskog procedure when the gas density is too low to allow the fluid to be assumed continuous. In this case the fluid is outside the scope of the Navier–Stokes equations of hydrodynamics. The problem of boundary conditions is of especial importance here. The second more general question concerns the method by which distribution functions are to be obtained even within the continuum approximation, but which are more fully specified than by the first three velocity moments alone. A method of answering these questions has been proposed by Grad in his so-called thirteen-moment approximation[1].

Moment equations are obtained from MB by multiplying MB throughout by a power of the momentum, and then integrating throughout the resulting equation over the momentum of the particles. The Enskog procedure considers the first three moments: the first and third relate respectively to the scalar density and temperature (2 moments) while the third relates to the mean velocity (3 moments). Five moments are therefore involved here. Grad suggests that rather than use these to obtain the momentum and heat fluxes, these two quantities should also be related directly to moments independently. Thus, the pressure tensor and heat flux vector are to be independent (6 moments) and each satisfy their own differential equations (2 moments). This total aggregation then provides thirteen moments at each point for the calculation of the future evolution of the distribution function. If the velocity and temperature of the gas do not vary appreciably over a mean free path, and further, if the properties of a small macroscopic volume of the gas do not change appreciably in the time associated with the mean time between collisions, then this formalism provides expressions for the pressure tensor and heat flux that have the same form as for conventional hydrodynamics. The thirteen-moment equation in this way includes, also, the Enskog method as a more restrictive case. It is not appropriate to consider these matters further here, since our main concern is with dense fluids, but they are worth bearing in mind as situations that the statistical theory must ultimately show itself competent to solve.

CHAPTER 9

NON-EQUILIBRIUM LIQUIDS

THE Maxwell–Boltzmann equation was derived in the last chapter on the essential assumption (represented explicitly in equation (8.17)) that the movement of each particle of the gas can be studied virtually independently of the movement of the remaining gas particles. This assumption is applicable to the description of dilute gases because then the interaction between the particles is that of binary elastic collisions. The form of the MB equation is intimately connected with the features of binary collisions and it is not easily applicable to more complicated encounters. In particular, this equation will not be applicable to fluids above a critical density, the exact value of which will depend upon the details of the particle interaction force. For liquid densities it is not possible to consider the motion of one particle in isolation from the remainder if the particle force is at all realistic.[1] Each particle is constantly in interaction with neighbouring particles and the concept of direct collisions is foreign to the discussion. The MB equation is consequently inapplicable and we are forced to search for an alternative equation characteristic of the short-ranged particle spatial ordering of the fluid. Appeal cannot, on the other hand, be made to the theory of crystalline solids which is based upon the simplification, valid for solids but not for liquids, that the particle motion can be resolved into independent modes of vibration at least to acceptable approximation.

There is not at the present time any full theory of simple non-uniform liquids which can be regarded in any way as final, although there is considerable work now going on designed to provide ultimately such a theory. Much of the work is of a formal nature, and unambiguous numerical values which can be compared with experimental data are very scarce indeed. Since any theory must ultimately be judged in terms of the success it has in accounting for the full range of experimental data which lies within its scope, it will be realised that the present position of the theory of liquids under non-equilibrium conditions is unsatisfactory. In the present chapter we consider one approach to the treatment of liquid non-equilibrium which has the present merit of being essentially the only treatment

)ased on particle dynamics and involving the Liouville equation which has
ed to numerical values of the liquid transport coefficients which are in
ιny way satisfactory. The method is due originally to Kirkwood[2] and later
o Eisenschitz[3] and bases the study of transport in liquids on equations
)f the Fokker-Planck and Smoluchowski types already met with earlier
n Chapter 7 (section 7.5(b)) in connection with the Brownian motion.
[t will be found that the following arguments do in fact provide a broad
ιnd consistent treatment of the liquid transport properties, which is based
)n the principles of particle dynamics.[4] While it cannot be regarded as a
inal theory, since it involves points that still need further resolution, it is
ikely to be included (though perhaps with considerable modification) in
ιny final theory when, eventually, this is developed. Reference to other
ιlternative work is made in Appendix 9.5. We restrict the arguments to
"ollow to pure liquids only; liquid mixtures will not be included.

9.1. THE FOKKER-PLANCK EQUATION FOR SINGLE PARTICLES

As a preliminary to the derivation of an equation for the structure of a
non-uniform liquid we will first explore the possibility of deriving an equation for the distribution of single particles where the interparticle interaction force is extended in time, and is not of the type of simple binary
encounters considered in the last chapter. The equation which results will
be the analogue of the MB equation but will differ from it significantly
in the form of its right hand side. This is because the particle interaction
is not now that appropriate to simple collisions. The equation will describe
a Markovian system, i.e. where the past history is irrelevant. The representation of a simple liquid as such a system is a principal assumption of
the theory.

Again we consider a system of N interacting particles contained in the
volume V, and we assume the particles to have no internal degrees of
freedom. The Nth order specific distribution satisfies the Liouville equation
(8.11) which is our starting point now as it was in Chapter 8. As for the
MB equations so now we integrate (8.11) over the phase of all the particles
except the one involved in the unknown singlet distribution. We arrive
then at the equation (8.12) and invoke also the expression (8.13a). To this
point our arguments are identical with those for the MB equation. From
this point onwards, however, they are different. We can no longer treat
the interaction between two particles as an isolated even, but suppose it
as part of an extended interaction in which neighbouring particles also

play a part. The treatment of the right hand side of (8.12) must now be made to account explicitly for the permanent interaction between any particle in the liquid and its neighbours. This we choose to do in what follows by using the form of Kirkwood's approach originally due to Eisenschitz,[3] introducing $f^{(1)}$ at a later stage in the argument without introducing $f^{(2)}$ at all. Thus the binary assumption (8.17) is avoided. Irreversibility is introduced into the theory by replacing the hypothesis of molecular chaos of gas theory by a generalisation appropriate to extended interactions and expressed in (9.43).

The right hand side of equation (8.12) is rewritten using the expressions (8.13)

$$ - \int \int \sum_{j=1}^{N} \left(\frac{d\mathbf{p}_j}{dt} \cdot \frac{\partial f^{(N)}}{\partial \mathbf{p}_j} \right) \prod_{k=2}^{N} d\mathbf{p}_k \, d\mathbf{r}_k. \tag{9.1} $$

The time-smoothed singlet specific distribution function (8.10) is the appropriate representation in the theory of the physical kinetic distribution and the left hand side of (8.12) is again arranged to involve the time-smoothed function $\bar{f}^{(1)}$ by time averaging. For the moment the value to be assigned to τ is left undefined; we say only that it must not be either too large or too small in a manner to be specified later. The result is that the left hand side is given by (8.15), referring to the time instant t. The right hand side of the equation that we are now constructing is the time average of (9.1), i.e.

$$ - \frac{1}{\tau} \int_0^\tau \int \int \sum_{j=1}^{N} \left(\frac{\partial \mathbf{p}_j}{dt} \cdot \frac{\partial f^{(N)}}{\partial \mathbf{p}_j} \right) \prod_{k=2}^{N} d\mathbf{p}_k \, d\mathbf{r}_k \, ds. \tag{9.2} $$

In evaluating this expression, those terms in which the integrand contains explicitly coordinates and momenta of the molecules 2, 3, ... N are eliminated from the argument due to purely mathematical reasons. Specifically, derivatives of $f^{(N)}$ with respect to the phase coordinates of the $N-1$ particles 2, 3, 4, ... N can be converted into surface terms through partial integration. These surface terms vanish because $f^{(N)}$ itself vanishes rapidly in the region of the phase boundary containing the particles. The reason for this is simply that the particles are restrained from moving outside some configuration region due to the action of the physical boundary walls; on the other hand, the particle momentum must always remain finite. This means that the summation in (9.2) is effectively to include only the particles 1 and 2. If $\Delta\mathbf{p}_1$ and $\Delta\mathbf{r}_1$ are respectively the increments of momentum and position of the particle 1 during the time interval τ, then (9.2) an be rewritten to become:

$$\frac{1}{\tau} \int \int [f^{(N)}(\mathbf{p}_1 - \Delta\mathbf{p}_1, \mathbf{r}_1 - \Delta\mathbf{r}_1) - f^{(N)}(\mathbf{p}_1, \mathbf{r}_1)] \prod_{k=2}^{N} d\mathbf{p}_k \, d\mathbf{r}_k. \quad (9.3)$$

Equating the two expressions (8.15) and (9.3) gives the integro–differential equation for $\bar{f}^{(1)}$ in the form:

$$\frac{\partial \bar{f}^{(1)}}{\partial t} + \left(\frac{\mathbf{p}_1}{m} \cdot \frac{\partial \bar{f}^{(1)}}{\partial \mathbf{r}_1}\right)$$

$$= \frac{1}{\tau} \int \int [\bar{f}^{(N)}(\mathbf{p}_1 - \Delta\mathbf{p}_1, \mathbf{r}_1 - \Delta\mathbf{r}_1) - \bar{f}^{(N)}(\mathbf{p}_1, \mathbf{r}_1)] \prod_{k=2}^{N} d\mathbf{p}_k \, d\mathbf{r}_k, \quad (9.4)$$

where we have neglected the presence of external forces (i.e. $\mathbf{X}_1 = 0$). By invoking the previous reduction formula (1.34) with $h = 2$, it is easily seen that (9.4) is equivalent to (8.16). Since we do not have binary encounters now there is no value in introducing $f^{(2)}$ into (9.4). Instead we expand the right hand side of (9.4) in a special way introducing explicitly the singlet distribution $f^{(1)}$.

Difficulties in integration arise because of the time increment τ between the two terms in the integral on the right hand side of (9.4). The second term, referring to time t, is readily written as $f^{(1)}$ according to (1.34) with $h = 1$. Thus the right hand side of (9.4) is rewritten as:

$$\frac{1}{\tau} \left[-f^{(1)}(\mathbf{p}_1, \mathbf{r}_1) + \int \int f^{(N)}(\mathbf{p}_1 - \Delta\mathbf{p}_1, \mathbf{r}_1 - \Delta\mathbf{r}_1) \prod_{k=2}^{N} d\mathbf{p}_k \, d\mathbf{r}_k \right]. \quad (9.5)$$

The second term in (9.5) will also be written in terms of $f^{(1)}$ by using a so-called conditional probability. This gives the probability distribution of the system for fixed values of the phase of one particle (or in the general case for a small group of particles) of the system. For our present purposes we require the conditional probability where the phase of particle 1 is chosen as fixed and the phases of the remaining $(N-2)$ particles allowed to vary. Expressed mathematically, the conditional probability distribution with particle 1 taken as standard is written:

$$f^{(N-1:1)}(\mathbf{p}_2, \mathbf{r}_2, \mathbf{p}_3, \mathbf{r}_3, \ldots \mathbf{p}_N, \mathbf{r}_N : \mathbf{p}_1, \mathbf{r}_1) \equiv f^{(N-1:1)}(\mathbf{p}^{N-1}, \mathbf{r}^{N-1} : \mathbf{p}_1, \mathbf{r}_1), \quad (9.6)$$

where the second expression uses an obvious notation also used in earlier chapters. Using this conditional probability distribution we write $f^{(N)}$ for the total system in the alternative form:

$$f^{(N)}(\mathbf{p}^N, \mathbf{r}^N) = f^{(1)}(\mathbf{p}_1, \mathbf{r}_1) f^{(N-1:1)}(\mathbf{p}^{N-1}, \mathbf{r}^{N-1} : \mathbf{p}_1, \mathbf{r}_1). \quad (9.7)$$

The conditional probability tells of the phase of the system relative to $\mathbf{p}_1\mathbf{r}_1$, while the probability $f^{(1)}$ describes the distribution for particle 1. It is obvious then that each side of (9.7) says exactly the same thing physically.

Introducing (9.7) into (9.5) we have:

$$\frac{1}{\tau}\left[-f^{(1)}(\mathbf{p}_1, \mathbf{r}_1) + \int\int f^{(1)}(\mathbf{p}_1-\varDelta\mathbf{p}_1, \mathbf{r}_1-\varDelta\mathbf{r}_1)f^{(N-1:1)}\right.$$

$$\left.\times(\mathbf{p}_{11}^{N-1}, \mathbf{r}_{11}^{N-1} : \mathbf{p}_1, \mathbf{r}_1, t-\tau)\prod_{k=2}^{N}\mathrm{d}\mathbf{p}_k\,\mathrm{d}\mathbf{r}_k\right], \qquad (9.8a)$$

where

$$\mathbf{p}_{11}^{N-1} = \mathbf{p}^{N-1}(t-\tau) \quad \text{and} \quad \mathbf{r}_{11}^{N-1} = \mathbf{r}^{N-1}(t-\tau). \qquad (9.8b)$$

In evaluating the integral in (9.8a) explicit account must be taken of the fact that it refers to time $(t-\tau)$ rather than t. To do this we follow Eisenschitz[3] and divide the integration into two parts, first that for which $\varDelta\mathbf{p}_1$ is constant, and then that accounting for all the values of $\varDelta\mathbf{p}_1$ that are possible during the time interval τ. With the integration performed in this way the expression (9.8a) is replaced by the alternative form:

$$\frac{1}{\tau}\left[-f^{(1)}(\mathbf{p}_1, \mathbf{r}_1) + \int\int f^{(1)}(\mathbf{p}_1-\varDelta\mathbf{p}_1, \mathbf{r}_1-\varDelta\mathbf{r}_1)\right.$$

$$\left.\times W(\varDelta\mathbf{p}_1, \varDelta\mathbf{r}_1)\,\mathrm{d}(\varDelta\mathbf{p}_1)\,\mathrm{d}(\varDelta\mathbf{r}_1)\right]. \qquad (9.9)$$

The function W appearing in (9.9) is the phase volume of the subspaces of the total phase of the system for which $\varDelta\mathbf{p}_1$ is constant. At this point the function W is undetermined and we will in fact not need to determine it explicitly. In any complete theory the function W would need to be evaluated explicitly. The problems associated with such an evaluation are those of the simultaneous movement of a large number of interacting particles, and no way of dealing with this rigorously is yet known. For the moment we circumvent the issue, although we will need to consider it later in the present section. It is, however, necessary for our present purposes to assume that W is virtually independent of the time. This can be expressed alternatively because from (9.8a) and (9.9) it follows that W is closely connected with the conditional probability $f^{(N-1:1)}$. In the approximation that this distribution function is essentially independent of the time, the time dependence in the total distribution $f^{(N)}$ arises entirely from the time dependence of $f^{(1)}$. This is a simplifying assumption of the theory. If this can be assumed to be the case, then $W(\varDelta\mathbf{p}_1, \varDelta\mathbf{r}_1)$ can be interpreted as a transition probability[6] for the increments $\varDelta\mathbf{p}_1$ and $\varDelta\mathbf{r}_1$ in the momentum and position respectively of particle 1 during the time interval τ. On this interpretation, W is also a function of the initial phase $r_1 - \Delta r_1$, $p_1 - \Delta p_1$ at time $(t-\tau)$. Because W is virtually time independent, the form at time $(t-\tau)$ is the same as that at time t. If this interpretation is made then the equation (9.9) has the form of the interaction integral in the Fokker–Planck equation describing the motion of a single Brownian particle.[†]

The momentum and position increments are related by the equations of particle dynamics, for

$$m\Delta r_1 = p_1 \tau, \qquad (9.10)$$

where m is the particle mass. In consequence we have

$$W(\Delta p_1, \Delta r_1; p_1, r_1) = W_1(\Delta p_1, p_1)\, \delta(m\Delta r_1 - \Delta p_1 \tau), \qquad (9.11)$$

where δ is the Dirac delta function, and the transition probability in phase space is reduced to a transition probability in momentum space. The configuration integration in (9.9) is immediately performed so that (9.9) becomes now:

$$\frac{1}{\tau}\left[-f^{(1)}(p_1, r_1) + \int f^{(1)}(p_1 - \Delta p_1) W_1(\Delta p_1, p_1)\, d(\Delta p_1) \right]. \qquad (9.12)$$

We now make the restriction on the magnitude of τ that the momentum increment during this time interval Δp_1 is small in comparison with p_1 for extended interactions,[7] i.e. that the relative particle momentum increment during τ is small. If we further assume that the corresponding increment in position is negligible during time τ (i.e. $\Delta r_1 \sim 0$), the integrand in (9.12) can be expanded in a Taylor series about p_1 and the integration performed. Thus we write:

$$f^{(1)}(p_1 - \Delta p_1) = f^{(1)}(p_1) - \left(\Delta p_1 \cdot \frac{\partial f^{(1)}}{\partial p_1}\right) + \tfrac{1}{2}(\Delta p_1 \cdot \Delta p_1)\frac{\partial^2 f^{(1)}}{\partial p_1^2} - \cdots . \qquad (9.13)$$

The mean increments of Δp_1 and $(\Delta p_1 \cdot \Delta p_1)$ can be defined in terms of the

[†] Improvements of the approximation that $f^{(N-1:1)}$ is to be assigned an equilibrium value result in the addition of further terms in the final equations (9.26). In particular, the left hand side of these equations is augmented by the term:

$$+\frac{\partial}{\partial p_1}(F^* \overline{f_1^{(1)}}),$$

where F^* is the mean force on the particle due to the departure of the environment of the particle from equilibrium. In applications of the present theory to the study of the Brownian motion such a correction is not necessary since the fluid as a whole is in equilibrium. For viscous flow, however, this is not so: but departures from equilibrium are of higher order of small quantities than those normally retained in the theory.

transition probability W_1 according to:

$$\langle \Delta \mathbf{p}_1 \rangle = \int_{-\infty}^{\infty} \Delta \mathbf{p}_1 W_1(\Delta \mathbf{p}_1) \, \mathrm{d}(\Delta \mathbf{p}_1), \tag{9.14a}$$

$$\langle \Delta \mathbf{p}_1 \cdot \Delta \mathbf{p}_1 \rangle = \int_{-\infty}^{\infty} (\Delta \mathbf{p}_1 \cdot \Delta \mathbf{p}_1) W_1(\Delta \mathbf{p}_1) \, \mathrm{d}(\Delta \mathbf{p}_1). \tag{9.14b}$$

The insertion of the expressions (9.13), and (9.14) into (9.12) then leads to the form:

$$\frac{1}{\tau} \left[-\frac{\partial}{\partial \mathbf{p}_1} (f^{(1)}\langle \Delta \mathbf{p}_1 \rangle) + \frac{1}{2} \frac{\partial^2}{2\partial \mathbf{p}_1^2} (f^{(1)}\langle \Delta \mathbf{p}_1^2 \rangle) + \frac{\partial}{\partial \mathbf{p}_1} \frac{\partial}{\partial \mathbf{p}_1} (f^{(1)}\langle \Delta \mathbf{p}_1 \, \Delta \mathbf{p}_1 \rangle) \right],$$

$$\tag{9.15}$$

where powers of the momentum increment higher than the second have been disregarded as being negligibly small, in comparison with the first and the second increments. Provided that the time dependence of $f^{(1)}$ is not too strong we can again invoke (8.18) as a basis for replacing $f^{(1)}$ by the time-smoothed function $\bar{f}^{(1)}$ in (9.15). The full equation determining $\bar{f}^{(1)}$ for the present case of continual particle interaction is obtained finally by replacing the right hand side of (9.4) by (9.15) with the result:

$$\frac{\partial \bar{f}^{(1)}}{\partial t} + \left(\frac{\mathbf{p}_1}{m} \cdot \frac{\partial \bar{f}^{(1)}}{\partial \mathbf{r}_1} \right)$$

$$= \frac{1}{\tau} \left[-\frac{\partial}{\partial \mathbf{p}_1} (\bar{f}^{(1)}\langle \Delta \mathbf{p}_1 \rangle) + \frac{1}{6} \frac{\partial^2}{\partial \mathbf{p}_1^2} (\bar{f}^{(1)}\langle \Delta \mathbf{p}_1 \cdot \Delta \mathbf{p}_1 \rangle) \right], \tag{9.16}$$

where mean cross products of components like the Cartesian $\langle \Delta \mathbf{p}_{1x} \, \Delta \mathbf{p}_{1y} \rangle$ are also neglected. Equation (9.16) is the Fokker–Planck equation in its general form. It was met with earlier in Chapter 7, equation (7.10), and it still remains to rearrange (9.16) into the form of (7.10) which is known to describe successfully the irreversible features of the Brownian motion. We assert here that equations of this type are sufficient also for describing liquid non-equilibria. To carry the arguments further it is necessary to show that the bracket expression on the right hand side of (9.16) is proportional to τ, i.e. that *both* $\langle \Delta \mathbf{p}_1 \rangle$ and $\langle \Delta \mathbf{p}_1^2 \rangle$ are each proportional to τ. This requirement will be found to lead to an expression for the friction constant of hydrodynamics controlling the irreversible movement to equilibrium. In addition it provides information about the magnitude of τ that can be assigned in the theory (see also section 9.3).

In order to evaluate the mean increments $\langle \Delta \mathbf{p}_1 \rangle$ and $\langle \Delta \mathbf{p}_1^2 \rangle$ it is necessary to specify the transitional probability W in terms of the particle phases, or what is the same thing, to define in detail the conditional distribution $f^{(N-1:1)}$. For this purpose we suppose that $f^{(N-1:1)}$ is independent of the time and is equal to its equilibrium value at the initial time $t = 0$. This is a simplifying assumption which seems unavoidable at the present state of the theory. The total distribution function $f^{(N)}$ is written in terms of its equilibrium value $f_0^{(N)}$ at time $t = 0$ by considering the increment of momentum of particle 1 during the subsequent time interval τ.

The momenta occur in the total distribution $f^{(N)}$ through the factor $\exp\{-\sum\limits_{j=1}^{N} \mathbf{p}_j^2/2mkT\}$, and the momenta at time t are given by $\mathbf{p}_j = \mathbf{p}_{j0}+\Delta\mathbf{p}_j$, where $\mathbf{p}_{j0}$ are the momenta at the initial time $t = 0$. If the increment of momentum during τ is small we can write:

$$f^{(N)} = f_0^{(N)} \left[1 - \frac{1}{mkT} \sum_{j=1}^{N} (\mathbf{p}_{j0}\cdot\Delta\mathbf{p}_j) + \dots \right], \qquad (9.17)$$

to first order in $\Delta\mathbf{p}_j$. The mean and mean square momentum increments for particle 1 during the time τ are respectively:

$$\langle\Delta\mathbf{p}_1\rangle = \int\int \Delta\mathbf{p}_1 f^{(N-1:1)}(\Delta\mathbf{p}_1) \prod_{k=2}^{N} d\mathbf{p}_k \, d\mathbf{r}_k, \qquad (9.18a)$$

$$\langle\Delta\mathbf{p}^2\rangle = \int\int (\Delta\mathbf{p}_1 \, \Delta\mathbf{p}_1) f^{(N-1:1)}(\Delta\mathbf{p}_1) \prod_{k=2}^{N} d\mathbf{p}_k \, d\mathbf{r}_k, \qquad (9.18b)$$

which are alternative expressions to (9.14). If $\mathbf{F}_1$ is the total force on particle 1 due to the remaining particles we also have the expression for $\Delta\mathbf{p}_1$:

$$\Delta\mathbf{p}_1 = \int_0^\tau \mathbf{F}_1(s) \, ds, \qquad (9.19)$$

giving $\Delta\mathbf{p}_1$ as the time average of the force on the particle during the interval τ. Using (9.19) and (9.17) in (9.18a) we have:

$$\langle\Delta\mathbf{p}_1\rangle = \int\int_0^\tau \mathbf{F}_1(s) \, ds \, f_0^{(N)} \left[1 - \frac{1}{mkT} \sum_{j=1}^{N} \mathbf{p}_{j1}\tau\mathbf{F}_1(0) + \dots \right] \prod_{k=2}^{N} d\mathbf{p}_k \, d\mathbf{r}_k, \quad (9.20)$$

where $\Delta\mathbf{p}_j$ appearing in the summation is given its value in terms of the force at time $t = 0$. The first term on the right hand side of (9.20) vanishes because the integration is made over the equilibrium total distribution. For the correct function $f^{(N)}$, which has not an equilibrium form, this contribution will not vanish but will lead to an effect due to a mean force arising from the collective effect of neighbours. The arguments here have also assumed a simple system: for mixtures a mean force will also arise because of the asymmetry of the particle species present. One term in the expansion of the second term in (9.20) will, however, not vanish, giving:

$$\langle \Delta \mathbf{p}_1 \rangle = -\frac{1}{mkT} \left\{ \int \int \int_0^\tau [\mathbf{F}_1(s) \cdot \mathbf{F}_1(0)] \, ds \, f_0^{(N)} \prod_{[k=2}^N d\mathbf{p}_k \, d\mathbf{r}_k \right\} \tau \mathbf{p}_{10}. \quad (9.21)$$

Let us introduce the function $\beta^{(1)}$ according to:

$$\beta^{(1)} = \frac{1}{3mkT} \int_0^\tau \langle \mathbf{F}_1(t) \cdot \mathbf{F}_1(t+s) \rangle_{N-1} \, ds, \quad (9.22)$$

where the phase average of the integrand is over the equilibrium distribution of the $(N-1)$ particles other than the particle 1 in question, i.e.:

$$\langle \mathbf{F}_1(t) \cdot \mathbf{F}_1(t+s) \rangle_{N-1} = \int \int (\mathbf{F}_1(t) \cdot \mathbf{F}_1(t+s)) f_0^{(N-1:1)} \prod_{k=2}^N d\mathbf{p}_k \, d\mathbf{r}_k. \quad (9.23)$$

This quantity $\beta^{(1)}$ is the time average over the time τ of the conditional phase average of the product of the force on particle 1 at times t and $(t+s)$. Because the force on the particle is considered at different times $\beta^{(1)}$ will not vanish even though the environment is in equilibrium. It will be studied further in section 9.3. For the moment let us assume that $\beta^{(1)}$ is a constant, the physical implications of this being left open for the moment. Then (9.21) simplifies in form to become:

$$\langle \Delta \mathbf{p}_1 \rangle = -\mathbf{p}_{10} \beta^{(1)} \tau, \quad (9.24)$$

where $\mathbf{p}_{10}$ is the particle momentum at the beginning of the time instant τ. Reference to Chapter 7, section 7.5(b), will remind us that (9.24) is exactly the average momentum increment for a Brownian particle during the interval τ, provided that $\beta^{(1)}$ is interpreted as the Stokes friction constant of hydrodynamics. If $\beta^{(1)}$ defined in (9.22) is interpreted as this friction constant, so that (9.24) refers to the momentum increment of the particle during the interval τ then the statistical theory has provided the fundamental formula (9.22) (which must elude normal hydrodynamics) relating the macroscopic friction effects associated with differential gross fluid movement to the underlying molecular structure. This is probably the most important new result of the entire theory (see also section 9.3).

The calculations of $\langle \Delta \mathbf{p}_1^2 \rangle$ and $\langle \Delta \mathbf{p}_i \, \Delta \mathbf{p}_j \rangle$ then follow similar lines to the calculation of $\langle \Delta \mathbf{p} \rangle$ and lead to the conclusion that:

$$\langle \Delta \mathbf{p}_1^2 \rangle = 6mkT\beta^{(1)}\tau, \quad (9.25a)$$

$$\langle \Delta \mathbf{p}_{1i} \, \Delta \mathbf{p}_{1j} \rangle = 0(\tau^2) \quad \text{where} \quad i, j = x, y, z \quad \text{but} \quad i \neq j. \quad (9.25b)$$

It will be seen that whereas $\langle \Delta \mathbf{p}_1 \rangle$ and $\langle \Delta \mathbf{p}_1^2 \rangle$ are each proportional to τ, $\langle \Delta \mathbf{p}_{1i} \, \Delta \mathbf{p}_{1j} \rangle$ is proportional to τ^2. We disregard terms proportional to τ^2, thus ensuring that the right hand side of (9.16) will be independent of τ. This is necessary if only non-equilibrium contributions are to be retained. Inserting (9.24) and (9.25) into (9.16) gives finally the Fokker–Planck equation for the single particle distribution in the form:

$$\frac{\partial \bar{f}^{(1)}}{\partial t} + \left(\frac{\mathbf{p}_1}{m} \cdot \frac{\partial \bar{f}^{(1)}}{\partial \mathbf{r}_1} \right) = \beta^{(1)} \left[\frac{\partial}{\partial \mathbf{p}_1} (\bar{f}^{(1)} \mathbf{p}_1) + mkT \frac{\partial^2 \bar{f}^{(1)}}{\partial \mathbf{p}^2} \right]. \qquad (9.26)$$

This equation is identical to the previous equation (7.10). The kinetic distribution can be introduced into (9.26) by using (8.21). If the fluid has a mean motion with velocity $\mathbf{V}_0$ the mean momentum increment is augmented by the quantity $m\mathbf{v}_0\tau$. As a consequence (9.26) is changed to become:

$$\frac{\partial \bar{f}^{(1)}}{\partial t} + \left(\frac{\mathbf{p}_1}{m} \cdot \frac{\partial \bar{f}^{(1)}}{\partial \mathbf{r}_1} \right) = \beta^{(1)} \left\{ \frac{\partial}{\partial \mathbf{p}_1} [(\mathbf{p} - m\mathbf{v}_0)\bar{f}^{(1)}] + mkT \frac{\partial^2 \bar{f}^{(1)}}{\partial \mathbf{p}_1^2} \right\}. \qquad (9.26a)$$

The analysis of this chapter is important in the study of liquids for three respects. First, it shows that an equation of the Fokker–Planck type is fully compatible with the Liouville equation and can be obtained by statistical arguments, using well-defined assumptions which are plausible in relation to the present concepts of liquid structure. Second, the important possibility is provided, through the expressions (9.22) and (9.23), of developing a mechanism for the calculation of the features of a dissipative mechanism controlling the irreversible motion in terms of particle dynamics. And finally, it acts as a guide for the contruction of an equation relating to the motion of pairs of particles relevant to liquid structure.

The Fokker–Planck equation for a single particle is alternatively applicable to the study of gases where the interparticle force is long-ranged and where binary encounters are unlikely. Such a situation also occurs in plasmas at low density, where the Coulomb force is more effective an interaction between particles than is direct collision. In this case the plasma can be controlled in its macroscopic behaviour by the manipulations of externally applied magnetic fields so that account must generally be made for the presence of a force (in this case the Lorentz force) of external origin. This is done by including the term:

$$\left(\frac{\mathbf{X}_1}{m} \cdot \frac{\partial \bar{f}^{(1)}}{\partial \mathbf{p}_1} \right)$$

on the left hand side of the expressions (9.26). Non-electromagnetic forces (such as gravitation) can also be included through such a term. In practice, for liquids such forces have negligible effect and will not be recognised in what follows.

So far the character of the interparticle force has been treated as a single unity over the full range of interactions, and any effects specifically associated with particle repulsion or attraction have not been explicitly isolated. There is, however, a real advantage in exploring the possibility of taking separate account of the repulsion and attraction characteristics of the interparticle force potential. This approach has been explored particularly by Rice and Allnatt,[8] and seems capable of providing a basis for a theory of transport in dense fluids. The central idea is to treat a direct encounter between two particles as consisting of a strong repulsive encounter followed by a random motion of the Brownian type in the fluctuating field of the neighbouring particles. The Brownian-type motion can be expected to destroy interaction correlations very rapidly, and it is plausible to regard successive repulsive interactions as statistically independent events uncoupled to the neighbouring particle environment. It will be realised that the actual particle interaction process is now separated into a component associated with the short time-scale of binary encounters (where the momentum increment is not small during the encounter), and a longer time-scale component, for which the idea of a small momentum increment can be applied.

With the interaction force separated in this way, the development of the Liouville equation according to the arguments of the present chapter is in a sense a mixture of those of the present chapter and of the last chapter. The effect is to add to the right hand side of (9.26) an integral term of the same form as that applying to the Maxwell–Boltzmann equation. The reader is referred to the original papers[8] for the details of the derivation, which is essentially a repetition of the analysis that we have already considered.

The theory in this form depends explicitly on the assumption that the approach to equilibrium is due to the independent action of two distinct interaction mechanisms. The strongly repulsive interactions (often termed hard) have an associated friction constant, which differs from the essentially independent friction constant for the weaker interactions (mainly attractive but possibly also including the weaker features of repulsion just beyond the core region), termed soft. In the general fluid system, these two interactions are not independent, but Rice and Allnatt assert that it is a sufficient approximation for application to simple liquids like argon where the repulsive potential has a large space gradient. Indeed, in their formulation of the theory, the interparticle potential is assumed to have a hard central core out to a distance σ (OA of Fig. 5), the larger distance potential form (entirely negative ψ) showing a weak remaining repulsion and an attraction according to the (12–6) potential form. It would seem, however, that the hardcore feature is not a cardinal feature and can be relaxed to some extent, with the general proviso that the repulsion must, nevertheless, remain sufficiently strong. This approach will be considered further in section 9.6.

9.2. FOKKER–PLANCK EQUATION FOR PARTICLE PAIRS

The arguments developed in the last section for the motion of a single particle can be extended to apply to a particle pair. The resulting equation will be considered as a possible contender for the calculation of liquid transport coefficients. The short-ranged liquid spatial order is represented theoretically by the pair configuration distribution $g^{(2)}$ by averaging $f^{(2)}$ over all the momenta available to the two particles. The resulting Fokker–Planck equation is somewhat more complicated than that for $f^{(1)}$ in that the interaction force between the particle pair described by $f^{(2)}$ must now also be accounted for.

The derivation of the equation for $f^{(2)}$ proceeds in exactly the same way as for $f^{(1)}$ explained in the last section. Again we start from the Liouville equation (8.11), and being concerned with the pair function $f^{(2)}$, we integrate over the phase of the remaining $(N-3)$ particles of the system. Time-smoothed functions are obtained by time averaging every term in the equation so constructed over the time interval τ which is macroscopically small though microscopically large. The left hand side of the final equation relating to the two particles numbered 1 and 2 is, in the absence of external forces:

$$\frac{\partial \bar{f}^{(2)}}{\partial t} + \left(\frac{\mathbf{p}_1}{m} \cdot \frac{\partial \bar{f}^{(2)}}{\partial \mathbf{r}_1} \right) + \left(\frac{\mathbf{p}_2}{m} \cdot \frac{\partial \bar{f}^{(2)}}{\partial \mathbf{r}_2} \right). \tag{9.27}$$

The right hand side of the equation to be married to (9.27) is

$$-\frac{1}{\tau} \int_0^\tau \int \int \frac{1}{m} \sum_{j=1}^N \left(\mathbf{F}_j \cdot \frac{\partial f^{(N)}}{\partial \mathbf{p}_N} \right) \prod_{k=3}^N d\mathbf{p}_k \, d\mathbf{r}_k \, ds, \tag{9.28}$$

where the summation appearing in the integrand is to be made over all particles of the system. The difficulty in the derivation of the Fokker–Planck equation for the particle pair is centred around the evaluation of the integrals in (9.28). The physics of the physical system is invoked in this evaluation. Some simplification of (9.28) is immediately possible (as it was previously in connection with (9.2)) since integrals involving j with values 3, 4, 5, ... N vanish. In the remaining two integrals, involving $\mathbf{F}_1$ and $\mathbf{F}_2$, the integration is not trivial since the force on each of the particles 1 and 2 arises from interactions with the remaining members of the system.

It is convenient in the treatment of the phase evolution of the pair of particles to introduce relative coordinates. In this way the configuration of the pair is written in terms of the motion of the centre of mass of the pair, and the relative movement of the particles about the mass centre. Thus, let us introduce the two distances $\mathbf{R}$ and ξ defined respectively by:

$$2\mathbf{R} = (\mathbf{r}_2 + \mathbf{r}_1) \quad \text{and} \quad 2\xi = (\mathbf{r}_2 - \mathbf{r}_1). \qquad (9.29)$$

The new momentum coordinates $\mathbf{P}$ and π are also introduced according to

$$\mathbf{P} = (\mathbf{p}_2 + \mathbf{p}_1) \quad \text{and} \quad \pi = (\mathbf{p}_2 - \mathbf{p}_1), \qquad (9.30)$$

so that $\mathbf{P}$ is the sum and π the difference of the particle momenta. Finally, total force on each particle will be replaced by the mean and relative forces, respectively $\mathscr{F}$ and $\boldsymbol{\phi}$, where

$$2\mathscr{F} = \mathbf{F}_2 + \mathbf{F}_1 \quad \text{and} \quad 2\boldsymbol{\phi} = \mathbf{F}_2 - \mathbf{F}_1. \qquad (9.31)$$

Using (9.29) and (9.30) in connection with (9.27), this latter expression is converted into the form involving the relative phase coordinates:

$$\frac{\partial \bar{f}^{(2)}}{\partial t} + \frac{1}{2m}\left\{\left(\mathbf{P} \cdot \frac{\partial \bar{f}^{(2)}}{\partial \mathbf{R}}\right) + \left(\pi \cdot \frac{\partial \bar{f}^{(2)}}{\partial \xi}\right)\right\}, \qquad (9.32)$$

where now

$$\bar{f}^{(2)} = \bar{f}^{(2)}(\mathbf{P}, \pi, \mathbf{R}, \xi, t). \qquad (9.32a)$$

The first term in the brackets in (9.32) refers to the position of the mass centre and the total momentum, while the second term refers to the momentum difference, and to the relative separation of the two particles of the pair. The expression (9.32) is entirely equivalent to the expression (9.27). The interaction term (9.28) becomes:

$$-\frac{1}{\tau}\int_0^\tau \int \int \frac{1}{m}\left[\left(\mathbf{F}_1 \cdot \frac{\partial}{\partial \mathbf{p}_1}\right) + \left(\mathbf{F}_2 \cdot \frac{\partial}{\partial \mathbf{p}_2}\right)\right] f^{(N)} \prod_{k=3}^{N} d\mathbf{p}_k\, d\mathbf{r}_k, \qquad (9.33a)$$

where

$$\mathbf{F}_1 = \sum_{j=2}^{N} \mathbf{F}_{1j} \quad \text{and} \quad \mathbf{F}_2 = \mathbf{F}_1 + \sum_{j=3}^{N} \mathbf{F}_{2j}. \qquad (9.33b)$$

The treatment of (9.33) proceeds analogously to the previous treatment of (9.2). The integrand is first converted to a form involving the total distribution before and after the time interval τ. The assumption is made that τ is sufficiently small microscopically for $\Delta p \ll p$ for each particle of the pair, and yet is large enough to include the full extent of the force correlation. In consequence, a Taylor expansion of $f^{(N)}(t+\tau)$ is permissible about the time t, and in this way expressions for the mean and mean square momentum increments can be defined in terms of the phase average of the $(N-2)$ particles engulfing the pair under discussion.

This procedure is given a mathematical formulation in terms of the relative coordinates in the following way. Using the definitions (9.30) and (9.31) for the relative coordinates, the expression (9.33a) becomes:

$$-\frac{1}{\tau}\int_0^\tau\int\int\frac{2}{m}\left[\left(\mathscr{F}\cdot\frac{\partial f^{(N)}}{\partial \mathbf{P}}\right)+\left(\phi\cdot\frac{\partial f^{(N)}}{\partial \pi}\right)\right]\prod_{k=3}^N d\mathbf{p}_k\,d\mathbf{r}_k, \qquad (9.34)$$

where now $f^{(N)}$ is a function of the relative coordinates. This expression is rewritten in the form:

$$\frac{2}{\tau}\int\int\left[f^{(N)}(\mathbf{P}-\varDelta\mathbf{P}, \pi-\varDelta\pi)-f^{(N)}(\mathbf{P}, \pi)\right]\prod_{k=3}^N d\mathbf{p}_k\,d\mathbf{r}_k. \qquad (9.34a)$$

The changes in the macroscopic position coordinates during τ can be neglected and so need not be shown explicitly in this expression.

The further arrangement of (9.34a) is made by introducing the conditional probability for a particle pair, $f^{(N-2:2)}$, analogous to $f^{(N-1:1)}$ introduced earlier in (9.6). Thus we write:

$$f^{(N)}(\mathbf{P}, \pi, P_{11}^{N-2}\pi_{11}^{K-2}) = f^{(N-2:2)}(\mathbf{P}_{11}^{N-2}, \pi_{11}^{N-2} ; \mathbf{P}, \pi)f^{(2)}(\mathbf{P}, \pi), \qquad (9.35)$$

where $(\mathbf{P}_{11}^{N-2}, \pi_{11}^{N-2})$ denotes the relative coordinates of all the N particles of the system other than the pair 1, 2 at time $(t-\tau)$. Then (9.34a) becomes:

$$\frac{2}{\tau}\left[-f^{(2)}(\mathbf{P}, \pi)+\int\int f^{(2)}(\mathbf{P}-\varDelta\mathbf{P}, \pi-\varDelta\pi)f^{(N-2:2)}(t-\tau)\prod_{k=3}^N d\mathbf{p}_k\,d\mathbf{r}_k\right]. \qquad (9.34b)$$

The integral is simplified at this stage by making an assumption about the form of $f^{(N-2:2)}$. This conditional distribution function will be written as the sum of an equilibrium term $f_0^{(N-2:2)}$, and a non-equilibrium term $\varDelta f^{(N-2:2)}$ i.e.:

$$f^{(N-2:2)} = f_0^{(N-2:2)}+\varDelta f^{(N-2:2)}. \qquad (9.36)$$

We now assume that $\varDelta f^{(N-2:2)}$ is negligibly small in comparison with $f_0^{(N-2:2)}$ so that the environment of the pair is in virtual equilibrium. Any time dependence of the total function $f^{(N)}$ then arises from the time dependence of the pair function $f^{(2)}$. Upon this restriction, $f_0^{(N-2:2)}$ can be interpreted as a time-independent transition probability for the momentum increments $\Delta\mathbf{P}$ and $\Delta\pi$ during the time interval τ, written $W_2(\Delta\mathbf{P}, \Delta\pi)$. W_2 will also be a function of the initial momenta $(\mathbf{P}_{11}, \pi_{11})$. Then (9.34b) can be written as an integral over all the mechanically possible values of the increments $(\Delta\mathbf{P}, \Delta\pi)$ in a way exactly similar to that for a single particle and set down in section 9.1. Infinite values of the momenta and momenta increments and configuration coordinates referring to points outside the volume V of the total system are excluded and (9.34b) reduces to the expression:

$$\frac{1}{\tau}\left[-f^{(2)}(\mathbf{P}, \pi) + \int\int f^{(2)}(\mathbf{P}-\Delta\mathbf{P}, \pi-\Delta\pi)\, W_2(\mathbf{P}, \pi)\, \mathrm{d}(\mathbf{P})\, \mathrm{d}(\pi)\right]. \quad (9.37)$$

The configuration is included by using the auxiliary mechanical relative expressions:

$$2m\,\Delta\mathbf{R} = \tau\Delta\mathbf{P}, \quad \text{and} \quad 2m\Delta\xi = \tau\Delta\pi. \quad (9.37a)$$

These expressions are analogous to the previous expression (9.10) referring to a single particle. The f‸ʰ‑ᵗor 2 appears in the left hand side of each expression because of the asy nn etric form of the definitions (9.29) and (9.30) for the relative coordina ⌣‑ and momenta.

Assuming that $\Delta\mathbf{P}$ and $\Delta\pi$ are small increments of relative momenta during the time interval τ, the integrand of (9.37) can be expanded about instant t and the full expression written in terms of the mean increments of relative momentum.

We define the mean increments $\langle\Delta\mathbf{P}\rangle$, $\langle\Delta\pi\rangle$, $\langle\Delta\mathbf{P}^2\rangle$, $\langle\Delta\pi^2\rangle$, $\langle\Delta\mathbf{P}\,\Delta\pi\rangle$ as follows. Let $\langle Q\rangle$ represent any of these mean increments, then:

$$\langle Q\rangle = \int Q\,W_2(\Delta\mathbf{P}, \Delta\pi)\, \mathrm{d}(\Delta\mathbf{P})\, \mathrm{d}(\Delta\pi). \quad (9.38)$$

At this stage it is not necessary to express the transition probability explicitly in terms of phase variables.[9]

By performing the Taylor expansion of the pair function $f^{(2)}(\mathbf{P}-\Delta\mathbf{P}, \pi-\Delta\pi)$ about $(\mathbf{P}, \pi)$ and using (9.38), the expression (9.37) takes the alternative expanded form:

$$\frac{1}{\tau}\left[-\frac{\partial}{\partial\mathbf{P}}\left(f^{(2)}\langle\Delta\mathbf{P}\rangle\right) + \frac{1}{2}\frac{\partial^2}{\partial\mathbf{P}^2}\left(f^{(2)}\langle\Delta\mathbf{P}^2\rangle\right) + \frac{1}{2}\frac{\partial^2}{\partial\mathbf{P}^2}\left(f^{(2)}\langle\Delta\mathbf{P}\,\Delta\pi\rangle\right)\right]$$

$$+\frac{1}{\tau}\left[-\frac{\partial}{\partial\pi}\left(f^{(2)}\langle\Delta\pi\rangle\right) + \frac{1}{2}\frac{\partial^2}{\partial\pi^2}\left(f^{(2)}\langle\Delta\pi^2\rangle\right) + \frac{1}{2}\frac{\partial^2}{\partial\pi^2}\left(f^{(2)}\langle\Delta\mathbf{P}\,\Delta\pi\rangle\right)\right].$$

$$(9.38a)$$

Provided the deviations from equilibrium are not too large, the arguments involving the previous equation (8.18) can be applied here with the result that the distribution $f^{(2)}$ in (9.38a) can be replaced by the time-smoothed function $\bar{f}^{(2)}$ to the present approximation. It is unlikely that the restrictions on τ implied by this substitution will conflict with the requirements associated with the Taylor expansion of $f^{(2)}(\mathbf{P} - \varDelta\mathbf{P}, \pi - \varDelta\pi)$.

The evaluation of the moments defined in (9.38) can be made only when the transition probability is known as an explicit function of the phase. The arguments of section 9.1 can again be applied with $f^{(N)}$ related to the equilibrium value $f_0^{(N)}$. For the pair of particles we have:

$$f^{(N)} = f_0^{(N)} \left[1 - \frac{(\mathbf{P} \cdot \varDelta\mathbf{P})(\pi \cdot \varDelta\pi)}{2mkT} \right], \qquad (9.38b)$$

in place of the previous expression (9.17). The factor 2 in the denominator of the bracket expression appears because of the way in which $\mathbf{P}$ and π have been defined, i.e. due to the form of (9.30). The mean moments of $\varDelta\mathbf{P}$ and $\varDelta\pi$ can be calculated from (9.38) using (9.38b), and the results are analogous to those given previously for a single particle. There is, however, one difference in that a different characteristic friction constant, written $\beta^{(2)}$, replaces the previous constant $\beta^{(1)}$. Explicitly, the friction constant $\beta^{(2)}$ for the particle pair is given by:

$$\beta_{ij}^{(2)} = \frac{2}{mkT} \int_0^\tau \langle \mathbf{Q}_i(t+s) \cdot \mathbf{Q}_i(t) \rangle_{N-2} \, \mathrm{d}s, \qquad (9.39)$$

where $\mathbf{Q}_i$ can be either $\mathcal{F}$ or ϕ. The phase integration in (9.39) is to be made over the $(N-2)$ particles other than the particle pair under consideration. The mean moments themselves are given by:

$$\langle \varDelta\mathbf{P} \rangle = -\tau[(\beta_{\mathcal{F}\mathcal{F}} \cdot \mathbf{P}) + (\beta_{\mathcal{F}\phi} \cdot \pi)]; \qquad (9.40a)$$

$$\langle \varDelta\pi \rangle = -\tau[(\beta_{\pi\pi} \cdot \pi) + (\beta_{\pi\mathcal{F}} \cdot \mathbf{P})] - 2\tau\langle\varphi\rangle; \qquad (9.40b)$$

$$\langle \varDelta\mathbf{P}^2 \rangle = 4mkT\beta_{\mathcal{F}\mathcal{F}}^{(2)}\tau, \quad \langle \varDelta\pi^2 \rangle = 4mkT\beta_{\phi\phi}^{(2)}\tau; \qquad (9.40c)$$

$$\langle \varDelta\mathbf{P}_i \varDelta\pi_j \rangle = 0(\tau)^2, \quad \text{where} \quad i \neq j. \qquad (9.40d)$$

All other higher moments are of order τ^2 or smaller. The expressions (9.4) for a particle pair differ from the previous expressions (9.24) and (9.25) for a single particle in one very important way connected with (9.40b). In particular, a mean relative force $\langle\phi\rangle$ appears which has no analogue in (9.24). The force on a single particle has a high degree of symmetry so that there is no effective mean force on this particle due to neighbours. For a particle pair, on the other hand, the immediate environment of each particle departs seriously from a symmetric form and there results then a marked mean force on each particle due to the neighbours. This mean force depends upon the structure of the liquid, and so to the spatial particle arrangement. In the absence of a full solution of the Liouville equation it is necessary to proceed indirectly. For this purpose we interpret the mean force appearing in (9.40b) by the expression (3.28) relating the mean force to the fluid particle spatial structure. Needless to say, the triplet and doublet functions appearing in (3.28) must be replaced by the non-equilibrium functions $f^{(3)}$ and $f^{(2)}$ for our present study. The mean force will be related to a mean potential function, Φ, as in (2.21) defined by (2.19) with $f^{(2)}$ replacing $g^{(2)}$.

The total Fokker–Planck equation for the particle pair in relative coordinates is obtained finally by equating the two expressions (9.32) and (9.38a), using also the expressions (9.40). This equation written out in full is

$$\frac{\partial \bar{f}^{(2)}}{\partial t} + \frac{1}{2m}\left(\left(\mathbf{P}\cdot\frac{\partial}{\partial \mathbf{R}}\right)+\left(\pi\cdot\frac{\partial}{\partial \xi}\right)\right)\bar{f}^{(12)} + \left(\langle\varphi\rangle\cdot\frac{\partial}{\partial \pi}\right)\bar{f}^{(2)}$$

$$=\frac{\partial}{\partial \mathbf{P}}\left\{\beta^{(2)}_{\mathcal{F}\mathcal{F}}\left(\mathbf{P}+\frac{\partial}{\partial \mathbf{P}}\left(2mkT\,\beta^{(2)}_{\mathcal{F}\mathcal{F}}\right)\right)\bar{f}^{(2)}\right\}+$$

$$+\frac{\partial}{\partial \mathbf{P}}\left\{\beta^{(2)}_{\mathcal{F}\phi}\left(\pi+\frac{\partial}{\partial \pi}\left(2mkT\,\beta^{(2)}_{\mathcal{F}\phi}\right)\right)\bar{f}^{(2)}\right\}+$$

$$+\frac{\partial}{\partial \pi}\left\{\beta^{(2)}_{\phi\phi}\left(\pi+\frac{\partial}{\partial \pi}\left(2mkT\,\beta^{(2)}_{\phi\phi}\right)\right)\bar{f}^{(2)}\right\}+$$

$$+\frac{\partial}{\partial \pi}\left\{\beta^{(2)}_{\phi\mathcal{F}}\left(\pi+\frac{\partial}{\partial \mathbf{P}}\left(2mkT\,\beta^{(2)}_{\phi\mathcal{F}}\right)\right)\bar{f}^{(2)}\right\}. \qquad (9.41)$$

$\bar{f}^{(2)}$ can be replaced by the kinetic distribution by writing $f^{(2)} = N^2 \bar{f}^{(2)}$. This is a very lengthy and complicated equation for the determination of the time-smoothed distribution $\bar{f}^{(2)}$. Its interpretation in physical terms will be clear from formulae such as (9.38a), but it is written out in detail here to show the magnitude of the mathematical task of using this expression for the rigorous determination of the phase distribution of a representative pair of particles of the system whether for the steady state or as function of the time.

Similar equations can, in principle at least, be constructed for the triplet and higher order functions, but their complexity makes it hardly worth while considering them at the present time.

The characteristic feature of the Fokker-Planck type equations is that at least some of the mean square increments of momentum are proportional to the time interval τ to which they refer, and not to τ^2. Consequently they are able to account for dissipative behaviour. By regarding the motion of the particles in a non-uniform liquid as behaving at least to sufficient approximation like Brownian particles of the same mass as the environment in which they are suspended, it is now asserted that the solution of the Fokker–Planck equation will be sufficient for elucidating many liquid non-equilibrium properties. The final test of such a conjecture can be made by a comparison between the calculated and experimental data. It is, at the present time, the only approach, unambiguously not applicable either to dilute gases or in its present form to crystalline solids, that has yielded significant numerical results for liquid transport coefficients. In what follows we shall assume that a knowledge of the phase of a representative particle pair is sufficient information for determining the liquid non-equilibrium properties. Further, we assert that this information is to be derived by solving the Fokker–Planck equation in pair space. The remainder of the present chapter is devoted to the development of these assumptions for the case of steady non-equilibrium conditions.

9.3. THE FRICTION CONSTANTS

Before the phase equation (9.41) can be used to determine the pair distribution, it is necessary to specify the functions $\beta_{ij}^{(2)}$ in terms of the momenta and configuration of the pair of particles. According to the expressions (9.22) and (9.23), and (9.39), the functions $\beta^{(i)}$ referring to one or two particles are defined in terms of the average motion of the particles comprising the liquid. The interpretation of the equations (9.26) and (9.41) as Fokker–Planck equations is possible only if the functions $\beta^{(i)}$ can be identified as a set of friction constants of the type met with in hydrodynamics, such as in Stokes' law of friction. Such an identification can be made only by making certain physical assumptions, particularly associated with the time interval τ. Consequently, before we even face the proper mathematical problem of solving (9.41) we must overcome the formidable physical-mathematical problem of calculating $\beta^{(i)}$; we consider this problem in the present section.

The simplest expression to consider is that for $\beta^{(1)}$ given in (9.22) and (9.23) relating to a single particle. If $\beta^{(1)}$ is to be independent of τ then the time correlation function

$$\Xi^{(1)}(s) \equiv \langle (\mathbf{F}_1(t) \cdot \mathbf{F}_1(t+s)) \rangle_{N-1}, \tag{9.42}$$

must vanish for values of s greater than some time interval τ_1 which is itself less than τ. Thus there must be assumed to exist some time interval $\tau_1 < \tau$ such that:

$$\Xi^{(1)}(s) \neq 0, \quad \text{for} \quad s < \tau_1,$$
$$\Xi^{(1)}(s) = 0, \quad \text{for} \quad s > \tau_1. \tag{9.43}$$

Because of the reversible nature of the underlying particle dynamics, τ_1 must be smaller than the Poincaré cycle. For if it were not, the physical system would not show irreversible effects and $\beta^{(1)}$ would have the value zero when averaged over the complete cycle. Alternatively, if τ_1 is chosen to be very small, the force on the particle at the beginning and end of τ_1 will be correlated, because the interaction between this particle and the remainder is well defined physically throughout this time interval. It is necessary, therefore, to assign to τ_1 a value which is neither too small nor yet too large on a microscopic time-scale. For macroscopic systems of physical interest the upper bound on τ_1 may still be small on a macroscopic time-scale. A natural upper limit on τ_1 is given in practical terms by the details of the measurement to be made. It is necessary to allow the measuring apparatus to reach at least quasi-equilibrium with the system under test if the derived data are to be significant. This means that τ_1 must be smaller than the relaxation time of the measuring apparatus. The lower bound on τ_1 can be the time for the occurrence of a few consecutive strong interactions between the particle and its neighbours. The crude picture then emerges of $\beta^{(1)}$ given by (9.22) increasing at first with τ, but reaching what Kirkwood termed[2] a plateau value for $\tau > \tau_1$. If (9.43) is applied rigorously, then τ may be given any value beyond τ_1 and the value of $\beta^{(1)}$ will remain unaffected. This, however, is not so in fact since ultimately $\beta^{(1)}$ must vanish as $\tau \to \infty$. It is for this reason that the value of $\beta^{(1)}$ appropriate to physical non-equilibria is to be associated with a *plateau value* and not with some asymptotic form for large τ. It is difficult to be more precise than this, in the absence of detailed mathematical analysis, since the very nature of an extended interaction between particles is contrary to the appearance of definite events which can be used to construct a microscopic time-scale. The time occupied by two particles during a direct collision can be used as a datum in the study of gases at low enough density, so that the present problem does not apply there.

It is postulated, then, that a time τ_1 exists which is neither microscopically very small or very large, such that the conditions (9.43) apply for the interacting particles comprising a liquid. These conditions are then interpreted as meaning that a time correlation of the force on a particle due to its neighbours exists only over a restricted time-interval, and beyond this interval the particle interactions are statistically independent events. This assumption, first proposed by Kirkwood,[2] is a means of introducing the irreversible features into the statistical theory of liquid non-equilibrium. It is a natural extension of the hypothesis of molecular chaos appearing in the theory of the dilute gas, according to which statistical correlation between the phase trajectories of two colliding particles does not persist beyond a very few collisions. The expressions (9.43) then describe for a macroscopic liquid a device by which information is continually lost in the sense of section 7.3. The assumed existence of the time interval τ_1, which is markedly less than the time period of the corresponding Poincaré cycle, is recognised as being a device for ensuring that once the system of a large number of particles has moved to its most probable equilibrium state, characterised by complete uniformity, it will stay there.

These general arguments can be made more precise only by the evaluation of the expressions such as (9.42) and (9.39). Strictly speaking, both $\beta^{(1)}$ and $\beta^{(2)}$ are tensor quantities but the simple liquid isotropy suggests that is is sufficient to write each of them in the approximate form:

$$\beta^{(1)} = \tilde{\beta}\tilde{\mathbf{I}}, \quad \text{and} \quad \beta^{(2)} = \gamma\tilde{\mathbf{I}}, \tag{9.44}$$

where $\tilde{\mathbf{I}}$ is the unit tensor and (β, γ) are two scalar quantities each having the dimensions of the inverse of a time. Then β is given in terms of the interparticle forces by

$$\beta = \frac{1}{3mkT} \int_0^\tau \langle [\mathbf{F}_1(t) \cdot \mathbf{F}_1(t+s)] \rangle_{N-1} \, ds, \tag{9.45a}$$

and γ by

$$\gamma = \frac{1}{3mkT} \int_0^\tau \langle [\mathbf{F}_2(t) \cdot \mathbf{F}_2(t+s)] \rangle_{N-2} \, ds. \tag{9.45b}$$

The integrand appearing in the expression (9.45a) for β is the average of the force product for particle 1, the average being taken over the phase of the remaining $(N-1)$ particles of the system. The integrand appearing in (9.45b) for γ is to be the average of the force on particles 1 and 2 due to the remaining $(N-2)$ particles. Because phase averages are involved, the contribution of the force of one particle of the pair upon the other over the time interval s will be proportional to s, and is to be neglected since γ must be constant for dissipation. Expressed in terms of the relative force, γ is to be calculated using the relative force between the particle pair at two different times, the direct interaction between the pair of particles being subtracted from the whole.[3]

The problem of evaluating expressions such as (9.45) even if the environment is in equilibrium involves the study of the simultaneous interaction between a large number of particles, made over a time interval. Such an analysis is comparable in complexity to that of the evaluation of the partition function in the equilibrium theory and is beyond the power of present mathematical techniques. Progress can be contemplated only if drastic simplifications are made, based essentially on the need to avoid mathematics rather than on physical criteria. Several authors have investigated such an approach and, although there was some early optimism that detailed and reliable general information about β and γ would be easily obtained, this now seems very unlikely. Nevertheless, some progress is being made which is able to lead to approximate information about β and γ, which is sufficient for some numerical purposes. The simplifications involved in such approximations must be made carefully. The most obvious possibilities, such as that where the particle moves in the average force field of the neighbours, lead to the result either that the friction constant is zero (i.e. there is no irreversibility), or alternatively that it is indefinitely large (i. e. the movement to equilibrium takes place instantaneously).

It is important to make clear the particular friction constant appropriate to the study of liquids. β of (9.45a) refers to the motion of single particles, and on the interpretation of physical diffusion as a problem of the random walk, it is β that describes the irreversible element in diffusion theory. The movement of a single liquid molecule can be interpreted as the motion of a particle in a potential well according to the concepts of the cell model. The time required for the particle to acquire sufficient energy from the neighbours to escape from the well is likely to be proportional to the factor $\exp[U/kT]$, where T is the temperature and U is the well potential barrier to be overcome. This time is essentially the correlation time to be used in (9.45a). On this basis, the friction constant β is likely to be proportional to this factor, and leads to the expectation of β having essentially an exponential temperature dependence, decreasing with increasing temperature. This factor will not appear in connection with γ which applies to a pair of particles. In this case, the indirect force is involved, and the correlation is not necessarily broken when potential barriers are crossed. It is to be expected, therefore, that γ will depend less sensitively on the temperature than does β. It is the constant γ that is to be associated with liquid transport effects, and it is usual now to regard it as virtually temperature-independent over small ranges of temperature. This means that the temperature dependencies of the liquid transport coefficients is not to be ascribed to the temperature dependence of γ. It should be mentioned in passing that since the distribution of single particles can be found when the distribution of particle pairs is known, then β is related to γ in some general way, and in principle we might expect to derive some knowledge of β in terms of that for γ.

Numerical estimates of γ have been made by several authors.[10] They differ from each other by, at worst, two orders of magnitude, although more recent values agree much more closely with each other than this. Calculations of the friction constant can hardly yet claim to have gone beyond the qualitative stage.

The first estimate of γ was given by Kirkwood[11] assuming the force correlation of (9.45b) to have the form of a Gaussian function. In this case,

$$\gamma \sim \frac{(2\pi)^{\frac{1}{2}} \langle \Delta \mathbf{F}^2 \rangle}{6kT\omega}, \tag{9.46a}$$

where $\langle \Delta \mathbf{F}^2 \rangle$ is the mean square of the force on the single particle and ω is some characteristic frequency describing the time changes of the force. An alternative expression for γ has been given by Rice and Kirkwood[12], viz.:

$$\gamma = \frac{4\pi m}{3} \int_0^\infty r^2 \left(\frac{\partial^2 \psi}{\partial r^2} + \frac{2}{r} \frac{\partial \psi}{\partial r} \right) g^{(2)}(r) \, dr, \tag{9.46b}$$

where $g^{(2)}(r)$ is the equilibrium radial distribution function referring to the spherically symmetric pair interaction potential ψ. Using data for ψ and $g^{(2)}$ adapted to liquid argon at 89°K, (9.46 b) leads to the result:[13]

$$\gamma = 7.3 \times 10^{12} \text{ sec}^{-1}. \tag{9.47a}$$

This value, in fact, is not very different from that of the Stokes friction constant of hydrodynamics, although this is probably a fortuitous result.

Other values are also available. Thus Orton[13] has derived an estimate of γ for argon near the melting point using the expression for the shear viscosity coefficient to be derived later in section 9.5, which is proportional to γ. Using experimental data for the shear viscosity and for the appropriate equilibrium pair distribution, Orton then found the value:

$$\gamma = 4.24 \times 10^{11} \text{ sec}^{-1}, \tag{9.47b}$$

Because the approximation is made that the environment of the particle pair is in equilibrium, the integral in (9.45b) can be evaluated using the collective coordinates met with previously in connection with the arguments of Chapter 4. On this basis, account is taken of the transference of energy throughout the liquid by the propagation of density fluctuations associated with the passage of sound-waves. The study of the force cor-relations in time are found to be more easily approximated in terms of the Fourier components than in terms of actual particle trajectories. Turner, and Eisenschitz and Wilford have independently applied this approach for estimating γ. Turner[14] finds for argon at 84° K,

$$\gamma = 0 \cdot 56 \times 10^{11} \ \sec^{-1}, \qquad (9.47c)$$

while Eisenschitz and Wilford[15] find, again for argon at 84° K,

$$\gamma = 3 \cdot 5 \times 10^{11} \ \sec^{-1}. \qquad (9.47d)$$

This last value is in relatively close agreement with the independent value (9.47b) given by Orton. The best value of γ at present available for liquid argon is presumably (9.47d). The evaluation of the expressions for the friction constants is one of the present great needs of the statistical theory of non-equilibrium. Until this is finally achieved no proper quantitative test of the theory is possible.

The assertion that the values of microscopic parameters separated by a time interval are uncorrelated if the time interval is larger than some macro-scopically small value has the appearance of providing a general and pow-erful method of describing the non-equilibria of systems, whose compo-nent particles are under continuous interaction. In the expressions for the friction constants introduced so far, it is the force correlation on a particle that is assumed to break down after a time interval which exceeds τ_1. Correlation functions other than for the force can be defined and may be of importance.

These time dependencies can arise from the application of a dynamic impulse to an equilibrium system, or from a fluctuation disturbance to the thermal distribution. This approach has led to transport coefficients that are correct in the linear approximation, and to this extent the theory of non-equilibrium can claim to be formally solved. The evaluation of these expressions to give numerical data is not yet possible, however, except in the special case of a dilute gas when the corresponding formulae reduce to the forms already known from alternative and conventional arguments. This approach to non-equilibrium situations is associated with the work of Kubo and others,[5] and is significant in that in the general case a correlation integral can be associated with a transport coefficient. The approach re-mains only formal, however, due to our present inability to evaluate the correlation integrals properly with any degree of precision for liquid densities. We will not, for this reason, pursue this line of inquiry further here.

9.4. THE SMOLUCHOWSKI EQUATION

In order to obtain expressions for the liquid transport coefficients, it is necessary to solve, on our present arguments, the Fokker–Planck equation (9.41) on the assumption that γ is a constant. The value to be assigned to the constant γ can then be treated as a separate issue later. The task of solving (9.41) is very formidable, but may be simplified considerably if the friction constant is large enough. In this case, the particle momenta reach equilibrium values appreciably more quickly than the particle configurations and the Fokker–Planck equation in phase space can be reduced to the Smoluchowski equation in configuration space, already met with in section 7.5(b). More precisely, γ must be sufficiently large for the condition $\gamma\tau_1 \gg 1$ to hold.[16] The reduction was first considered by Kramers[17] in connection with the Brownian motion, and has more recently been considered further by Suddaby and Miles.[18]

Reference to the expressions (7.26) and (7.23) for the pressure tensor and the energy flow vector involve the interparticle force potential, and so can be evaluated only when the configuration pair distribution for the specific non-equilibrium is known. It is not necessary for liquids, where the second term of each expression (7.26) and (7.23) provides the overwhelming contribution to the total expression, to have detailed information about the probability distribution of particle momentum. The determination of the liquid transport coefficients is, in this way, assumed to be based on the concepts of particle forced diffusion, including particle interactions.[3] The forces controlling the diffusion processes arise from viscous stresses due to macroscopic velocity gradients, or heat or mass fluxes arising from macroscopic temperature or particle concentration gradients.

The Smoluchowski equation for a single particle follows here from (9.26) by integration over the momentum $\mathbf{p}_1$, and the equation for a particle pair follows from (9.41) by integration over the momenta $\mathbf{p}_1$ and $\mathbf{p}_2$, or equivalently over the relative momenta $\mathbf{P}$ and π. We will consider now the case of a particle pair, so that we will be concerned with equation (9.41). We will not distinguish now between the time-smoothed probability $\bar{f}^{(2)}$ and the unsmoothed probability $f^{(2)}$. This is justified if deviations from equilibrium are not too large.

The last two terms on the left hand side of (9.41) and all the terms on the right hand side refer to the particle interactions. Momentum is conserved during the interaction, and the energy remains finite, so that the result of integrating of (9.41) is:

$$\frac{\partial n^{(2)}}{\partial t} + \frac{\partial \mathbf{J}}{\partial \mathbf{R}} + \frac{\partial \mathbf{j}}{\partial \xi} = 0, \qquad (9.48)$$

where

$$n^{(2)}(\mathbf{r}, t) = \int \int f^{(2)}(\mathbf{p}, \mathbf{r}, t) \, d\mathbf{P} \, d\pi, \tag{9.49a}$$

$$\mathbf{J} = \frac{1}{2m} \int \mathbf{P} f^{(2)}(\mathbf{p}, \mathbf{r}, t) \, d\mathbf{P} \, d\pi, \tag{9.49b}$$

$$\mathbf{j} = \frac{1}{2m} \int \pi f^{(2)}(\mathbf{p}, \mathbf{r}, t) \, d\mathbf{P} \, d\pi. \tag{9.49c}$$

The first term in (9.48) involves the configuration pair distribution $n^{(2}$ $(\mathbf{R}, \xi, t)$, defined in (9.49a). $\mathbf{J}$ in the second term, defined in (9.49b) and $\mathbf{j}$ in the third term, defined in (9.49c), are the two components of the relative flux of momentum in the fluid. The equation (9.48) is, then, the expression for the continuity of pairs in the liquid, and ultimately of particles.

The continuity equation (9.48) contains the three unknowns $n^{(2)}$, $\mathbf{J}$, and $\mathbf{j}$. It is reduced to an equation involving the single unknown $n^{(2)}$ when alternative expressions are available for $\mathbf{J}$ and $\mathbf{j}$ in terms of $n^{(2)}$. The expression (9.48) is the most general configuration information (within our present context) derivable from the Liouville equation without specifying the nature of the particle interactions.

The expressions for $\mathbf{j}$ and $\mathbf{J}$ are now to be obtained from the Fokker-Planck equation (9.41). This is done by multiplying this equation throughout first by $\mathbf{P}$, and alternatively by π and each time integrating throughout[19] over the momenta $\mathbf{P}$ and π. We replace the friction tensor appearing in (9.41) by the single constant γ, and make the approximation that in the evaluation of terms for the momentum integration of expressions involving the product of the momenta and the space gradient of $f^{(2)}$, the equilibrium value of the term is used.[20] This is fully compatible with the situation in which the particle momenta achieve equilibrium in a short time, while the particle configurations are still not in equilibrium. Thus in terms like:

$$\int \int (\mathbf{P} \cdot \mathbf{P}) \frac{\partial f^{(2)}}{\partial \mathbf{R}} \, d\mathbf{P} \, d\pi = \frac{\partial}{\partial \mathbf{R}} \int \int (\mathbf{P} \cdot \mathbf{P}) f^{(2)} \, d\mathbf{P} \, d\pi, \tag{9.50a}$$

the equilibrium distribution is used so that this particular term is replaced by

$$\frac{\partial}{\partial \mathbf{R}} (2m \, kTn^{(2)}), \tag{9.50b}$$

and so on.

The replacement of $\beta^{(2)}$ by γ is not critical. The replacement of terms like (9.50a) by the equilibrium form (9.50b) has been shown by Kirkwood to involve the neglect of terms proportional to $1/\gamma^2$. This introduces negligible error if γ is large enough. In these assumptions the Fokker-Planck equation (9.41) leads, after a lengthy although straightforward analysis which will not be reproduced here, to the following uncoupled expressions for $\mathbf{J}$ and $\mathbf{j}$:

$$\mathbf{J} = \frac{1}{\gamma} \left[\frac{\partial}{\partial \mathbf{R}} \left(\frac{kT}{2m} n^{(2)} \right) + \frac{\partial \mathbf{J}}{\partial t} \right], \tag{9.51a}$$

$$\mathbf{j} = \frac{1}{\gamma} \left[\frac{\partial}{\partial \xi} \left(\frac{kT}{2m} n^{(2)} \right) + \frac{\partial \mathbf{j}}{\partial t} - \frac{\langle \mathbf{\Phi} \rangle}{m} n^{(2)} \right] \tag{9.51b}$$

where $\langle \mathbf{\Phi} \rangle$ is the mean relative force acting on the particle pair.

One further assumption will be made before the expressions (9.51) are inserted into (9.48) and that is that the time dependence of the momentum fluxes will be neglected, i.e. we assume $\partial \mathbf{J}/\partial t = \partial \mathbf{j}/\partial t = 0$. It follows from (9.48) and (9.41) that these terms are proportional to $1/\gamma$, and since γ is already supposed large in the derivation of (9.51) the retention of the time dependent terms in these expressions is unnecessary. The insertion of

$$\mathbf{J} = \frac{1}{\gamma} \frac{\partial}{\partial \mathbf{R}} \left(\frac{kT}{2m} n^{(2)} \right) \quad \text{and} \quad \mathbf{j} = \frac{1}{\gamma} \left[\frac{\partial}{\partial \xi} \left(\frac{kT}{2m} n^{(2)} \right) - \frac{\langle \mathbf{\Phi} \rangle}{m} n^{(2)} \right]$$

into the continuity equation (9.48) gives finally the Smoluchowski equation in configuration space:

$$\frac{\partial n^{(2)}}{\partial t} + \left[\frac{\partial}{\partial \mathbf{R}} \cdot \frac{\partial}{\partial \mathbf{R}} \left(\frac{kT}{2m\gamma} n^{(2)} \right) \right]$$

$$+ \left\{ \frac{\partial}{\partial \xi} \cdot \left[\frac{\partial}{\partial \xi} \left(\frac{kT}{2m\gamma} n^{(2)} \right) - \frac{\langle \mathbf{\Phi} \rangle}{m\gamma} n^{(2)} \right] \right\} = 0. \tag{9.52}$$

This equation referring to a particle pair has the same form as (7.11) quoted previously for the Brownian motion of a single particle. The quantity $(kT)/(2m\gamma)$ is, according to (7.13), interpretable as a diffusion coefficient for the pair motion. By calculating the non-equilibrium configuration pair distribution according to (9.52) the transport of momentum, energy, etc. is regarded as a diffusion process under the action of the average force of particle interaction.

The Smoluchowski equation (9.52) has been derived from the Fokker-Planck equation by neglecting all terms of the order $1/\gamma^2$ or less. More accurate data result if terms involving $1/\gamma^2$ are retained, with higher order terms still neglected.[15,21] This is achieved by replacing terms like (9.50a) by more accurate approximations, and retaining the time-dependent terms in the expressions (9.51) for the relative currents. The basis of this improved information is again the Fokker–Planck equation which now is first multiplied on each side by the square or product of the relative momenta before integration over the momenta is performed. In this way the Smoluchowski equation (9.52) is the lowest order approximation of a more general equation, the hierachy of equations representing essentially an expansion in powers of γ^{-1}. This series has been considered in some detail by Suddaby[18,21] who showed, in particular, that in the next approximation (9.52) is to be replaced by a fourth order differential equation. It is rather lengthy and will not be written down here, although it will be referred to again later (in section 9.5(a)). The complexity of these more general equations rules them out at the present time as the basis for numerical computations of the liquid transport coefficients, unless the first equation of the hierarchy (9.52) should prove inadequate in tests with experiment.[22]

The problem of finding solutions of (9.52) relevant to specific conditions of liquid non-equilibrium depends in its details upon the nature of the non-equilibrium. For equilibrium conditions it is easily seen by direct substitution that, for spherical particles,

$$g^{(2)}(\mathbf{R}, \xi, t) = An \exp\left\{-\frac{\Phi}{kT}\right\} \tag{9.53}$$

is a solution of (9.52), where n is the constant number density of the fluid. Φ is the potential of the mean force associated with the difference coordinate ξ such that

$$2\langle\phi\rangle = -\frac{\partial\Phi}{\partial\xi}. \tag{9.53a}$$

For non-equilibrium conditions we proceed in the same way as for gases (see Chapter 8, section 8.5). We assume the non-equilibrium pair distribution $n^{(2)}(t)$ to be related to $g^{(2)}$ given by (9.53) according to

$$n^2(\mathbf{r}_1, \mathbf{r}_2, t) = g^{(2)}(\xi)[1+w]. \tag{9.54}$$

For small deviations from equilibrium the unknown function w is a small correction term. Its form is dictated by the exact details of the macroscopic fluid non-uniformities (for instance, the details of the velocity or temperature gradients), and it will be time dependent for non-steady conditions. The derivation of w is made by inserting (9.54) into the Smoluchowski equation (9.52), and solving the resulting equation for the single unknown function w under the appropriate boundary conditions.

9.5. THE STEADY NON-UNIFORM STATE

The liquid transport coefficients are calculated by considering a liquid either in motion with a steady velocity gradient, or a steady temperature gradient, or with other separate relevant space gradients. Because conditions are assumed steady, the Smoluchowski equation (9.52) does not now contain the time. In the present section we consider separately the form of the Smoluchowski equation for the two cases of a steady isothermal velocity gradient and a steady temperature gradient in a fluid at rest. Possible compression effects are also mentioned later. These considerations lead eventually to expressions for the liquid viscosity and thermal conductivity in the next section.

(a) *Viscous Shear Flow*

The liquid is assumed to be flowing isothermally and with macroscopic velocity $\mathbf{v}_0$ which can be an arbitrary function of the position for the moment. Fluid compressibility is irrelevant for describing simple shear, so there is no loss of generality if we assume the liquid to be completely incompressible. We then have at each point in the fluid:

$$\text{div}_r \, \mathbf{v}_0 = 0. \tag{9.55}$$

The mean velocity affects the mean momentum increment and must appear in the equation (9.52) when calculations of the viscosity are made. Before doing this, however, some simplification of the Smoluchowski equation (9.52) is possible for the present viscous problem. Viscous forces arise when contiguous macroscopic fluid elements are in relative motion. This relative motion is independent of the motion of the centre of mass of the total liquid, so that viscous effects are to be studied from the treatment of relative motions. Consequently the pair distribution relevant to viscous flow is a function only of the relative separation distance ξ. The pair distribution $n^{(2)}$ for non-equilibrium is, for the present case, separable into a function of $\mathbf{R}$ and a function of ξ, and only the latter function need be retained.

The insertion of (9.54) into the Smoluchowski equation (9.52) then gives, for the steady viscous flow of an incompressible liquid, the equation for the unknown function w:

$$\nabla^2 w + \frac{1}{kT} (\langle \boldsymbol{\phi} \rangle \cdot \text{grad} \, w) = -\frac{\gamma m}{kT} (\mathbf{v}_0 \cdot \langle \boldsymbol{\phi} \rangle), \tag{9.56}$$

where the viscous flow velocity $\mathbf{v}_0$ has been introduced. The configuration variables in (9.56) are the relative coordinates ξ. This equation is to be solved subject to the condition that at infinity the flow is equal to $|v_0 g^{(2)}|$, where $g^{(2)}$ is the equilibrium form (9.53). This requirement provides a boundary condition for the equation (9.56) since the flow vector $\mathbf{j}$ for the present problem is, according to (9.51b):

$$\mathbf{j} = g^{(2)} \left[\frac{kT}{\beta m} \operatorname{grad} w - \mathbf{v}_0 \right],$$

where steady conditions are assumed and terms of the small magnitude $|w \, \mathbf{v}_0|$ have been neglected. The condition that $|\mathbf{j}| = |n^{(2)} \, \mathbf{v}_0|$ at infinity means that

$$\operatorname{grad} w = 0, \quad \text{and} \quad \xi \to \infty. \tag{9.57}$$

The equation (9.56) is reduced further by specifying $\mathbf{v}_0$. Let us assume that the flow is laminar, and that the rate of shear is $\tfrac{1}{2} a$, with Cartesian components $\alpha_x = \alpha_z = 0$; $\alpha_{xy} = \alpha$. This means that the fluid flow is along the direction of the y-axis, with a gradient parallel to the x-axis. Further, we will assume that the mean force $\langle \mathbf{\phi} \rangle$ is to be derived from the mean potential Φ according to (9.53a). The mean potential is itself supposed related to $n^{(2)}$, remembering the previous expression (9.53). The present analysis is correct only to terms of order wv_0, so that $n^{(2)}$ can be replaced by its equilibrium value $g^{(2)}$ in calculating Φ for use in the second term on the left hand side of (9.56). The right hand side of (9.56) becomes in the conventional polar coordinates:

$$-a \frac{\partial \Phi}{\partial \xi} \xi \sin^2 \vartheta \sin \varphi \cos \varphi, \tag{9.58a}$$

where

$$a = \frac{\gamma m}{(kT)^2} \alpha. \tag{9.58b}$$

If we assume the solution of (9.56) to have the same angular dependence as the right hand side we write:

$$w(\xi, a) = au(\xi) \sin^2 \vartheta \sin \varphi \cos \varphi, \tag{9.59}$$

where $u(\xi)$ is an unknown function of the pair separation. The insertion of (9.53a), (9.58a), and (9.59) into (9.56) then provides the ordinary second order differential equation for $u(\xi)$:

$$\frac{d^2 u}{d\xi^2} + \left(\frac{2}{\xi} - \frac{1}{kT} \frac{d\Phi(\xi)}{d\xi} \right) \frac{du}{d\xi} - \frac{6u}{\xi^2} = -\frac{d\Phi}{d\xi} \xi a. \tag{9.60}$$

The angular terms do not appear in this expression. This is the form of the Smoluchowski equation for the present viscosity problem, and was derived in this form by Eisenschitz.[23] Kirkwood[24] and his collaborators also obtained this equation in relation to the present problem.

The equation (9.60) is a second order equation and the solution requires for its unique specification the assignment of two boundary conditions. To begin with, the condition that the flow vector for the particle pair shall vanish at infinity, so that equilibrium conditions shall prevail according to (9.57), is satisfied by

$$u(\xi) = 0, \quad \text{as} \quad \xi \to \infty. \qquad (9.61)$$

Both Eisenschitz and Kirkwood agree about this condition. There is, however, disagreement about the second condition. Kirkwood and his collaborators make the weak condition that the function $u(\xi)$ must remain finite everywhere and so assume

$$u(\xi) = 0, \quad \text{as} \quad \xi \to 0. \qquad (9.62)$$

Eisenschitz, on the other hand, points out that the condition (9.62), while ensuring that u shall always remain finite, nevertheless would allow a degree of anisotropy of the shear flow which is not supported experimentally. Consequently, the Kirkwood weak condition (9.62) is rejected by Eisenschitz who postulates instead the further strong condition for infinite pair separation:

$$r^3 u(\xi) = 0, \quad \text{as} \quad \xi \to \infty. \qquad (9.63)$$

The objection to the condition (9.63) that it will allow $u(\xi)$ to become infinite at $\xi = 0$ is countered by Eisenschitz, who claims that this region is irrelevant provided that the calculated viscosity remains finite. We shall see later that the viscosity does in practice remain finite whether either condition (9.62) or (9.63) is used with (9.61), because of the strong repulsive behaviour of the actual particle interaction at essentially zero particle separation distances.

It turns out that the effect of the different boundary conditions (9.62) and (9.63) on the solution of (9.60) is quite distinctive. A study of (9.60) under the strong conditions (9.61) and (9.63) shows that $u(\xi)$ is strongly dependent upon the potential energy which determines the particle motion in the liquid: since the potential energy itself is dependent upon the temperature, it is seen that $u(\xi)$ is now to be expected to be fairly strongly temperature-dependent. The effect is smaller for higher temperatures where the difference between the controlling potential energy and the particle energy is smaller. The expression (9.69a) for the shear viscosity given later shows that a marked temperature-dependence of $u(\xi)$ leads to a similar marked dependence on the temperature for the shear viscosity itself. The strong boundary conditions (9.61) and (9.63) applied to solutions of (9.60) give expressions $u(\xi)$ which are markedly temperature-dependent. This is not the case if the weak boundary conditions (9.61) and (9.62) are used. While the corresponding solution of the differential equation (9.60) is now also dependent upon the temperature, the dependence using the weak Kirk-wood conditions (9.61) and (9.62) is much weaker than the dependence arising from the use of the strong Eisenschitz conditions (9.61) and (9.63). Because the experimentally determined data for the shear viscosity is known to be strongly temperature-dependent, the difference between the weak and strong boundary conditions becomes significant for the theory. Presumably this discrepancy is a feature of the use of the Smoluchowski equation, and would not appear if the more correct Fokker–Planck equation in pair space were used, instead, as the basis of calculation.[27]

Meanwhile, some further information is available about the boundary conditions. Eisenschitz and Suddaby[21] have considered the fourth order equation which is the next approximation mentioned earlier to replace the second order Smoluchowski equation (9.52). It appears that unique solutions of this fourth order equation follow from an application of the strong boundary conditions, whereas the weak conditions lead to some ambiguity. Eisenschitz and Cole[25] have also shown that the strong boundary conditions can also be applied to more general interparticle force laws than those for spherical particles such as when the particles carry a dipole. The strong boundary conditions were introduced to eliminate any marked anisotropy in the flowing liquid, and their accuracy of use can then be studied from the degree of anisotropy actually observed in practice. Champion[26] has reported measurements of the small anisotropy actually observed and his experiments are continuing. For the present the existence of both the weak and strong boundary conditions must be admitted. While the preference still needs further investigation, the strong boundary conditions seem to be more plausible at the present time.

(b) *Temperature Gradients*

Let the fluid be at rest, but the temperature T differ throughout the liquid, subject only to the restriction that it be a harmonic function, i.e. that $\nabla^2 T = 0$. Since the fluid is at rest, the centre of gravity of the total fluid is stationary and the second term in the Smoluchowski (9.52) disappears. The temperature in (9.52) is now a function of the position and the Smoluchowski equation for the present problem is obtained by inserting (9.54) into (9.52). Neglecting terms of magnitude w grad T, grad$^2 T$, and so on, as being small, the equation for the determination of the temperature-dependent correction function w to the equilibrium pair distribution becomes:

$$\nabla^2 w - \left(\frac{1}{kT} \operatorname{grad} \Phi \cdot \operatorname{grad} w\right) = \frac{\Phi}{(kT)^2 T_0} (\operatorname{grad} \Phi \cdot \operatorname{grad} T), \quad (9.64)$$

where T_0 is the temperature at the origin of coordinates. Here again we have used (9.53a). This equation was given by Eisenschitz.

To make conditions definite for calculations, suppose a constant temperature gradient $\aleph$ to exist along the z-axis of a Cartesian coordinate frame. Then:

$$T = T_0(1 + \aleph z),$$

and grad $zT = \aleph T_0$ is the only non-vanishing temperature gradient. The right hand side of (9.64) becomes now:

$$\frac{\aleph \Phi}{(kT)^2} \frac{\partial \Phi}{\partial \xi} \cos \vartheta$$

in polar angular terms. We therefore assume for w the form:

$$w = v(\xi) \cos \vartheta, \quad (9.65)$$

and the insertion of (9.65) into (9.64) provides the ordinary differential equation for $v(\xi)$:

$$\frac{d^2 v}{d\xi^2} + \left(\frac{2}{r} - \frac{1}{kT} \frac{d\Phi(\xi)}{d\xi}\right) \frac{dv}{d\xi} - \frac{2v}{\xi} = \frac{\aleph \Phi}{(kT)^2} \frac{\delta \Phi}{d\xi}. \quad (9.66)$$

This equation for the temperature distribution differs from (9.60) for the viscous flow in the last term on the left hand side, and on the right hand side.

The two boundary conditions to be applied to (9.66) are derived to ensure that the energy flow shall remain always finite. Eisenschitz[23] assumes the two conditions:

$$\frac{dv}{d\xi} = -\aleph, \quad \text{and} \quad \frac{v}{\xi} = -\aleph, \quad \text{as} \quad \xi \to \infty. \quad (9.67)$$

The equation (9.66) with conditions (9.67) was also obtained in essentially the same form by Zwanzig, Kirkwood, Oppenheim, and Alder.[28] A study of the solutions of (9.66) shows that no strong temperature dependence is to be anticipated for $v(\xi)$. It seems, therefore, that the Smoluchowski equation is able to be applied to viscous flow and heat conduction in a consistent manner, and that different temperature dependencies of the solution of the relevant equations arise due entirely to the different boundary conditions which separately apply.

(c) *Bulk Viscosity*

In the study of viscous shear flow it was assumed that the flowing liquid is incompressible. If the fluid is compressible, and yet at rest, dissipative effects arise from compression or rarefaction of the liquid. These effects are describable by a bulk viscosity which appears in hydrodynamics, but about which there is still controversy and uncertainty. Relaxing the condition (9.55) which does not now apply, and accounting for the time rate of shear in the momentum flux, Kirkwood, Buff, and Green[24] derive the Smoluchowski equation for the present problem in the form:

$$\frac{d^2s}{d\xi^2} + \left(\frac{2}{\xi} - \frac{1}{kT} \frac{d\Phi(\xi)}{d\xi} \right) \frac{ds}{d\xi} = -\frac{\xi}{kT} \frac{d\Phi(\xi)}{d\xi}. \tag{9.68}$$

This is to be solved subject to the conditions:

$$\frac{ds}{d\xi} = 0, \quad \text{as} \quad \xi \to \infty, \tag{9.68a}$$

$$\xi^2 \frac{ds}{d\xi} = 0, \quad \text{as} \quad \xi \to 0. \tag{9.68b}$$

Study of (9.68) under these boundary conditions makes it unlikely that $s(\xi)$ is strongly temperature-dependent.

9.6. VISCOSITY AND THERMAL CONDUCTIVITY

The expressions for the stress tensor (7.23) and (7.20), and the heat flux vector (7.21) and (7.26) lead to expressions for the shear and bulk viscosities, and the thermal conductivity. In the expressions (7.26) and (7.23) the first term relates to the free movement of single particles and is in this way applicable to dilute gases. The second term of each expression includes the action of the interparticle forces and is the predominant term for liquids. It is only necessary to consider these second terms for liquids.

By carrying through the momentum averages in (7.26) and (7.23) the following expressions are derived for the shear viscosity η, the bulk vis-

osity ξ, and the thermal conductivity λ. For spherically symmetric interaction potentials:

$$\eta = A_1 \frac{\gamma n^2}{kT} \int_0^\infty \frac{\mathrm{d}\psi(\xi)}{\mathrm{d}\xi} u(\xi) g^{(2)}(\xi, T)\xi^3 \, \mathrm{d}\xi, \tag{9.69a}$$

$$\zeta = A_2 \frac{\gamma n^2}{kT} \int_0^\infty \frac{\mathrm{d}\psi(\xi)}{\mathrm{d}\xi} s(\xi) g^{(2)}(\xi, T)\xi^3 \, \mathrm{d}\xi, \tag{9.69b}$$

$$\lambda = \frac{A_3 n^2}{kT\gamma} \int_0^\infty \int_0^\pi \int_0^{2\pi} g^{(2)}(\xi) \left[\left(\xi \frac{\mathrm{d}\psi(\xi)}{\mathrm{d}\xi} - \Phi(\xi) \right) \left(\frac{\mathrm{d}v(\xi)}{\mathrm{d}\xi} + \frac{\Phi(\xi)}{kT} \right) \cos^2 \vartheta \right.$$

$$\left. + \left(\frac{\xi}{2} \frac{\mathrm{d}\psi(\xi)}{\mathrm{d}\xi} - \Phi(\xi) \right) \left(\frac{v(\xi)}{\xi} + \frac{\Phi(\xi)}{kT} \right) \sin^2 \vartheta \right] \sin \vartheta \, \mathrm{d}\xi \, \mathrm{d}\vartheta \, \mathrm{d}\varphi. \tag{9.69c}$$

In these expressions A_1, A_2, and A_3 are numerical constants. $A_1 = \pi/15$; $A_2 = \pi/9$; $A_3 = \pi/2$. $u(\xi)$ in (9.69a) is the solution of (9.60) using either the strong boundary conditions (9.61) and (9.63), or the weak boundary conditions (9.61) and (9.62). $s(\xi)$ appearing in (9.69b) is obtained by solving (9.68) subject to the boundary conditions (9.68a) and (9.68b). Finally, $v(\xi)$ in (9.69c) is obtained as solution of (9.66) under the boundary conditions (9.67). In the expressions (9.69) the equilibrium liquid structure appears explicitly.

TABLE 5

Source	$\eta \times 10^3$ poise	$\gamma \times 10^{-11}$ sec^{-1}
A	1·27	73
B	0·84	0·35
C	1·91	3·5
D	assumes 2·39	4·24

It is seen that the viscosity coefficient, whether for shear or bulk motion is proportional to the friction constant. On the other hand, the thermal conductivity is proportional to the inverse of the friction constant. The product $\eta\lambda$ or $\zeta\lambda$ is consequently independent of γ and could be used as an absolute check on the theory at the present time.

A number of numerical predictions of the theory exist for using inter-particle force potentials that represent the case of liquid argon very well: alternatively, experimental information is available to act as a standard for comparison with the calculations. We end this chapter with such a comparison, made in broad terms. Values of the viscosity and thermal conductivity, calculated using the arguments of the present chapter, must be based on a knowledge of the fluid non-uniform microscopic structure: and this has been assumed to differ from the corresponding uniform structure by only a small amount. A knowledge of the uniform structure is therefore essential, on our present arguments, for the calculation of the transport coefficients. It was seen in the earlier chapters of the book that the equilibrium pair distribution used to describe the uniform structure is still known only imperfectly, partly because the equation to be used for its calculations is still open to doubt and partly because our knowledge of the pair interaction potential may still require refinement. It follows that calculated values of the liquid transport coefficients must not be expected to have fine numerical accuracy, and too close an agreement with experiment must not be given unwarranted significance of itself. The theory can be expected, however, to show the correct qualitative behaviours, such as the correct dependence on the fluid temperature.

The first numerical data deduced from the theory are those obtained by Kirkwood and his co-workers. These are the first two entries in Table 5. Source A in this table is Kirkwood, Buff, and Green.[24] The weak boundary conditions were used in obtaining solutions of (9.60). The equilibrium pair distribution was taken as an analytic form adapted to the known experimental X-ray data, and particular attention was paid to fitting the region of the first maximum of the intensity curve. The interparticle force potential was chosen separately as the (12–6) potential with the associated parameters adapted for argon except that a hard central core was assumed at very small distances. Although this is probably a good representation of the pair potential it should be noted that the pair distribution data used was not derived using this potential function. The friction constant used was not based on a molecular model leading to the decay of the correlation function.[12] The value used $(7 \cdot 3 \times 10^{12} \sec^{-1})$ is thus an estimate and is probably high. The source B is Zwanzig, Kirkwood, Stripp, and Oppenheim.[23] These authors improved on the specification of γ, but obtained a rather lower value for the shear viscosity. These authors gave also as value for the bulk viscosity $\zeta = 0 \cdot 42 \times 10^{-3}$ poise, derived from using equation (9.69b). This is of the same general order of magnitude as their calculated value for the shear viscosity. These authors also used the "stretching" procedure met with earlier in Chapter 6, aimed at choosing that value of $g^{(2)}$ which gives the best prediction of thermodynamic data. This meant in practice replacing $g^{(2)}(r)$ by $g^{(2)}(1 \cdot 026r)$: the effect was to lower the calculated viscosity value.

The data C is derived from (9.69a) using the strong conditions (9.61) and (9.63) of Eisenschitz in the evaluation of equation (9.60). The friction constant used was that of Eisenschitz and Wilford[15] quoted in (9.47d), based on the representation of the thermal molecular movement in a liquid as a process of density wave propagation. The theory is, then, an example of the use of collective coordinates akin to the procedure used earlier by Bohm and Pines in the theory of plasma oscillations. The data for $g^{(2)}$ was again taken from the experimental curves, and the interparticle potential used by Kirkwood was again used here.

Finally, the data D are those due to Orton,[13] who employed the experimental value $\eta = 2 \cdot 39 \times 10^{-3}$ poise along with (9.69a), and experimental data for $g^{(2)}$ and $\psi(r)$ to determine γ. These data are added to the table for completeness.

Measurement for the shear viscosity of liquid argon has been reported for several temperatures and pressures.[29] More data are, however, necessary before a full experimental knowledge of the shear viscosity of liquid argon can be claimed to be available. Two points are, however, of direct interest here. First, there would seem to be a linear increase of viscosity with pressure, at least over the pressure range 50–500 atmospheres, the value of the viscosity at 101·8°K increasing from $1 \cdot 6 \times 10^{-3}$ poise to $2 \cdot 8 \times 10^{-3}$ poise in this range. And second, the effect of temperature *at constant fluid density* would seem to be rather weak. This result contradicts the earlier conclusions of Andrade,[5] and should be the subject of further experimental investigations. Indeed, it seems now likely that only about one quarter of the measured dependence of viscosity upon temperature is a true temperature effect, the remainder being a density effect. If this is, indeed, the case then the case for the strong boundary conditions is vitiated, and the weak conditions become the more obvious ones to use.

The Rice–Allnatt theory has also been used for the calculation of shear viscosity of liquid argon and the agreement with experiment is, from quoted values,[8] not worse than about 40 per cent. Remembering the uncertainties in the equilibrium pair distribution and in the specification of pair interaction potential, such agreement should not be the reason for early rejoicing. Almost every piece of information used on the calculations is open to some doubt (even including the actual numerical values of viscosity derived from experiment); but the fact that calculated data, having the correct magnitude, do result from the theory is certainly significant and it can be concluded from this that the Rice–Allnatt theory does give a useful first order qualitative description of molecular processes in simple liquids.

Some calculated data are also available for the thermal conductivity of liquid argon. There was for some time confusion over the interpretation of the expression (9.69c) for the thermal conductivity, in that the contribution due to the relative movement of the particle pair was neglected. The value given by Zwanzig, Kirkwood, Stripp, and Oppenheim[23] of $\lambda = 2\cdot4\times10^{-4}$ cal/g/sec/deg is therefore only an order of magnitude estimate, but no better data seem available at the present time. It is surprisingly near to the experimental value $\lambda = 2\cdot9\times10^{-4}$ cal/g/sec/deg. This apparently hopeful situation was, however, shown to be largely spurious by these authors who showed that if $g^{(2)}(r)$ is the pair distribution leading to the figure $2\cdot4\times10^{-4}$ just quoted, the small stretching of r so that $g^{(2)}(1\cdot026\ r)$ is the new pair distribution gives $\lambda = 4\cdot1\times10^{-4}$. It seems that λ is very critically dependent upon the exact details of the equilibrium pair distribution.

Some experimental data for the thermal conductivity of liquid argon are available[30] but, as for shear viscosity, more data is still necessary for any decisive test of the theory. The widest test of theory against what experimental data there are is probably that using the Rice–Allnatt theory.[8] As for viscosity, so for thermal conductivity, the result of the comparison probably leads to a too optimistic assessment of the theory. It is probably safe to say no more than that the theory is able to account qualitatively for the observed thermal conductivity effects, although the truly quantitative test must await the various refinements of the theory, such as improved data of the equilibrium fluid structure and the interparticle force potential. A central feature in the calculation of the transport coefficients is the problem of calculating the friction constant: the numerical deduction of the friction constant from the principles of molecular dynamics alone is still to be achieved.

With the friction constant known only approximately, it is probably better at the present time to consider the product $\eta\lambda$ rather than its factors separately. Certainly, the theory is able to account for the magnitude of this result even though its precise numerical value may be outside our certain competence at the present time.

The theories mentioned here, that is those of Kirkwood and Eisenschitz and the special form due to Rice and Allnatt, all depend upon the validity of the Smoluchowski equation. The deduction of this equation on the basis of molecular dynamics is, therefore, of cardinal importance to the development of the theory. It must be admitted that this deduction is still not satisfactory and that more work remains to be done in this direction. The discussion hinges upon the value of the friction constant, for if this constant is too low, the Smoluchowski equation ceases to be a satisfactory approximation to the Fokker–Planck equation. The exact critical value is open to doubt, but Suddaby and Miles[18] have suggested that it might be s high as 4×10^{12} sec $^{-1}$. Further work is needed to clarify this point. Alternatively, it may prove possible (or indeed necessary) to seek a link between the Smoluchowski and Liouville equations that does not involve the phase equation of Fokker and Planck directly. The validity of the Smoluchowski equation, for the determination of the deviation of the liquid microscopic structure from the equilibrium value, is a central assertion of the distribution function approach to the calculation of the transport phenomena in simple liquids. Further study of this circumstance is necessary for the further development of the theory. Although the theory of transport in liquids has not yet reached its final form, it is able to account for the observed liquid properties in qualitative detail and as to orders of magnitude. Further assessment of the theory must involve a fuller knowledge of the fluid equilibrium state. Alternative approaches to the problems of liquid transport (such as the approach involving the fluctuation dissipation theorem, or the approach of Prigogine and his co-workers) have not yet yielded numerical predictions for liquid transport. These alternative approaches must ultimately be linked with the distribution function approach treated in this book. It may be that it will be in this way that the arguments considered here will be refined.

REFERENCES AND COMMENTS

GENERAL REFERENCES

The following treatises are standard references for the principles of equilibrium statistical mechanics.

. C. Tolman, 1938, *The Principles of Statistical Mechanics*, London, Oxford University Press.

E. Meyer and M. G. Meyer, 1940, *Statistical Mechanics*, New York, Wiley.

. H. Fowler, 1936, *Statistical Mechanics*, London, Cambridge University Press.

. W. Gibbs, 1948, *Collected Works*, New Haven, Yale University Press.

. L. Hill, 1956, *Statistical Mechanics*, New York, McGraw-Hill.

. D. Landau and E. M. Lifshitz, 1958, *Statistical Physics*, London, Pergamon Press.

. S. R. Chisholm and A. H. de Boer, 1958, *An Introduction to Statistical Mechanics*, London, Pergamon Press.

. Huang, 1963, *Statistical Mechanics*, New York, Wiley.

There is as yet no comparable standard treatise for non-equilibrium situations, although exts of limited scope are available.

'or gases, the best text is still:

. Chapman and T. G. Cowling, 1939, *The Mathematical Theory of Non-uniform Gases*, London, Cambridge University Press.

lso of interest is:

.. A. Guggenheim, 1960, *Elements of the Kinetic Theory of Gases*, Oxford, Pergamon Press.

. very readable discussion of gas theory is contained in:

.. Huang, 1963, *Statistical Mechanics*, New York, Wiley.

. broad survey of the statistical theory of non-equilibria (though not suitable as an ntroductory text) is:

.. Eisenschitz, 1958, *Statistical Theory of Irreversible Processes*, London, Oxford University Press.

here are now several books specifically devoted to dense fluids. These are:

. S. Green, 1952, *Molecular Theory of Fluids*, London, Cambridge University Press.

. O. Hirschfelder, C. F. Curtiss and R. B. Bird, 1954, *Molecular Theory of Gases and Liquids*, New York, Wiley.

. N. Bogoliubov, 1946, *Dynamical Theory in Statistical Physics*. English translation, Problems of a Dynamical Theory in Statistical Physics, in *Studies in Statistical Mechanics*, vol. 1 (eds. J. de Boer and G. E. Uhlenbeck), Amsterdam, North-Holland.

. Frenkel, 1946, *Kinetic Theory of Liquids*, London, Oxford University Press.

.. Darmois, 1947, *L'Etat Liquid de la Matière*, Paris, Albin Michel.

. S. Green, 1960, The Structure of Liquids, *Handbuch der Physik*, **10**, 1.

Z. Fisher, 1964, *Statistical Theory of Liquids*, Chicago University Press.

. A. Rice and P. Gray, 1965, *The Statistical Mechanics of Simple Liquids*, Interscience.

. L. Frisch and J. L. Lebowitz, 1964, *The Equilibrium Theory of Classical Fluids*, Benjamin

CHAPTER 1

A useful summary of liquid properties is:
J. S. ROWLINSON, 1959, *Liquids and Liquid Mixtures*, New York, Academic Press.

1.1. For a discussion of the macroscopic treatment of non-Newtonian situations see
A. S. LODGE, 1964, *Elastic Liquids*, New York, Academic Press.

1.2. General references for X-ray studies are:
J. T. RANDALL, 1934, *The Diffraction of X-rays and Electrons by Amorphous Solids, Liquids, and Gases*, London, Chapman & Hall.
R. W. JAMES, 1948, *The Optical Principles of the Diffraction of X-rays*, London Bell.
W. SPROULL, 1946, *X-rays in Practice*, New York, McGraw-Hill.
A. H. COMPTON and S. K. ALLISON, 1935, *X-rays in Theory and Experiment*, New York, Van Nostrand.
For historical papers see:
C. G. BARKLA and T. AYERS, 1911, *Phil. Mag.* **21**, 275.
W. FRIEDRICH, P. KNIPPING, and M. VON LAUE, 1912, *Sitzb. Math.-Phys. Klasse Bayer. Akad. Wiss. München.*
W. FRIEDRICH, 1915, *Physik. Zeits.* **14**, 397.
P. DEBYE and P. SCHERRER, 1916, *Göttingen Nachr.* **16**.
W. H. KEESOM and J. DE SMEDT, 1922, *Proc. Acad. Sci. Amst.* **25**, 118; 1923, *ibid* **26**, 112.
F. ZERNIKE and J. PRINS, 1927, *Z. Phys.* **41**, 184.
J. PRINS, 1929, *Z. Phys.* **56**, 617.
P. DEBYE and H. MENKE, 1931, *Ergeb. d. Tech. Röntgenk.* II.

1.3. For neutron diffraction details see for instance:
P. A. EGELSTAFF, 1962, *Adv. Phys.* (*Phil. Mag.* Supp.) **11**, 203.
G. H. VINEYARD, 1960, *Phys. Rev.* **119**, 1150.
G. T. CLAYTON and LEROY HEATON, 1961, *Phys. Rev.* **121**, 649.
A. RAHMAN, K. S. SINGUI and A. SJÖLANDER, 1961, *Phys. Rev.* **122**, 9.
N. S. GINGRICH and LEROY HEATON, 1961, *J. Chem. Phys.* **34**, 873.
Theory was considered by:
L. VAN HOVE, 1954, *Phys. Rev.* **95**, 249.

1.4. Experimental data specifically for liquids are given in:
N. S. GINGRICH, 1943, *Rev. Mod. Phys.* **15**, 90.
For liquid bromine see:
G. CAGLIOTI and F. P. RICCI, 1962, *Nuovo Cim.* **24**, 103.
Data for liquid neon between the critical and triple points are given in:
D. STIRPE and C. W. TOMPSON, 1962, *J. Chem. Phys.* **36**, 392.

1.5. The Fourier transform of the function $h(r)$ can be written in alternative notation. Denoting the Fourier transform of the total correlation function $h(r)$ by $\bar{h}(r)$ then we write:

$$\bar{h}(s) = i(s) = \frac{I(s) - I_0}{I_0}.$$

1.6. For a discussion, see for instance:
G. FOURNIER, 1949, *C. R. Acad. Sci. Paris*, **228**, 1421, 1801.
Experimental methods can be used to determine $i(s)$ experimentally so that the Fourier transform of $h(s)$ is to be regarded as an experimentally determined function. In Chapter 5 of the main text, the total correlation is related to the direct correlation function $c(r)$ according to the main text equation (5.2). We now take

the Fourier transforms throughout (5.2) to obtain:

$$\tilde{h}(s) = \tilde{c}(s) + n\tilde{c}(s)\,\tilde{h}(s),$$

so that

$$\tilde{h}(s) = i(s) = \frac{\tilde{c}(s)}{1 - n\tilde{c}(s)}\,.$$

Consequently, the direct correlation is related to $i(s)$ by

$$\tilde{c}(s) = \frac{i(s)}{1 + ni(s)}\,.$$

Apparently, the direct correlation function is itself a function that can be deduced from experiment through its Fourier transform. This procedure has been used by M. D. JOHNSON, P. HUTCHINSON, and N. H. MARCH (1965, *Proc. Roy. Soc.* (London) A **282**, 283) to obtain the direct correlation function for liquid argon and liquid rubidium, using the neutron diffraction data of D. G. HENSHAW (1957, *Phys. Rev.* **105**, 976) and N. S. GINGRICH and L. HEATON (1961, *J. Chem. Phys.* **34**, 873). This work will be considered further in Chapter 6 of the main text.

1.7. For small-angle scattering, the main text equation (1.12) becomes, for spherical particles:

$$1 + i(0) = 1 + 4\pi n \int_0^\infty h(r)r^2 \, dr.$$

This expression does not depend upon the wavelength of the incident radiation and will apply, therefore, to optical wavelengths. Consequently, information about fluid structure can be determined from optical experiments. See:

J. YVON, 1937, *Fluctuations en Densité, La Propogation et la Diffusion de la Lumière*, Paris, Hermann.

L. S. ORNSTEIN and F. ZERNICKE, 1914, *Proc. Acad. Sci. Amst.* **17**, 793.

M. FIXMAN, 1962, *J. Chem. Phys.* **36**, 1965.

S. KIELICH, 1960, *Acta Physica Polonica*, **14**, 149, 573, 711; 1961, *ibid.* **20**, 83.

1.8. This expression can be integrated between the two separation distances r_1 and r_2 to give the number dN of particles in the shell of thickness $(r_2 - r_1)$ and of mean radius $\left(\dfrac{r_1 + r_2}{2}\right)$. The result is:

$$dN = 4\pi n \int_{r_1}^{r_2} r^2 g^{(2)}(r) \, dr.$$

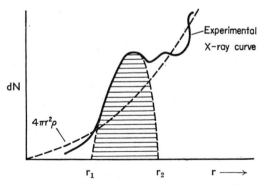

FIG. 18. The location of the first coordination shell using experimental data. The shaded area refers to the first coordination shell.

By choosing $(r_2 - r_1)$ to cover successively the spatial ranges of those distances for which $g^{(2)}(r) > 1$ we obtain the number of particles in those shells where the occupation number for particles is greater than the average. Each shell is called a coordinate shell, and the number of particles in each shell is called the coordination number. The first coordination shell for a typical simple fluid is sketched in Fig. 18, where interest is focused on the first coordination shell.

It is found that the coordination number for the first coordination shell in a simple liquid is always less than the number of nearest neighbours in the corresponding solid crystal. For example, for liquid argon at 84·4°K and 0·8 atmospheres pressure, there are 10·5 nearest neighbours at a mean distance of 3·79 Å, so that the first coordinate number is 10·5 and the first coordination distance 3·79 Å. For solid argon, there are 12 nearest neighbours at a mean distance of 3·52 Å. See:

E. R. DOBBS and G. O. JONES, 1957, *Rep. Prog. Phys.* **20**, 560.

N. S. GINGRICH and C. W. TOMPSON, 1962, *J. Chem. Phys.* **36**, 2398.

It should be noticed that the coordination number is a mean number over the time and is not a strict constant. The deviation of this number about the mean value is a measure of the molecular motion in the fluid.

1.9. See, for instance:

J. I. FRENKEL, 1946, *Kinetic Theory of Liquids*, London, Oxford University Press.

CHAPTER 2

2.1. A good comprehensive survey of interparticle force fields, together with many references, is contained in part III of the book:

J. O. HIRSCHFELDER, C. F. CURTISS, and R. B. BIRD, 1954, *Molecular Theory of Gases and Liquids*, New York, Wiley.

See also the review article:

I. E. DZYALOSHINSKII, E. M. LIFSHITZ, and L. P. PITAEVSKII, 1961, *Adv. Phys.* (*Phil. Mag.* Supp.) **10**, 165.

2.2. This assumption of additivity must be viewed with caution in general application. While it turns out to be adequate for the study of the rare elements in the liquid phase, it is not always applicable for the solid phase. The expression (2.1) of the main text is useful in the initial construction of a theory of fluids because of its simplicity: it may prove to need modification ultimately for calculations of very high accuracy.

2.3. For details see:

G. MIE, 1903, *Ann. Phys. Lpz.* **11**, 657.

J. E. LENNARD-JONES, 1937, *Physica*, **4**, 941.

E. R. DOBBS and G. O. JONES, 1957, *Rep. Prog. Phys.* **20**, 560, which refers particularly to argon. Other data for argon is given by:

G. S. RUSHBROOKE, 1940, *Proc. Roy. Soc. Edin.* **60**, 182. This reference gives $4\varepsilon\sigma^{11\cdot4} = 3\cdot62 \times 10^{-8}$, and $4\varepsilon\sigma^6 = 1\cdot11 \times 10^{-10}$, with ε in ergs and σ in angstrom units.

2.4. The various values of m are very often selected on the basis of a comparison between calculated and experimental data for the second virial coefficient for a particular fluid.

2.5. We are concerned here only with fluid conditions; for solids the situation can be more complicated. Formulae such as the Buckingham–Corner (exp-6) expression are often more appropriate then. For details see previous ref. 2.1.

2.6. E. A. GUGGENHEIM and McGLASHAN, 1962, *Proc. Roy. Soc.* (London), **225**, 456. The specification is not made in terms of a single formula covering all separation distances but rather is made to involve three separate regions. Each region has a fairly critical effect on the numerical value of specific calculated data, and selection is made in order that theory and experiment shall have a good fit in these cases. Explicitly:

$$\psi(r) = \infty, \quad \text{for} \quad \frac{r}{\sigma} < 1,$$

$$\psi(r) = -\varepsilon + K \frac{(r-r_0)^2}{r_0^2} - \alpha \frac{(r-r_0)^3}{r_0^3} \frac{(2r-r_0)}{r_0}, \quad \text{for} \quad r_1 \leqslant r \leqslant r_2,$$

$$\psi(r) = -\lambda \left(\frac{r_0}{r}\right)^6, \quad \text{for} \quad r \geqslant r_3.$$

It is seen that there is a hard central core for $r < \sigma$, and at large distances ($r > r_3$) the potential vanishes like r^{-6}. In between, the region of the potential minimum, located at r_0, is specified carefully in powers of $(r-r_0)$ in conformity with earlier arguments of D. K. RICE (1941, *J. Am. Chem. Soc.* **63**, 3). For argon, GUGGENHEIM and McGLASHAN in their paper give the following best values for the various parameters:

$$\frac{\varepsilon}{k} = 137 \cdot 6° \text{ K,} \qquad \frac{K}{k} = 44 \cdot 9° \text{ K,} \qquad r_1 = 3 \cdot 60 \text{ Å,}$$

$$\frac{K}{k} = 19 \cdot 6 \times 10^{30} \text{ K,} \qquad \sigma = 3 \cdot 2 \text{ Å,} \qquad r_2 = 4 \cdot 15 \text{ Å,}$$

$$\frac{\lambda}{k} = 150° \text{ K,} \qquad r_0 = 3 \cdot 812 \text{ Å,} \qquad r_3 = 5 \cdot 40 \text{ Å.}$$

The potential has been used by Khan for numerical studies of argon (1964, *Phys. Rev.* **134**, A 367) and of krypton (1964, *Phys. Rev.* **136**, A 1260). These calculations are considered in Chapter 6 of the main text.

There is still a real need for simple expressions to represent the interparticle force potential and further modifications of existing expressions can be expected in the future. Wider possibilites would seem possible through the use of computers because simple analytic expressions for the potential are not then necessary.

2.7. We list here details of the idealised potential forms (see Fig. 19) that are most often used in calculations.

(i) *The hard-sphere potential*

This is the simplest interparticle force law and the potential is defined by the one-parameter expressions:

$$\psi(r) = \infty, \quad \text{for} \quad \frac{r}{\sigma} < 1,$$

$$\psi(r) = 0, \quad \text{for} \quad \frac{r}{\sigma} > 1, \qquad \text{(A2.1)}$$

where σ is the diameter of the sphere.

There is a discontinuity at $r = \sigma$ so that the force is impulsive and has the mathematical form of a Dirac delta function $\delta(r-\sigma)$. The particle is completely impenetrable and particle interaction involves actual contact. This potential can be used to describe the conditions in a gas at very high temperatures.

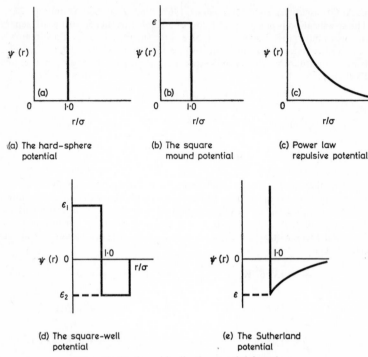

(a) The hard-sphere potential

(b) The square mound potential

(c) Power law repulsive potential

(d) The square-well potential

(e) The Sutherland potential

FIG. 19. Various idealised potential functions

There is no explicit attraction between particles according to (A2.1) but average attractive effects between particles can appear indirectly due to the shielding effect of one particle by another. The hard-sphere potential excludes the appearance of temperature effects in calculated physical quantities because it describes a purely impulsive interaction process.

(ii) *The square-mound potential*

A temperature effect can be introduced into calculated macroscopic data by relaxing the hard-sphere model as follows:

$$\psi(r) = \varepsilon, \quad \text{for} \quad \frac{r}{\sigma} < 1,$$

$$= 0, \quad \text{for} \quad \frac{r}{\sigma} > 1, \tag{A2.2}$$

This is a two-parameter potential form.

(iii) *The power-law repulsion*

The discontinuous strong repulsion of models (i) and (ii) can be relaxed through the use of the expression:

$$\psi(r) = A \left(\frac{\sigma}{r}\right)^m. \tag{A2.3}$$

This is to apply for all distances r. A and m are two adjustable parameters apart from the distance scale; m is a pure number, where A has the dimensions of energy. m will usually need to be assigned a value of at least 12.

(iv) *The square-well potential*

This potential accounts formally for both repulsive and attractive regions. It is defined by the expressions:

$$\psi(r) = \infty, \quad \text{for} \quad \frac{r}{\sigma} < 1,$$

$$\psi(r) = -\varepsilon, \quad \text{for} \quad 1 < \frac{r}{\sigma} < g, \quad \text{(A2.4)}$$

$$\psi(r) = 0, \quad \text{for} \quad \frac{r}{\sigma} > g.$$

Here, there is an indefinitely strong repulsion of unit range, and an attractive region of magnitude ($\varepsilon > 0$) of range ($g - 1$). Beyond this, the potential is zero.

Mathematically, the simplest situation is when the repulsive and attractive ranges are equal, so that $g = 2$. This assignment also has some practical value for the simpler molecules, a sis seen from Table 6. Here values of σ, g, and ε/k are listed which have been derived from virial equation data for gases.

TABLE 6

Gas	σ in Å	g	ε/k °K
Neon	2·38	1·87	19·5
Argon	3·16	1·85	69·4
Krypton	3·36	1·85	98·3
N_2	3·30	1·87	53·7
CO_2	3·92	1·83	119·0
Ethane	3·53	1·65	244
CCl_3F	4·53	1·55	399
CH_4	2·90	1·27	692
Steam	2·61	1·20	1290
Propane	4·42	1·46	34·7

It is seen that $g = 2$ is a fair approximation for the first five entries in the table, although it is not good for the remainder. The actual value of (ε/k) in each case is not critical.

(v) *The Sutherland potential*

The attractive region of the potential suffers a definite cut-off in the square-well potential form. The known dependence of r^{-6} for the attractive region of simple spherical particles can be accounted for by defining $\psi(r)$ as:

$$\psi(r) = \infty, \qquad \text{for} \quad \frac{r}{\sigma} < 1,$$

$$\psi(r) = -4\varepsilon \left(\frac{\sigma}{r}\right)^6, \qquad \text{for} \quad \frac{r}{\sigma} > 1. \tag{A2.5}$$

This potential form was suggested by Sutherland and has proved useful in some practical cases.

(vi) *The Stockmayer potential contribution*

Although our main concern is with spherical particles representing non-polar molecules, the arguments can be applied readily to simple polar cases. For, if a representative molecule carries a dipole μ then it will interact with other molecules through the dipole interaction as well as through the normal interparticle force. In spite of showing a resultant dipole, and so having a shape that deviates from that of a perfect sphere, the deviation from spherical symmetry may be sufficiently small to be neglected. Then the total interaction potential is the simple sum of a non-polar contribution ψ (of the type (i) to (v) above, for example) and a polar contribution ψ_s. W. H. STOCKMAYER (1941, *J. Chem. Phys.* **9**, 398) has derived an expression for ψ_s. The dipole interaction is to apply only external to each particle (i.e. for $r > \sigma$). Then if (ϑ_1, ϕ_1) and (ϑ_2, ϕ_2) are the angular orientation of two dipole particles, the Stockmayer potential contribution is:

$$\psi_s = -\frac{\mu^2}{r^3}\left[2\cos\vartheta_1\cos\vartheta_2 - \sin\vartheta_1\sin\vartheta_2\cos(\phi_2 - \phi_1)\right], \qquad \text{for} \quad \frac{r}{\sigma} > 1, \tag{A2.6}$$

where r is the separation distance of the particles measured from their centres.

The total interparticle potential is then obtained by joining (A2.6) to one of the appropriate forms (A2.1) to (A2.5).

It must be borne in mind always that any simple expression for the interparticle force potential, including the form (2.5) of the main text, is no more than a more or less good approximation in particular cases. There is also the possibility that no single analytic potential form will be adequate for the detailed study of different phases of matter. Thus, what is best for a gas, or a liquid, is not necessarily adequate for a solid.

2.8. General references for classical mechanics are:

S. GOLDSTEIN, 1950, *Classical Mechanics*, Addison-Wesley.

C. LANCZOS, 1949, *The Variational Principles of Mechanics*, University of Toronto Press.

M. BORN, 1929, *Mechanics of the Atom*, ch. 1, London, Bell.

J. W. LEECH, 1959, *Classical Mechanics*, London, Methuen Monographs on Physical Subjects.

D. TER HAAR, 1961, *Elements of Hamiltonian Mechanics*, Amsterdam, North-Holland.

2.9. For a further discussion of the virial theorem, see:

E. PARKER, 1954, *Phys. Rev.* **96**, 1686.

J. O. HIRSCHFELDER, 1962, Paper No. 34, pp. 386–92, in the collection *Progress in Internation Research on Thermodynamic and Transport Properties* (published by Academic Press for ASME). This paper is very stimulating in suggesting the wide scope of application of the theorem.

2.10. See, for instance:

R. C. TOLMAN, 1938, *Introduction to the Principles of Statistical Mechanics*, p. 48, London, Oxford University Press.

2.11. See, for instance:
R. C. TOLMAN, 1938, *Introduction to the Principles of Statistical Mechanics*, London, Oxford University Press.
J. DE BOER, 1948, *Rep. Prog. Phys*, **12**, 315.

2.12. See ref. 2.10, p.47 and pp.65–70.

2.13. The ergodic theorem is referred to in many books on statistical mechanics. For more details see:
A. I. KHINCHIN, 1948. *Mathematical Foundations of Statistical Mechanics*, New York, Dover.
Ergodic Theories, 1961, Proceedings of the International School of Physics, Enrico Fermi, New York, Academic Press.
I. E. FARQUHAR, 1961, *Nature*, **190**, 17.
See also:
H. POINCARÉ, 1894, *Rev. Gen. des Sci.* 516.
P. EHRENFEST and T. EHRENFEST, 1911, *Encyclop. der Math. Wissenschaften*, IV. Art 32.
C. CARATHEODORY, 1919, *Berl. Ber.* **580**.
G. D. BIRKHOFF, 1922, *Acta Math.* **43**, 113.

CHAPTER 3

3.1. An excellent and yet concise discussion of statistical thermodynamics is:
E. SCHRODINGER, 1948, *Statistical Thermodynamics*, London, Cambridge University Press.
See also:
R. C. TOLMAN, 1938, *Introduction to the Principles of Statistical Mechanics*, London, Oxford University Press.
For a review see:
J. DE BOER, 1948, *Rep. Prog. Phys.* **12**, 305.

3.2. We choose here to assign a specific form for the function $f^{(N)}$ for a closed system of N particles, but the equation (3.11) can be deduced alternatively. On our present approach, the validity of the canonical form is to be tested ultimately by the successful comparison of the thermodynamic functions that it yields with appropriate experimental data. In particular it is necessary to show that the entropy derived from (3.11), using equation (3.13), is a maximum. The more usual procedure now is to go the other way round, and ask of the form of $f^{(N)}$ that is necessary for the entropy to have the maximum possible value. For more information see references in 3.1. above.

3.3. If the total energy of the system at temperature T is increased by an amount dQ, then the consequent increase of internal energy ΔU and the consequent work done by the system dW in increasing its volume by amount dV are related by:

$$dQ = dU + p\, dV.$$

The change of entropy of the system dS is given by:

$$T\, dS = dU + p\, dV = dU + p\, dV - S\, dT + S\, dT.$$

Therefore,

$$d(U - TS) = -S\, dT - p\, dV.$$

Introducing the function F, called the free energy of Helmholtz, according to $F = U - TS$ it follows that:

$$dF(V, T) = \frac{\partial F}{\partial V}\bigg|_{T} dV + \frac{\partial F}{\partial T}\bigg|_{V} dT.$$

Comparison with the equation above leads immediately to the equations (3.22a) and (3.22c) of the main text. The equation (3.22b) for the internal energy is then obtained from equation (3.19) of the main text. A knowledge of the free energy as function of volume and temperature is sufficient to allow all the thermodynamic properties to be calculated. To show this, we list now the more important thermodynamic quantities apart from those appearing in the main text in a form that displays explicit dependence on $F(V, T)$. Now V will be the specific volume.

(i) *Enthalpy (or total heat)*, H_e is:

$$H_e = U + pV,$$

i.e.

$$H_e = -T^2 V \left\{ \frac{1}{V} \frac{\partial}{\partial T} \left(\frac{F}{T} \Big|_V \right) + \frac{1}{T} \frac{\partial}{\partial V} \left(\frac{F}{T} \Big|_T \right) \right\}.$$

(ii) *Specific heat at constant volume*, C_V is:

$$C_V = \frac{\partial U}{\partial T} \Big|_V = T \frac{\partial S}{\partial T} \Big|_V = -T \frac{\partial^2 F}{\partial T^2} \Big|_V.$$

(iii) *Specific heat at constant pressure*, C_p is:

$$C_p = \frac{\partial H_e}{\partial T} \Big|_V = T \frac{\partial S}{\partial T} \Big|_p = C_V - T \left(\frac{\partial p}{\partial T} \Big|_V \right) \left(\frac{\partial V}{\partial T} \Big|_p \right).$$

In terms of F:

$$C_p = -T \frac{\partial^2 F}{\partial T^2} \Big|_V + T \left(\frac{\partial^2 F}{\partial T \partial V} \Big|_T \right) \left(\frac{\partial V}{\partial T} \Big|_p \right).$$

It follows further that C_p and C_V satisfy the relations:

$$\frac{\partial C_V}{\partial V} \Big|_T = T \frac{\partial^2 p}{\partial T^2} \Big|_V,$$

$$\frac{\partial C_p}{\partial p} \Big|_T = -T \frac{\partial^2 V}{\partial T^2} \Big|_p.$$

(iv) *The ratio of the specific heats*, γ, is then:

$$\gamma = 1 - \left(\frac{\partial p}{\partial T} \Big|_V \right) \left(\frac{\partial V}{\partial T} \Big|_p \right) \left(\frac{\partial^2 F}{\partial V^2} \right)^{-1}.$$

Various coefficients arise from the description of controlled thermodynamic changes.

(v) *The isothermal dependence of enthalpy on pressure* leads to the recognition of the pressure coefficient Φ_E defined by:

$$\Phi_E = \frac{\partial H_e}{\partial p} \Big|_T = V + T \left(\frac{\partial^2 F}{\partial V \partial T} \right) \left(\frac{\partial^2 F}{\partial V^2} \right)^{-1}.$$

(vi) *When the enthalpy is constant*, the dependence of fluid temperature on pressure defines the Joule–Thomson coefficient, μ_T. Then:

$$\mu_T = \frac{\partial T}{\partial p} \Big|_H = \frac{1}{C_p} \left[T \frac{\partial V}{\partial T} \Big|_p - V \right],$$

i.e.

$$\mu_T = \frac{T \dfrac{\partial^2 F}{\partial V \partial T} + V \dfrac{\partial^2 F}{\partial V^2} \Big|_T}{T \left\{ \dfrac{\partial^2 F}{\partial V^2} \Big|_T \dfrac{\partial^2 F}{\partial T^2} \Big|_V - \left(\dfrac{\partial^2 F}{\partial V \partial T} \right)^2 \right\}}.$$

(vii) *The isothermal compressibility* $\varkappa$ is defined by:

$$\varkappa = -\frac{1}{V} \frac{\partial V}{\partial p} \Big|_T = \left(V \frac{\partial^2 F}{\partial V^2} \Big|_T \right)^{-1}.$$

(viii) *The isentropic compressibility* K_s is:

$$K_s = -\frac{1}{V}\frac{\partial V}{\partial p}\bigg|_s = \frac{1}{V}\frac{\partial^2 F}{\partial T^2}\left(\frac{\partial^2 F}{\partial V^2}\frac{\partial^2 F}{\partial T^2} - \left(\frac{\partial^2 F}{\partial V\partial T^2}\right)^2\right)^{-1}$$

(ix) *The isobaric coefficient of volume expansion* β is:

$$\beta = -\frac{1}{V}\frac{\partial V}{\partial T}\bigg|_p = -\frac{\partial^2 F}{\partial V\partial T}\left(V\frac{\partial^2 F}{\partial V^2}\right)^{-1}.$$

(x) *The speed of sound* c_s is then given by:

$$c_s^2 = V^2\frac{\dfrac{\partial^2 F}{\partial V^2}\dfrac{\partial^2 F}{\partial T^2} - \left(\dfrac{\partial^2 F}{\partial V\partial T}\right)^2}{\dfrac{\partial^2 F}{\partial T^2}}$$

(xi) *Finally, the Gibbs free energy* is given by:

$$G = F + pV,$$

i.e.

$$G = F - V\frac{\partial F}{\partial V}\bigg|_T.$$

It will be seen from these more important examples that a knowledge of the Helmholtz free energy for the fluid, as function of volume and temperature, allows the full range of fluid thermodynamic functions to be inferred.

3.4.   For a study of the grand canonical ensemble, see:
R. H. FOWLER and E. A. GUGGENHEIM, 1939, *Statistical Thermodynamics*, ch. VI, London, Cambridge University Press.

The canonical ensemble is conceptually deficient in that experimental situations are never associated with closed (i.e. isolated) systems, nor can the number of particles be specified exactly constant as is required by the concept of the canonical ensemble. But experiment can yield finer information than the average number of particles enclosed in some volume of matter. The observed fact, that for many macroscopic systems this average number is sensibly constant, must be treated as on the same level of validity as the statement of magnitudes of other thermodynamic quantities. The grand canonical ensemble is the natural statement of this situation, with the distribution over phase and particle number both being controlled by conditions external to the physical system. The grand canonical ensemble does not contain more information than the canonical ensemble (from which it may be derived) and the two ensembles are entirely equivalent for the calculation of thermodynamic data. This result relies for its deduction on the physical condition that, for normal real matter, N is astronomically large.

By using equation (3.28a) of the text, the grand canonical distribution can be written alternatively:

$$f_G^{(N)}(p^N, r^N) = \frac{z^N}{N!\,h^{3N}}\exp\left\{-\frac{pV}{kT}\right\}\exp\left\{-\frac{\mathcal{H}(p^N, r^N)}{kT}\right\},$$

a form that is sometimes useful in that it includes the macroscopic pressure and volume explicitly.

The grand canonical ensemble is a valuable concept in the theoretical description of fluctuations and is used in this connection in section 3.6.

3.5.   All that is derived in section 3.5. of the main text, using the canonical ensemble can equally well be derived using the grand canonical ensemble. The difference between the two developments involves terms of order $(1/N)$ and such terms have negligible magnitude for real fluids. The one exception arises from fluctuation theory and is the result (3.46) of the main text. But that result is thus derived using the grand ensemble. The h-th order distribution in the grand canonical ensemble is given by:

$$\Xi n^h g^{(h)}(\mathbf{r}^h) = \sum_{N \geqslant h} \frac{z^N}{(N-h)!} \int \cdots \int \exp\left\{-X(\mathbf{r}^N)\right\} d\mathbf{r}^{N-h},$$

which reduces to the canonical form in real matter where only the single strongly peaked mean number of particles $\langle N \rangle$ contributes to the sum over N. In practical terms, the difference between the results of the canonical and grand canonical ensembles is simply that the definite number N of the canonical ensemble is to be replaced by the average number $\langle N \rangle$ of the grand ensemble, with $\langle N \rangle \sim N$.

As an example, consider the derivation of the formula for the internal energy, U. Since the number of particles are not now constant we must write for the Helmholtz free energy, F:

$$F = \langle U \rangle - TS,$$

so that the average value of the internal energy $\langle U \rangle$ is now to be deduced from the thermodynamic relation:

$$\langle U \rangle = \langle N \rangle \mu + TS - pV,$$

where μ is the chemical potential for one particle. Consequently,

$$\langle U \rangle = \langle N \rangle \mu + kT^2 \frac{\partial \ln \Xi}{\partial T}\bigg|_{V, \mu}.$$

It follows directly that, for identical particles:

$$T \frac{\partial \Xi}{\partial T}\bigg|_{V, \mu} = \sum_{N \geqslant 2} \frac{z^N}{N!} \int X(\mathbf{r}^N) \exp\left\{-X(\mathbf{r}^N)\right\} d\mathbf{r}^N + \left(\frac{3\langle N \rangle}{2T} - \frac{\langle N \rangle \mu}{kT^2}\right) \Xi T.$$

The integral contains $N(N-1)/2$ pair contributions as usual so that:

$$kT^2 \frac{\partial \ln \Xi}{\partial T}\bigg|_{V, \mu} = \frac{1}{\Xi} \int \chi(\mathbf{r}_{12}) \sum_{N \geqslant 2} \frac{z^N}{N!} \frac{N(N-1)}{2} \int \exp\left\{-X(\mathbf{r}^N)\right\} d\mathbf{r}^{N-2} d\mathbf{r}_1 d\mathbf{r}_2$$

$$+ \frac{3}{2} \langle N \rangle kT - \langle N \rangle \mu.$$

Using the definition for $g^{(2)}$ given above, it follows that, for spherical particles:

$$\frac{\langle U \rangle}{\langle N \rangle kT} = \frac{3}{2} + \frac{n}{2} \int \chi(r) g^{(2)}(r) 4\pi r^2 \, dr.$$

This is identical to the equation (3.36) of the main text.

Further discussion of this important parallelism between the canonical and grand canonical ensembles can be studied further in:

T. L. HILL, 1956, *Statistical Mechanics*, ch. 6, pp. 233–51, New York, McGraw-Hill.

The chemical potential μ can also be expressed in terms of the pair distribution using the concept of the grand canonical ensemble. Because the number of particles N is large, then μ defined by the main text equation (3.22e) can be expressed in terms of the two statistical integrals $Z(N)$ and $Z(N-1)$ by using (3.20). Consequently

$$\mu = F(N, V, T) - F(N-1, V, T)$$

$$= -kT \ln \left[\frac{Z(N, V, T)}{Z(N-1, V, T)}\right],$$

i.e.

$$\mu = -kT \ln \left[\frac{Z_r(N)}{Z_r(N-1)}\right] - \frac{3}{2} kT \ln \left(\frac{2\pi mkT}{h^2}\right).$$

We next rearrange the term involving the partition function. For this purpose, introduce a coupling parameter between the particle that is at position r_1 (say) and the remaining $(N-1)$ particles. The total potential Ψ is thus written, in an obvious notation

$$\Psi(N) = \xi \sum_{j \geqslant 2}^{N} \Psi(1, j) + \Psi(N-1)$$

(see also main text equation (4.23)).
Here ξ is the coupling parameter continuous in the range $0 \leqslant \xi \leqslant 1$ (see also Section 4.2(b) of the main text). It follows, then, that

$$Z_r(N; \xi = 0) = V Z_r(N-1; \xi = 1)$$

and that

$$\ln \left[\frac{Z_r(N)}{Z_r(N-1)} \right] = \ln V + \int_0^1 \frac{\partial}{\partial \xi} \ln Z_r(\xi) \, d\xi.$$

The integrand in this formula can be rearranged by an appeal to equation (3.14b) of the main text. Explicitly

$$\frac{\partial Z_r(\xi)}{\partial \xi} = -\frac{1}{N!} \int \cdots \int \exp \left\{ -\frac{\Psi(N, \xi)}{kT} \right\} \left(\sum_{j=2}^{N} \chi(1, j) \right) dr^N$$

$$= -Z_r(\xi) \frac{n^2}{NkT} \int \psi(r_{12}) \, g^{(2)}(r_{12}, \xi) \, dr_1 \, dr_2.$$

For spherically symmetric particles we have, therefore,

$$\frac{\partial}{\partial \xi} \ln Z_r(\xi) = \frac{1}{Z_r(\xi)} \frac{\partial Z_r(\xi)}{\partial \xi} = -\frac{n}{kT} \int \psi(r) g^{(2)}(r) \, 4\pi r^2 \, dr.$$

This expression is then inserted into the formulae set out above to yield the expression for the chemical potential for a system composed of spherical particles:

$$\mu = \frac{3}{2} kT \ln \left(\frac{h^2 n^{2/3}}{2\pi m kT} \right) + n \int_0^1 d\xi \int_0^\infty \psi(r) g^{(2)}(r, \xi) \, 4\pi r^2 \, dr.$$

The fugacity can also be expressed in molecular terms and involving explicitly the pair distribution by appeal to equation (3.25) of the main text.

3.6. The expressions (3.36) and (3.38) for fluid internal energy and pressure were first introduced by:
H. S. GREEN, 1947, *Proc. Roy. Soc.* (London) A **189**, 103.
See also:
M. BORN and H. S. GREEN, 1949, *A General Kinetic Theory of Liquids*, London, Cambridge University Press.
The expression (3.38), derived in the text using the virial theorem, was derived originally by H. S. GREEN directly from equation (3.22a). We start from the expressions (3.22a) and (3.16). Then,

$$p = kT \frac{\partial}{\partial V} \ln Z = \frac{kT}{Z_r} \frac{\partial Z_r}{\partial V}.$$

Introduce a new length scale L which is a characteristic dimension of the container, so that the total fluid volume is essentially $L^3 = V$. The distance r can be written in terms of L as,

$$r = zL,$$

where $z =$ is a new distance variable. Then,

$$\frac{\partial}{\partial V} = \frac{L}{3V}\frac{\partial}{\partial L}.$$

Further,

$$Z_r = \frac{L^{3N}}{N!}\int \exp\left\{-X(L^{3N}, z^N)\right\}\,\mathrm{d}z^N = L^{3N}Z(L).$$

L does not now occur in the integration limits. Consequently we have:

$$pV = kT\left[N + \frac{L}{3Z(L)}\frac{\partial Z(L)}{\partial L}\right].$$

But,

$$\frac{\partial Z(L)}{\partial L} = \int \frac{\partial X(L^{3N}, z^N)}{\partial L}\exp\left\{-X(L,^{3N} z^N)\right\}\,\mathrm{d}z^N,$$

so that

$$\frac{L}{Z(L)}\frac{\partial Z(L)}{\partial L} = -\frac{L^3}{N!Z_r}\int -\left(\frac{\partial X}{\partial L}\right)L\exp\left\{-X(L^{3N}, z^N)\right\}\,\mathrm{d}z^N.$$

We can at this stage revert to the origin distance variable and so obtain:

$$\frac{L}{Z(L)}\frac{\partial Z(L)}{\partial L} = -\frac{(N-1)NV}{2Z_rN!}\int \left(\frac{\partial\chi(\mathbf{r}_{12})}{\partial\mathbf{r}_{12}}\cdot\mathbf{r}_{12}\right)\exp\left\{-X(\mathbf{r}^N)\right\}\,\mathrm{d}\mathbf{r}^N.$$

Consequently, for spherical particles and remembering the expression defined $g^{(2)}$:

$$p = nkT - \frac{n^2}{6}\int_0^\infty g^{(2)}(r)\frac{\partial\psi(r)}{\partial r}4\pi r^3\,\mathrm{d}r,$$

which is identical with the equation (3.38) of the main text. The mathematical trick of introducing a dimension which is characteristic of the total fluid volume is generally useful for the evaluation of expressions in statistical thermodynamics which involve the volume differentiation of volume integrals.

3.7. There are a number of discussions of fluctuation theory to which reference can be made. Among the books are:

R. C. TOLMAN, 1938, *Introduction to the Principles of Statistical Mechanics*, pp. 629–49, London, Oxford University Press.

J. O. HIRSCHFELDER, C. F. CURTISS, and R. B. BIRD, 1954, *Molecular Theory of Gases and Liquids*, New York, Wiley.

E. SCHRODINGER, 1948, *Statistical Thermodynamics*, ch. V, pp. 22–6, London, Cambridge University Press.

T. L. HILL, 1956, *Statistical Mechanics*, pp. 97–113, New York, McGraw-Hill.

R. H. FOWLER, 1929, *Statistical Mechanics*, ch. 20, London, Cambridge University Press.

For papers see:

M. J. KLEIN, and L. TISZA, 1949, *Phys. Rev.* **76**, 1861.

A. EINSTEIN, 1910, *Ann. Phys. Lpz.* **33**, 1275.

M. SMOLUCHOWSKI, 1908, *Ann. Phys. Lpz.* **25**, 225.

S. CHANDRASEKHAR, 1943, *Rev. Mod. Phys.* **15**, 1.

J. G. KIRKWOOD and R. J. GOLDBERG, 1950, *J. Chem. Phys.* **18**, 54.

W. H. STOCKMAYER, 1950, *J. Chem. Phys.* **18**, 58.

H. WEIGELAND, 1962, *Fundamental Problems in Statistical Mechanics*, p. 33 (ed. E. G. D. Cohen), Amsterdam, North-Holland.

3.8.   The formula (3.46b) can be inverted to yield directly $\partial p/\partial n|_{T,\,N}$ if $h(r)$ is replaced by a suitable function, $c(r)$ say. In particular, define the new function $c(r)$ through the convolution equation:

$$h(\mathbf{r}_{12}) = c(\mathbf{r}_{12}) + n \int_0^\infty h(\mathbf{r}_{23})\, c(\mathbf{r}_{13})\, d\mathbf{r}_3.$$

This equation is exactly that of the main text (5.2), used to define the direct pair particle correlation function. Using this equation, the compressibility equation (3.46b) of the text can be converted into the reciprocal form:

$$\frac{1}{kT}\frac{\partial p}{\partial n}\bigg|_{T,\,N} = 1 - 4\pi n \int_0^\infty c(r)\, r^2\, dr.$$

This equation is as valuable as equation (3.46) of the main text in determining the fluid pressure. Apparently, both the functions $h(r)$ and $c(r)$ are equally useful in specifying the particle correlations. This circumstance is used in Chapter 5 as a basis for deriving an equation for the fluid pair distribution.

3.9.   The construction of a theory of imperfect gases involving the so-called cluster integrals has proved one of the great achievements of statistical physics. Since the theory does not involve particle correlation functions, it falls outside our main interests and is not directly relevant to the development of the arguments of the main text. Certain results of the cluster theory are, however, valuable in our main studies, such as the exact expressions for the various virial coefficients as function of the interparticle force, and for this reason some of the main features of the cluster theory are given in this Appendix

The cluster expansion technique is a construction for evaluating systematically the integrals appearing in the expansion (3.50) for the partition function. The starting point is, therefore, the expression.

$$N!\, Z(V,\, T) = \int d\mathbf{r}^N [1 + (\alpha(1,2) + \alpha(1,3) + \dots$$
$$+ (\alpha(1,2)\,\alpha(1,3) + \alpha(1,2)\,\alpha(1,4) + \dots) + \dots]. \tag{A3.1}$$

The evaluation of the first term presents no problems; it gives simply V^N. The second term is the sum of all the $\frac{1}{2}N(N-1)$ pair terms of which the typical member is:

$$V^{(N-2)} \int\int \alpha(1,2)\, d\mathbf{r}_1\, d\mathbf{r}_2.$$

For the short-ranged forces typical of simple fluids, this expression can be re-written:

$$V^{(N-2)} \int\int \alpha(1,2)\, d\mathbf{r}_1\, d\mathbf{r}_2 = V^{(N-1)} \int_0^\infty \alpha(r)\, 4\pi r^2\, dr = V^{(N-1)}\beta_1,$$

where the second integral defines the quantity β_1, i.e.

$$\beta_1 = \int_0^\infty \alpha(r)\, 4\pi r^2\, dr. \tag{A3.2}$$

Consequently, the second term in the expansion (A3.1) becomes:

$$\frac{N(N-1)}{2} V^{(N-1)}\beta_1 = N! \left(\frac{V^N}{N!}\frac{N(N-1)}{2V}\beta_1\right) \sim N! \left(\frac{V^N}{N!}\right)\frac{N^2}{2V}\beta_1,$$

where the last step is possible because N is very large.

Discussion of further terms is a complicated matter and it has proved convenient in treating these contributions to construct a pictorial representation of each
term separately. For this purpose, we suppose there are N circles drawn on a plane,
each circle being associated with one of the N particles of which the physical
system is composed (see Fig. 20 where twenty-four particles are considered).
It is to be agreed that the appearance of the function $\alpha(i, j)$ in the mathematical
integral is represented pictorially by a single line joining two circles marked i and j.
Each integral in the expansion (A3.1) is then represented pictorially by a characteristic set of lines joining specific circles in the diagram. The complex of lines
will become more complicated the higher the associated term in the series. As a
matter of nomenclature, the words diagram and graph are used interchangeably
in the general literature to describe drawings of which Fig. 20 is typical.

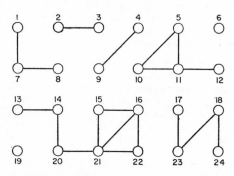

FIG. 20. Cluster diagram showing some elementary linkages.

From the way that the diagram has been constructed it is clear that circles which
are not joined represent particles which are outside the range of the interaction
effects of each other. The particular value of the present approach follows primarily from the short-range character of the interparticle force.

Figure 20, therefore, represents the space integration over twenty-four particles,
two of which are not in interaction with the rest. The integral then is:

$$\int \ldots \int dr_1 \ldots dr_{24}[\alpha(1, 7)\,\alpha(7, 8)\,\alpha(2, 3)\,\alpha(9, 4)\,\alpha(10, 5)\,\alpha(5, 11)$$

$$\times \alpha(10, 11)\,\alpha(11, 12)\,\alpha(13, 14)\,\alpha(14, 20)\,\alpha(20, 21)$$

$$\times \alpha(21, 15)\,\alpha(15, 16)\,\alpha(16, 22)\,\alpha(21, 16)\,\alpha(21, 22)$$

$$\times \alpha(17, 23)\,\alpha(23, 18)\,\alpha(18, 24)].$$

This is an extremely complicated integral to evaluate, and simplifications are far
from superfluous. For this purpose, the total integral is reduced to a number of
more elementary units containing only linked particles on the diagram. In is
these more elementary units that are called clusters. An l-cluster is, then, defiedt
as being an l-graph in which every circle is attached to the whole unit by at least
one line: consequently, every circle is joined either directly or indirectly to the
remaining $(l-1)$ particles of the group. There are six such reduced graphs in
Fig. 20.

The simplest graph is that for $l = 1$, i.e. for a single particle. This represents
the integration over the volume V. The next most simple graph is that linking two

particles only (e.g. the lines joining particles 2 and 3, and joining 9 and 4 in Fig. 20). Consequently, we have:

$$①—② = \int \alpha(1, 2) \, dr_1 \, dr_2.$$

Interchange of particles does not affect this integral.

The next member of the series involves three particles, and this can be treated as the prototype of more complex graphs. The important point is that interchange of particle does not affect the resulting integration. Three particles can be joined in our scheme in four ways, shown in Fig. 21. These are associated with the integrals:

$$\int \alpha(1, 2) \; \alpha(1, 3) \, dr_1 \, dr_2 \, dr_3,$$

$$\int \alpha(1, 2) \, \alpha(1, 3) \, \alpha(2, 3) \, dr_1 \, dr_2 \, dr_3,$$

$$\int \alpha(1, 3) \, \alpha(2, 3) \, dr_1 \, dr_2 \, dr_3,$$

$$\int \alpha(1, 2) \, \alpha(2, 3) \, dr_1 \, dr_2 \, dr_3.$$

These integrals are not all different: indeed the first, third, and fourth integrals have the same value. Further integrals associated with possible particle groupings follow in the same way although the number of contributions increases rapidly. Thus, there are ten terms associated with a group of four particles, and so on. We will not go further into these separate particle groupings but will consider the summed contributions to the configurational integral Z_r.

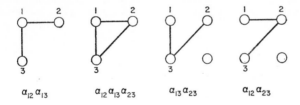

FIG. 21. Various ways of forming a cluster from three particles.

The various contributions can be collected together systematically, using the concept of the cluster integral b_l defined as follows. For a cluster composed of l-particles in direct or indirect interaction, the cluster integral b_l is defined as being:

$$b_l = \frac{1}{l! \, V} \int \cdots \int \sum_{1 \leqslant i < j \leqslant l} \Pi \alpha(i, j) \, dr_1 \, dr_2 \ldots \, dr_l, \qquad (A3.3)$$

where the summation here is to be made over all products of $\alpha(i, j)$ consistent with the corresponding particles being members of the same cluster of l particles. The first three cluster integrals are:

$$b_1 = \frac{1}{V} \int dr_1 = 1, \qquad (a)$$

$$b_2 = \frac{1}{2V} \iint \alpha(1, 2) dr_1 \, dr_2 = \frac{1}{2} \int 4\pi r^2 \alpha(r) \, dr, \qquad (b) \qquad (A3.4)$$

$$b_3 = \frac{1}{6V} \iiint [\alpha(1, 2) \, \alpha(1, 3) + \alpha(1, 3) \, \alpha(2, 3) + \alpha(1, 2) \, \alpha(2, 3)$$
$$+ \alpha(1, 2) \, \alpha(1, 3) \, \alpha(2,3)] \, dr_1 \, dr_2 \, dr_3. \qquad (c)$$

Comparison with (A3.4b) and (A3.2) shows that $2b_2 = \beta_1$: comparison with equation (3.55a) of the main text shows that $B_2 = -2b_2$. Provided l is not sufficiently large for the corresponding cluster to have dimensions comparable with the total volume V, the cluster integrals are independent of V.

The configurational partition function Z_r can be expressed as the sum of cluster integrals. If there are m_l clusters each composed of l particles, so that

$$N = \sum_{l \geqslant 1} l m_l, \tag{A3.5}$$

then combinatorial arguments lead to the relation:

$$Z_r = \sum_{m_l} \prod_l \left(\frac{N b_l}{n} \right)^{m_l} \frac{1}{m!}, \tag{A3.6}$$

where $n = N/V$. The configurational partition function is then expanded in the form (3.50) of the main text, and each term can be associated with a cluster of definite size. The formula (A3.6) is subject to the auxiliary condition (A3.5).

With the configurational partition function known in explicit form, the corresponding thermodynamic functions are in principle open to calculation through a series of integrations. Unfortunately, the evaluation of the necessary integrals is a difficult task other than for b_1 and b_2, and some simplifying procedure is essential. A high degree of complexity is removed from the calculations if the various terms in the expansion (A3.6) are arranged to display their dependence on a restricted class of integrals, called the irreducible integrals. The main point is shown clearly by reference to the set of equations (A3.4). There are three separate types of integral in the set but they are not directly the trio (b_1, b_2, b_3). Certainly b_1 and b_2 are separate integrals, but b_3 is not entirely different.

The integral in the expression (A3.4) is β_1 defined in (A3.2). This will be called the first irreducible integral. The first three integrals in b_3 defined by (A3.4c), are readily seen to be equal to each other and to $V\beta_1^2$. The remaining term in (A3.4c) defined the second irreducible integral β_2:

$$\beta_2 = \frac{1}{2V} \iiint \alpha(1, 2)\, \alpha(1, 3)\, \alpha(2, 3)\, dr_1\, dr_2\, dr_3.$$

Clearly,

$$b_3 = \frac{1}{2} \beta_1^2 + \frac{1}{3} \beta_2.$$

The essential feature of the irreducible integral is, as its name implies, that it cannot be reduced further into a combination of more simple units. A reduction is possible whenever two groupings within a given cluster are joined by each having one particle in common, but with no other lines between particles of the two separate groups. For, integration can be carried out over the particles of the two groups other than the shared particle and the total integral written as the product of two separate integrals. The two particle groupings are said to be singly connected. The integral β_2 is not singly connected in this sense. In any diagram in which every circle is joined to at least two others (i.e. any diagram which is at least doubly connected), it follows that the associated integral cannot be factorised into a simpler product form, since there are no two regions which are essentially independent in the integration process. It is possible to pass from any circle of the diagram to any other by at least two separate paths. The integral associated with such a diagram is said to be irreducible.

In general, the irreducible integral β_k is defined as the suitably normalised configurational integral over the volume available to a group of $(k+1)$ particles, which are at least doubly connected (in the sense explained above). Explicitly,

β_k is defined by the integral:

$$\beta_k = \frac{1}{k!V} \int \cdots \int \sum_{1 < j < i \leqslant k+1} \prod \alpha(i,j) \prod_{s=1}^{k+1} d\mathbf{r}_s.$$

This is the equation (3.51) of the main text. In these terms, the expression (A3.6) for the configurational partition function is transformed into the form (3.52a) of the main text. The development of the thermodynamic functions then proceeds as in the main text.

3.10. Further thermodynamic functions can be expanded in the same way, and we have the following members among others:

$$S = Nk \left[\ln \left(\frac{2\pi mkT}{h^2} \right)^{3/2} n + \frac{3}{2} + \sum_{j>1} \frac{1}{(j+1)} \frac{\partial}{\partial T} (T\beta_j) n^j \right] ;$$

$$H_e = NkT \left[\frac{5}{2} - \sum_{j>1} \frac{1}{(j+1)} \left(j\beta_j - T \frac{\partial \beta_j}{\partial T} \right) n^j \right] ;$$

$$C_V = Nk \left[\frac{3}{2} + \sum_{j>1} \left(\frac{1}{k+1} \right) \left(\frac{\partial}{\partial T} \left(T^2 \frac{\partial \beta_j}{\partial T} \right) \right) n^j \right] ;$$

$$\frac{\partial p}{\partial \ln V} \bigg|_T = -nkT \left[1 - \sum_{j>1} j\beta_j n^j \right] ;$$

$$-\frac{\partial^2 F}{\partial T \partial V} = nk \left[1 - \sum_{j>1} \left(\frac{j}{j+1} \right) \frac{\partial}{\partial T} (T\beta_j) n^j \right].$$

These expressions are arranged to display the virial coefficients directly and the temperature derivatives by using also equation (3.54c) of the main text.

3.11. The virial expansion in powers of the density is, in fact, a Taylor expansion about zero pressure. For the pressure, for example, we have

$$p(n) = p(0) + n \frac{\partial p}{\partial n} \bigg|_{n=0} + \frac{n^2}{2!} \frac{\partial^2 p}{\partial n^2} \bigg|_{n=0} + \frac{n^3}{3!} \frac{\partial^3 p}{\partial n^3} \bigg|_{n=0} + \cdots .$$

The virial expansion (3.53a) follows from the statements:

$$p(0) = 0, \quad \frac{\partial p}{\partial n} \bigg|_{n=0} = kT, \quad \frac{\partial^2 p}{\partial n^2} \bigg|_{n=0} = 2kTB, \quad \frac{\partial^3 p}{\partial n^3} \bigg|_{n=0} = 6kTC,$$

and so on.

It is not to be expected that the knowledge of the coefficients of such an expansion will give direct information about conditions at liquid densities. Knowledge of the coefficients might be of indirect value, however, in representing a low-density limit to act as a test for alternative formulae designed primarily for liquid densities (see Chapter 6).

3.12. Other variables can be added to the scheme. For instance, if each particle carries a dipole of strength μ, the dimensionless dipole strength μ^* can be introduced according to:

$$\mu^{*2} = \frac{\mu^2}{\varepsilon \sigma^3}.$$

Including a dipole, the law of corresponding states can be put into the form:

$$p^* = p^*(V^*, T^*, \mu^*).$$

The law of corresponding states has been considered so far only in its classical form. An extension to quantum conditions must also be contemplated and this must be associated with quantum corrections to the statistical partition integral. Any rigorous theory of interacting moving particles must, in principle, be based on quantum arguments, and it is important for our present classical theory to be sure of the effect of quantum corrections.

The general statistical integral is expanded in powers of the Planck constant about the classical form:

$$Z_N \text{ (quantum)} = Z_N \text{ (classical)} \left[1 - \frac{h^2}{4\pi^2} b + \ldots \right],$$

where

$$b = \frac{1}{24mkT} \sum_{1 \leqslant j \leqslant N} \frac{\partial^2}{\partial \mathbf{r}_j^2} \langle X(\mathbf{r}^N) \rangle.$$

The brackets in the expression for b denote an average over the phase. If X is the sum of a two-parameter interaction between particle pairs (such as equation (2.5) of the main text) then the free energy can be expanded in the form:

$$F \text{ (quantum)} = F \text{ (classical)} \left[1 + \left(\frac{\Lambda}{T^*} \right)^2 \omega(T^*, V^*) + \ldots \right],$$

where

$$\omega(T^*, V^*) \sim 1, \quad T^* = \frac{Tk}{\varepsilon}, \quad V^* = \frac{V}{N\sigma^3},$$

$$\Lambda = \frac{h}{2\pi\sigma\sqrt{m\varepsilon}}.$$

Λ is a dimensionless parameter whose importance in the present connection was first stressed by DE BOER (1948, *Rep. Prog. Phys.* **12**, 315). (Λ/T^*) is a measure of the importance of quantum effects and decreases steadily as both the temperature and the particle mass increase. For a given temperature, the relative importance of quantum corrections is to be judged from the magnitude of Λ. The law of corresponding states must be recast to include the new parameter Λ. The effect is:

$$p^* = p^*(T^*, V^*, \Lambda), \quad \text{and} \quad U^* = U^*(V^*, T^*, \Lambda).$$

Λ is composed of molecular constants only, unlike T^* and V^*. Therefore, while reduced pressure and volume are open to experimental control for a given fluid, this is not the case for Λ. The law of corresponding states now becomes more restricted in this quantum form than in the fully classical limit.

The introduction of the new parameter Λ is a complication that we would wish to avoid: whether this can be avoided depends upon the collective effects of the magnitude of the trio (m, σ, ε).

TABLE 7

Element	Λ	Element	Λ
He	0·42	Ar	0·03
Ne	0·09	Kr	0·02
		Xe	0·01

With $\omega(T^*, V^*)$ being a dimensionless function of order unity, it is seen that only helium offers a sufficiently large φ of Λ to make a quantum correction necessary, although neon is only slightly below this level. For argon, krypton, and xenon the correction is entirely unnecessary (see Table 7). In studying these last three fluids, therefore, the classical limit is fully adequate and the theory of the main text can be used without account of quantum physics.

3.13. The main text develops the statistical theory of liquids on the basis of the lower order distribution functions, but alternative approaches have also been made. These alternative treatments have been based on a variety of starting points and cover a wide range of points of view. But they have usually regarded a liquid as a relaxed crystalline solid or as a rather dense dilute gas. Because they have not treated a liquid as a structural entity in its own right, they have been of only limited value and have remained only semi-quantitative in application. With no final alternative statistical theory available they have had in the past, and indeed still do have, value as a means of systematising experimental information. We mention one or two of the more important theories now. Although not claiming to have the rigour required by the statistical theory even in principle, it might be hoped that this simpler approach, being more amenable to calculation than the correct theory, will nevertheless prove useful as an exploratory tool especially in connection with complex liquids.

(i) *The cell model.* This model exploits the similarity between the microscopic conditions in a liquid and in a solid for the calculation of liquid properties. The molecules in a liquid can move only within a limited volume of space due to the close presence of neighbours: this limited volume formed by neighbours is called a cell. The liquid, then, is regarded as a collection of cells containing molecules. In the most simple case each cell contains a single molecule: variants of the model can involve empty cells or a proportion of cells occupied by more than one particle. Each cell is assumed representative of the remainder. The configuration partition function Z_r is to be evaluated, on this basis, by first estimating the average contribution to Z_r of each of the N particles comprising the fluid, and raising this to the N-th power to obtain an estimate of Z_r. The accuracy associated with this calculated function Z_r depends upon the accuracy of the assessment of the average contribution. With Z known, the several thermodynamic functions can be determined as function of volume and temperature. Comparison between calculated and experimental data can be used to modify systematically the details of the initial model so as to reconcile theory and measurement as closely as possible.

Each representative cell is supposed to be centred at one of the lattice points of a virtual cubic face-centred lattice, where there are twelve nearest neighbours to each particle (coordination number $z = 12$). We assume at first the number of cells is equal to the number of particles and each cell contains only one particle. The average volume of each cell is $v = V/N$: the homogeneity of the model leads to an identity of cells.

The mean potential of the force inside each cell, which dictates the particle motion within the cell, depends upon the mean positions of the remaining particles in a way that can be calculated. The total potential energy of the liquid particles is then the sum for all particles of the superposition for each particle of the energy at the centre of the cell (ψ_0) and that due to molecular movement within the cell relative to the centre (and written $\psi(r)$). The configurational partition function Z is then given by:

$$Z_r = \frac{v_f^N}{N} \exp\left\{ -\frac{1}{2} z \frac{\psi_0}{kT} N \right\},$$

where v_f is the free volume defined by:

$$v_f = \int^{r_{\max}} 4\pi r^2 \exp\left\{-\frac{z}{kT}\psi(r)\right\} dr.$$

The upper integration limit $r_{\max}$ is related to the volume of the cell according to:

$$\frac{4\pi}{3} r_{\max}^3 = v.$$

For a face-centred cubic lattice structure, the distance between nearest neighbours is given by $\sqrt{2}\,v = a^3$. For the Lennard-Jones (12–6) interaction potential between pairs of particles it follows from the theory that:

$$\psi_0 = z\varepsilon[(v^*)^{-4} - 2(v^*)^{-2}],$$

$$\psi(r) - \psi_0 = z\varepsilon\left[\frac{l(y)}{(v^*)^4} - 2\frac{m(y)}{(v^*)^2}\right],$$

where

$$l(y) = (1 + 12y + 25\cdot 2y^2 + 12y^3 + y^4)\,(1-y)^{-10} - 1,$$
$$m(y) = (1+y)\,(1-y)^{-4} - 1,$$

and

$$v^* = \frac{v}{\sigma^3}, \quad \text{and} \quad y = \left(\frac{r}{a}\right)^2.$$

Here, z is the number of nearest neighbours for any molecule, and is twelve for a face-centred cubic lattice: σ is the length scale parameter which appears in the interparticle pair potential function. The thermodynamic functions then follow, with Z_r known, from the general formulae of statistical mechanics.

Various modifications of the theory have been explored, involving empty cells or multiple occupancy, and interactions between other than nearest neighbours have been included. In these ways, the known density fluctuations in a liquid are accounted for. But these extensions of the theory greatly complicate both its basis and its structure, and introduce an undesirable *ad hoc* element into the theory. Indeed, by suitable modification of the theory it is possible to reproduce many experimental features. Unfortunately, the cell model can hardly be reduced to a reasonable group of postulates that can form the basis of a definite theory. The cell model is closely allied to a sophisticated example of dimensional analysis. Although its most extensive development involves equilibrium fluid conditions, the cell model can be modified to include, also, non-equilibrium situations. Closely allied to the cell model is the hole model which stresses particularly the role of empty cells. There is an extensive literature for these lattice theories of liquids, and we list here a broadly representative sample.

E. A. GUGGENHEIM, 1932, *Proc. Roy. Soc.* (London) A **135**, 181.

J. S. ROWLINSON and C. F. CURTISS, 1951, *J. Chem. Phys.* **19**, 1519.

J. DE BOER, 1952, *Proc. Roy. Soc.* (London) A **215**, 4.

J. M. RICHARDSON and S. R. BRINKLEY, JR, 1960, *J. Chem. Phys.* **33**, 1467.

J. S. DAHLER and J. O. HIRSCHFELDER, 1960, *J. Chem Phys.* **32**, 330

J. GRINDLAY, 1961, *Proc. Phys. Soc.* (London) **77**, 1001.

J. DE BOER, 1953, *Nuovo Cim.* **10**, 225.

F. CERNUSCHI and H. EYRING, 1939, *J. Chem. Phys.* **7**, 547

S. ONO, 1947, *Mem. Fac. Eng. Dynsha*, **10**, 190.

H. M. PEEK and F. L. HILL, 1950, *J. Chem. Phys.* **18**, 1252.

K. ARAKAWA, 1954, *J. Phys. Soc. Japan*, **9**, 647.

P. JANSSENS and I. PRIGOGINE, 1950, *Physica* **16**, 895.

J. A. POPLE, 1951, *Phil. Mag.* **41**, 459.

E. G. D. Cohen, J. de Boer, and Z. W. Salsburg, 1955, *Physica*. **11**, 1.
H. S. Chung and J. S. Dahler, 1962, *J. Chem. Phys.* **37**, 1620.
L. H. Lund, 1960, *J. Chem. Phys.* **33**, 1086.
Z. W. Salsburg and W. W. Wood, 1962, *J. Chem. Phys.* **37**, 798.
H. S. Chung and J. S. Dahler, 1962, *J. Chem. Phys.* **37**, 1620.
J. A. Barker, 1957, *Proc. Roy. Soc.* (London) A **240**, 265.
For a recent monograph, see:
J. A. Barker, 1963, *Lattice Theories of Liquids*, Oxford, Pergamon Press.
The cell theories can be linked, at least formally, to the more rigorous aspects of
the statistical theory. See:
J. G. Kirkwood, 1950, *J. Chem. Phys.* **18**, 380.
H. S. Green, 1956, *J. Chem. Phys.* **24**, 732.

These arguments have so far not been developed beyond the initial formal stages.
It is quite possible that the cell model will ultimately be found useful as a means
of supplying primitive approximate information for use in the statistical theory
developed in the main text. For instance, it may yet be of value in the development
of the form of the superposition approximation. But there has, so far, been
virtually no exploration along this direction.

The initial exploration of the crystal representation of liquids is probably that
of the so-called blurred crystal models of Prins and Petersen. These papers are
still of interest for the study of their physical ideas:
J. A. Prins, 1931, *Natürwissenschaften*, **19**, 435.
J. A. Prins and J. H. Petersen, 1936, *Physica*, **3**, 147.
J. D. Bernal, 1937, *Trans. Faraday Soc.* **33**, 27.
The book of Frenkel (see General References) should also be consulted in this
connection.

(ii) *A theory of fluids based on the so-called tunnel model* has been discussed by:
J. A. Barker, 1959, *Aust. J. Chem.* **13**, 187; 1961, *Proc. Roy. Soc.* (London)
A **264**; 1962, *J. Chem. Phys.* **37**, 1061.
According to this model, the fluid is represented by lines of molecules considered
as moving in essentially one-dimensional tunnels formed by neighbouring molecules themselves arranged in a line structure. As for the cell model, so now the
fluid structure is hypothetically broken down into a form which permits an approximate evaluation of Z_r. The model allows for density fluctuations, and the random relative arrangement of molecules in different tunnels mirrors to some extent
the random nature of the fluid structure.

(iii) *The problems associated with specifying liquid structure* are closely related
to the geometrical problem of the close packing of particles. This geometrical
problem has been considered by:

J. D. Bernal, 1958, *Acta Phys. Hungary*, **8**, 269; 1959, *Nature*, **183**, 141; 1960,
Nature **185**, 68; 1960, *Scientific American*, **203**, 124.
For a study of the packing of spheres, see:
G. D. Scott, 1960, *Nature*, **188**, 908.
J. D. Bernal and J. Mason, 1960, *Nature*, **188**, 910.
The central role that must be accorded to the construction of a statistical geometry
in any final theory of liquids has been particularly stressed by Bernal; see:
J. D. Bernal, 1965, *Liquids: Structure, Properties, Solid Interactions* (ed. T. J.
Hughel), Elsevier.
This general approach has not yet progressed beyond the preliminary stages, but
may well have important future significance.

(iv) *Laboratory models* have been used in the past for the indirect study of
liquid structure. This approach is not based on the application of theoretical

statistical arguments. Thus, G. D. SCOTT, J. D. BERNAL, J. MASON, and K. R. KNIGHT (1962, *Nature* **144**, 957) have studied the geometrical arrangements in the packing of some 1000 steel balls. Alternatively, a system of gelatine spheres (some of which are coloured for purposes of recognition) floating in a liquid of essentially the same density and refractive index have been studied by W. E. MORRELL and J. H. HILDEBRAND (1936, *J. Chem. Phys.* **4**, 224). See also, E. DARMOIS, 1947, *L'État Liquid de la Matière*, p. 102. The system is shaken and photographic records of the subsequent particle arrangements are used to determine the probability of finding given separation distances between two particles chosen at random. Pair distribution functions have been deduced in this way which fit the experimental curves for simple liquids and dense gases remarkably well. These studies could presumably also be used to deduce empirical information about the triplet function which would be pertinent to the assessment of the value of the superposition approximation. This model approach to the study of fluids might well be valuable in future studies, even as a supplement to machine calculations in three dimensions.

3.14. A critical account of some of the predictions of theories of the liquid state with experimental data has been given by:

J. M. H. LEVELT and E. G. D. COHEN, 1964, *Studies in Statistical Mechanics*, vol. **2**, p. 107 (eds. J. de Boer and G. E. Uhlenbeck), Amsterdam, North-Holland.

CHAPTER 4

4.1. J. G. KIRKWOOD, 1935, *J. Chem. Phys.* **3**, 300.

The approximation was used in calculations of liquid structure by:
J. G. KIRKWOOD and E. M. BOGGS, 1942, *J. Chem. Phys.* **10**, 394.

4.2. Our arguments are concerned primarily with liquid densities where an expansion in powers of the density is not directly relevant to a main statement. But because the various formulae can be evaluated and compared with alternative exact expressions in the low density limit, consistency tests can be devised in this limit. Although not giving firm information about liquid densities, they are nevertheless of interest in providing the opportunity of handling solutions of the equations of physical interest. For further discussion of this low density limit, see ref. 4.8.

4.3. M. BORN and H. S. GREEN, 1946, *Proc. Roy. Soc.* (London) A **188**, 10; 1949, *A General Kinetic Theory of Liquids*, London, Cambridge University Press.

J. YVON, 1935, La Théorie Statistique des Fluides et L'Equation d'État, *Act. Sci. Ind.* **203**, Hermann.

N. N. BOGOLIUBOV, 1946, *J. Phys.* (Moscow) **10**, 256.

4.4. The equations (4.18) and (4.20) of the main text can be derived directly and alternatively by considering the mean force on a group of h particles due to the presence of the remaining $(N-h)$ particles of the system. The derivation runs as follows.

Let $\Phi(\mathbf{r}^h)$ be the potential of mean force for the chosen group of h particles. Suppose now one particle (say particle 1) of the group of h particles undergoes an elementary displacement. The gradient of the mean potential is given by

$$\frac{\partial \Phi(\mathbf{r}^h)}{\partial \mathbf{r}_1} = \frac{\int \frac{\partial X(\mathbf{r}^N)}{\partial \mathbf{r}_1} \exp\left\{-X(\mathbf{r}^N)\right\} d\mathbf{r}^{N-h}}{\int \exp\left\{-X(\mathbf{r}^N)\right\} d\mathbf{r}^{N-h}},$$

where the proper normalisation is also included. In this expression, $X(\mathbf{r}^N)$ is the total reduced potential for the total system of N particles and the integrations are over the remaining $(N-h)$ particles of the system. The integrals can be expressed in terms of the distribution functions $g^{(h+1)}$ and $g^{(h)}$. Explicitly, we have, for pair interaction forces:

$$\frac{\partial \Phi(\mathbf{r}^h)}{\partial \mathbf{r}_1} = \frac{\partial X(\mathbf{r}^h)}{\partial \mathbf{r}_1} + \frac{n}{(N-h)} \int \frac{\partial \chi(1, h+1)}{\partial \mathbf{r}_1} \frac{g^{(h+1)}(\mathbf{r}^{h+1})}{g^{(h)}(\mathbf{r}^h)} \, d\mathbf{r}_{h+1},$$

where $X(\mathbf{r}^h)$ is the total potential for the group of h particles. Introducing the mean force $\langle \mathbf{F}_1 \rangle$ according to:

$$[\langle \mathbf{F}_1 \rangle = -\frac{\partial \Phi(\mathbf{r}^h)}{\partial \mathbf{r}_1} = -kT \frac{\partial}{\partial \mathbf{r}_1} \ln g^{(h)}(\mathbf{r}^h),$$

and assuming that $N \gg h$, so that $N-h \sim N$, the equation (4.18) of the main text results. For the special case of a pair of particles, setting $h = 2$ above gives the equation (4.20) of the main text.

4.5. J. G. KIRKWOOD, 1935, *J. Chem. Phys.* **3**, 300.
J. G. KIRKWOOD and E. MONROE, 1941, *J. Chem. Phys.* **9**, 514.
J. G. KIRKWOOD and E. M. BOGGS, 1942, *J. Chem. Phys.* **10**, 395.
Extensions of this approach of variable particle coupling to include the case when all the N particles of the system are subjected to partial coupling have also been explored. See:
G. H. A. COLE, 1959, *Proc. Phys. Soc.* (London) **73**, 713; 1960, *ibid.* **75**, 671; 1959, *Adv. Phys.* (*Phil. Mag.* Supp.) **8**, 225.
T. L. HILL, 1956, *Statistical Mechanics*, New York, McGraw-Hill.
These extensions have not been used so far as the basis of numerical calculations.

4.6. G. H. A. COLE, 1958, *J. Chem. Phys.* **28**, 912.

4.7. I. Z. FISHER, 1962, *Uspekhi Fiz. Nauk*, **76**, 499 (English translation, *Soviet Phys., Uspekhi*, **5**, 239).

4.8. We follow here, particularly, the arguments of:
N. N. BOGOLIUBOV, 1946, Problems of a Dynamical Theory in Statistical Physics (English translation), in *Studies in Statistical Mechanics*, vol. **1** (eds. J. de Boer G. E. Uhlenbeck), Amsterdam, North-Holland.
But see also:
J. E. MAYER and E. MONTROLL, 1941, *J. Chem. Phys.* **9**, 2.
J. DE BOER, 1949, *Rep. Prog. Phys.* **12**, 305.
E. E. SALPETER, 1958, *Ann. Phys.* **5**, 183.

4.9. These arguments allow the pair distribution to be expressed in powers of the density. Of equal interest is the expansion of the direct correlation function $c(r)$, see equation (5.2) of the main text, in powers of the density. This expansion is relevant to the arguments of Chapter 5 and is considered in Appendix 5. The density expansion of $c(r)$ was given by:
G. S. RUSHBROOKE and H. I. SCOINS, 1953, *Proc. Roy. Soc.* (London) A **216**, 203.

4.10. When the Y_j are all set equal to zero, we revert to the form appropriate to the original Kirkwood superposition approximation (4.3) of the main text. This special form of the equations of the main text was considered by:
G. S. RUSHBROOKE and H. I. SCOINS, 1951, *Phil. Mag.* **42**, 582.
B. R. A. NIJBOER and L. VAN HOVE, 1952, *Phys. Rev.* **85**, 777.
The corresponding treatment for the Kirkwood equation (4.25) of the main text and using the Kirkwood superposition approximation (4.3) was reported by:
G. STELL, 1962, *J. Chem. Phys.* **36**, 1817.

4.11. For low densities, where a density expansion of the various quantities is valid, some progress is possible. Here an evaluation of the lower coefficients of the expansion of $g^{(3)}$ in powers of n is not entirely out of the question and direct information can be obtained in this way. This work is not of direct value for liquids, and leads to the consideration of simple clusters. For details see:

E. E. SALPETER, 1958, *Ann. Phys.* **5**, 183.

S. A. RICE and J. LEKNER, 1964, *Bull. Am. Phys. Soc.* **9**, 661.

At liquid densities the approach of Fisher (see section 4.2(d) of the main text) has not been used in practice. However, numerical calculations suggest that in this case the superposition approximation may not be bad. See:

B. J. ALDER, 1964, *Phys. Rev. Letters*, **12**, 317.

A. RAHMAN, 1964, *Phys. Rev. Letters*, **12**, 575.

4.12. Other equations, not discussed in the main text because so far they have not been developed within the modern theory, should at least be referred to here.

To begin with, the derivation of the Born–Green–Yvon equation or Kirkwood equation has been made by differentiating the expression defining the pair distribution, by respectively the position of one particle of the pair or the coupling parameter between one particle of the pair and the remainder. These two procedures are, in fact, special cases of a general argument, in which the effect on the pair distribution is investigated of some arbitrary parameter which appears in expressions for the distribution functions based on the grand canonical ensemble. This variational approach was proposed by Mayer:

J. E. MAYER, 1947, *J. Chem. Phys.* **15**, 187.

S. ONO, 1950, *Prog. Theor. Phys.* (Japan) **5**, 822.

A set of integral equations was derived by Kirkwood and Salsburg without using a variational principle. See:

J. G. KIRKWOOD and Z. SALSBURG, 1953, *Discussions Farad. Soc.* **15**, 28.

The method is related broadly to that of the cell model in that it selects one representative molecule located at the position r_1 (though a particular molecule cannot be specified because the grand ensemble is involved) for special consideration. The procedure resembles closely that of the Mayer cluster expansion for an imperfect gas, and the absolute activity is introduced explicitly into the arguments. The result is the equation for the fluid pair distribution:

$$g^{(2)}(\mathbf{r}_{12}) = \frac{z}{n} \exp\left\{-\chi(\mathbf{r}_{12})\right\} \left[1 + n \int g^{(2)}(\mathbf{r}_{23}) K^{(2)}(1, 2, 3) \, d\mathbf{r}_3\right],$$

where $z = \exp\left\{-\mu/kT\right\}$ is the inverse of the absolute activity, and:

$$K^{(2)}(1, 2, 3) = \alpha(1, 3) F^{(2)}(1, 2, 3)$$

with

$$F^{(2)}(1, 2, 3) = 1 + \sum_{s \geq 1} \frac{n^s}{(s+1)!} \int \cdots \int \frac{g^{(s+2)}(2, 3, \ldots s+3)}{g^{(2)}(2, 3)} \prod_{t=4}^{s+3} \alpha(1, t) \, d\mathbf{r}_t.$$

The central problem is that of the evaluation of the triplet function $F^{(2)}$ and this requires a knowledge of the hierarchy of distribution functions. Presumably, some form of closure procedure, like the superposition approximation, would be necessary in this connection. No calculated data for the fluid pair distribution has so far been reported using this procedure. For more details of the derivation of the Kirkwood–Salsburg equation the reader is referred to:

T. L. HILL, 1956, *Statistical Mechanics*, p. 251, New York, McGraw-Hill, and to the original paper of Kirkwood and Salsburg quoted above.

CHAPTER 5

5.1. L. S. ORNSTEIN and F. ZERNIKE, 1914, *Proc. Acad. Sci. Amst.* **17**, 793.
See also:
J. S. ROWLINSON, 1965. *Rep. Prog. Phys.* **28**, 169.
G. S. RUSHBROOKE, 1965. *Statistical Mechanics of Equilibrium and Non-Equilibrium*, p. 222 (ed. Meixner), Amsterdam, North-Holland.

5.2.   The hypernetted chain equation was the end-product of a great deal of work of which the more important steps were given by:

E. MEERON, 1958, *J. Chem. Phys.* **28**, 630; 1958, *Phys. Fluids*, **1**, 139.
E. MEERON and E. R. RODEMICH, 1958, *Phys. Fluids*, **1**, 246.
T. MORITA, 1958, *Prog. Theor. Phys.* (Japan) **20**, 920.
R. ABE, 1959, *J. Phys. Soc. Japan*, **14**, 10.
VAN LEENWEN, J. M. J. GROENEVELD, and J. DE BOER, 1959, *Physica*, **25**, 792.
E. MEERON, 1960, *J. Math. Phys.* **1**, 192.
T. MORITA and K. HIROIKE, 1960, *Prog. Theor. Phys.* (Japan) **23**, 385.
G. S. RUSHBROOKE, 1960, *Physica*, **26**, 259.
L. VERLET, 1960, *Nuovo Cim.* **18**, 77.
L. VERLET and D. LEVESQUE, 1962, *Physica*, **28**, 1124.

The work centres about the expansion of $c(r)$ in powers of the density given by:

G. S. RUSHBROOKE and H. I. SCOINS, 1953, *Proc. Roy. Soc.* (London) A **216**, 203.

These authors treated $c(r)$ in the expansion:

$$c(r) = \sum_{i \geq 2} c_i n^{i-2}, \qquad (A5.1)$$

where the coefficients are given by:

$$c_2(\mathbf{r}_{12}) = \alpha(\mathbf{r}_{12}), \qquad (a)$$

$$c_3(\mathbf{r}_{12}) = \int \alpha\,(1,\,2)\,\alpha\,(1,\,3)\,\alpha\,(2,\,3)\,dr_3, \qquad (b)$$

$$c_4(\mathbf{r}_{12}) = \frac{1}{2!} \int \int dr_3\,dr_4 \{ 2\alpha\,(1,\,2)\,\alpha\,(1,\,3)\,\alpha\,(3,\,4)\,\alpha\,(2,\,4) \qquad (A5.2)$$

$$+\alpha(1,\,3)\,\alpha(2,\,3)\,\alpha(1,\,4)\,\alpha(2,\,4)$$

$$+4\alpha(1,\,2)\,\alpha(1,\,3)\,\alpha(3,\,4)\,\alpha(2,\,4)\,\alpha(1,\,4)$$

$$+\alpha(1,\,2)\,\alpha(1,\,3)\,\alpha(1,\,4)\,\alpha(2,\,3)\,\alpha(2,\,4) \qquad (c)$$

$$+\alpha(1,\,3)\,\alpha(3,\,4)\,\alpha(2,\,4)\,\alpha(1,\,4)\,\alpha(2,\,3)$$

$$+\alpha(1,\,2)\,\alpha(1,\,3)\,\alpha(2,\,4)\,\alpha(3,\,4)\,\alpha(1,\,4)\,\alpha(2,\,3) \},$$

and so on.

Their first suggestion was that the essential features of $c(r)$ are fully represented by the first two terms of the expansion, i.e. by:

$$c(r) = \alpha(r) + nc_3(r). \qquad (A5.3)$$

Here, the direct pair correlation is restricted in range to that of $\alpha(r)$ itself. The insertion of (A5.3) into equation (5.2) of the main text proves an expansion for $h(r)$ in powers of the density, but of restricted scope. For example, the insertion of (A5.3) into the pressure equation (5.3) of the main text gives an expression that goes no further than the third virial coefficient. A modification of the expansion for $h(r)$, which we will not pursue here, led Rushbrooke and Scoins to the so-called netted chain equation.

The hypernetted chain equation arises from the expression of both $h(r)$ and $\ln g^{(2)}(r)$ into the sum of terms formed from three basic constituent interactions.

To explain these contributions we use again the diagram concepts of Appendix 3.9, but extend these slightly to include new terms of description. These are as follows.

(i) *Clusters of particles* where all routes from one particle outside the integration (base point) to the other base point all pass through at least one particle point in Fig. 22 (node point). For example, in Fig. 22, points 1 and 2 are base points while points 3 and 4 are node points. Cutting at points 3 or 4 divides the total diagram into subunits. There can be two types of chain, viz. a simple chain in which every integrated point is a node, and a netted chain, formed by adding not more than one integrated point from each simple chain link. The netted-chain approximation mentioned above involved the formation of netted chains in the coefficients of n^2 and higher in the density expansion of $h(r)$.

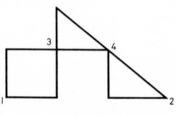

FIG. 22

(ii) *A bundle.* This is a parallel collection of links without nodes. There is, therefore, always at least two separate paths from one base point to the other.

(iii) *An elementary cluster.* This is any cluster which is neither a cluster nor a bundle. The name is very deceptive, for the associated integrations are almost always far from elementary in their structure.

We now denote the set of all chain clusters to be denoted by $G(r)$, the bundles by $B(r)$, and the elementary clusters by $E(r)$. The expansion of $h(r)$ is in terms of all clusters so that we can write generally:

$$h(r) = G(r) + B(r) + E(r). \tag{A5.4}$$

Reference to the expressions (A5.2) shows that $c(r)$ does not involve nodes, so that we have (see references at the beginning of this Appendix):

$$c(r) = B(r) + E(r). \tag{A5.5}$$

It follows from the theory (see references) that the expansion of the mean potential is the same as that for $h(r)$ except for the exclusion now of all bundles. Consequently,

$$\ln y(r) = G(r) + E(r). \tag{A5.5}$$

It further follows that an integral relation can be deduced relating G, B, and E. Starting from one base point of a diagram, called point 1, there will be a selection of bundles and elementary diagrams until the first node point 3 is reached. This total entity between base point and node is not a chain. But the entity between the node and the second field point 2 can contain nodes and so can contain chain contributions. Consequently, the total sett of chains in the system of particles between the base points 1 and 2 is:

$$G(\mathbf{r}_{12}) = n \int [B(\mathbf{r}_{13}) + E(\mathbf{r}_{13})] \, h(\mathbf{r}_{23}) \, d\mathbf{r}_3. \tag{A5.6}$$

From the expressions (A5.4) and (A5.5) it follows that:

$$B(r) = h(r) - \ln y(r):$$

the use of this relation and (A5.5) in (A5.6) gives finally:

$$\ln y(r_{12}) - E(r_{12}) = n \int [h(r_{13}) - \ln y(r_{13}) + E(r_{13})] \tag{A5.7}$$

$$\times h(r_{23}) \, dr_3 .$$

This is an equation for $g^{(2)}$ and is exact if E is specified exactly. The hypernetted chain approximation is the statement that $E = 0$. From (A5.5) this means assuming for the direct pair correlation function, the form:

$$c(r) = h(r) - \ln y(r). \tag{A5.8}$$

This is exactly the primitive assumption (5.4) of the main text, and in this approximation the equation (A5.7) reduces to become the main text equation (5.7). Improvements on the hypernetted chain equation must centre around the proper account of the contribution E of the elementary clusters.

5.3. The approximation

$$c_p(r) = \alpha(r) y(r), \tag{A5.9}$$

can be approached in several ways for gases, but still must remain an assumption for liquid densities. From cluster arguments, G. STELL (1963, *Physica*, **29**, 517) showed that $c(r)$ can be written generally:

$$c(r) = \alpha(r) y(r) + D(r),$$

where $D(r)$ involves cluster contributions that can be enumerated. The condition $D(r) = 0$, which defines the Percus–Yevick approximation, in fact includes the condition $E = 0$ relating to elementary diagrams, and includes also elementary clusters and certain bundles. In these terms, the Percus–Yevick approximation is more drastic than is the hypernetted chain approximation.

Stell has also given another reason for choosing the approximation (A5.9). The expansion (A5.1) for the direct correlation function has the first term:

$$c_0(r) = \alpha(r).$$

From the expansion (4.42) of the main text, written

$$y(r) = \sum_{j \geqslant 0} y_j n ,$$

it follows that $y_0(r) = 1$. Consequently, we have

$$c_0(r) = \alpha(r) y_0(r). \tag{A5.8}$$

From (4.43) of the main text we have, further, that

$$y_1(r) = \int \alpha(2, 3) \alpha(1, 3) \, dr_3 .$$

Comparison with equation (A5.2b) shows that

$$c_1(r) = \alpha(r) y_1(r). \tag{A5.9}$$

These results are exact: let us generalise them by assuming that this same relationship between coefficients holds to all orders of the density, so that:

$$c_j(r) = \alpha(r) y_j(r), \tag{A5.10}$$

for all $j \geqslant 2$. This generalised assertion, which is demonstrably not true in fact, is an expression of the Percus–Yevick approximation. The assumption (5.8) of the main text is an immediate consequence. Unfortunately, although it is clear that (A5.10) is an approximation, it is not possible to say in numerical terms on this basis how serious an approximation it is. Some indication of this can, of course, be deduced by a comparison between thermodynamic data calculated using (A5.10) and alternative data.

5.4. The original literature should also be consulted for this provides also yet another approach, (indeed, the original approach) to the problem using the so-called collective coordinates. The approach involves the rearrangement of the Hamiltonian for the system of N particles into a form allowing a more convenient evaluation of Z_r than is allowed by the original Hamiltonian (2.9) of the main text. This rearrangement of the Hamiltonian is achieved by replacing the particle phase coordinates by the Fourier components of the expansion of the fluid number density together with the space coordinates of the centre of mass of the total system. Approximation enters the theory in the selection of the Fourier components for a system with a finite number (i.e. $(3N-3)$) degrees of freedom. Any assessment of the quantitative error introduced by a chosen procedure is about as difficult to perform as it is to estimate the errors introduced by using the superposition approximation. The method is the application to insulating fluids of that previously applied to plasmas, by D. BOHM and D. PINES (1953, *Phys. Rev.* **92**, 609), and for general systems of particles by N. N. BOGOLIUBOV and D. N. ZUBAREV (1955, *Soviet Phys. JETP*, **1**, 71). Further information is contained in the collection of papers entitled *Many-body Problem* (ed. J. K. Percus), Interscience. The application to insulating fluids is given by:
J. K. PERCUS and G. J. YEVICK, 1958, *Phys. Rev.* **110**, 1.
The relation between the collective coordinate approach and other approximations is considered by:
J. K. PERCUS, 1962, *Phys. Rev. Letters*, **8**, 462.
Although the collective coordinate approach to the derivation of the Percus–Yevick equation is apparently not without problems, it does refer to the higher fluid densities appropriate to liquids. Thus, the combination of collective coordinates and diagram techniques can act as support for the assumption of the form of the direct correlation over the full range of fluid densities, including those for liquids.

5.5. Functional differentiation represents a natural generalisation of the usual Taylor expansion for several variables to the case of continuous variables.
For the normal Taylor series, if A is a function of the variables b_j then the change db in this set of variables leads to the change dA in A given by:

$$\mathrm{d}A_i = \sum_j \frac{\partial A_i}{\partial b_j}\,\mathrm{d}b_j + \frac{1}{2!}\sum_{j,k}\frac{\partial^2 A_i}{\partial b_j\,\partial b_k}\,\mathrm{d}b_j\,\mathrm{d}b_k + \ldots \tag{A5.11}$$

We pass to continuous variables so that the summations are replaced by integrations. More specifically, if the function A is a functional of the function B then the change ΔB in B leads to the change ΔA in A given by:

$$\Delta A(j) = \int \frac{\delta A(j)}{\delta B(k)}\bigg|_{\Delta B=0} \Delta B(k)\,\mathrm{d}k$$
$$+ \frac{1}{2!}\int\int \frac{\delta^2 A(j)}{\delta B(k)\,\delta B(l)}\bigg|_{\Delta B=0} \Delta B(k)\,\Delta B(l)\,\mathrm{d}k\,\mathrm{d}l + 0(\Delta B^3). \tag{A5.12}$$

It will be seen that the quantities $\delta A/\delta B$, and so on, are generalisations of the ordinary partial derivative. See:

V. VOLTERRA, 1959, *Theory of Functionals*, Dover.

N. N. BOGOLIUBOV, Problems of a Dynamical Theory in Statistical Physics (English translation, 1962) in *Studies in Statistical Mechanics*, vol. **1**, Amsterdam, North-Holland.

The application to statistical physical problems seems first to have been made by: M. A. LEONTOVICH, 1935, *J. Expt. Theor. Phys.* **5**, 41.

The application to fluid problems was seriously pursued, following the paper by: J. YVON, 1958, *Supp. Nuovo Cim.* **9**, 144.

5.6. L. VERLET, 1964, *Physica*, **30**, 95.
For a discussion, see also:
G. S. RUSHBROOKE, 1965, *Statistical Mechanics of Equilibrium and Non-Equilibrium* (ed. Meixner), Amsterdam, North-Holland.

CHAPTER 6

6.1. D. MCQUARRIE, 1964, *J. Chem. Phys.* **40**, 3455.
G. H. A. COLE, 1966, *J. Chem. Phys.* **44**, 338.

6.2. The expression $a_1(r)$ for the hard-sphere gas was given first by
J. G. KIRKWOOD, 1935, *J. Chem. Phys.* **3**, 300.

6.3. The formulae (6.5), with the functions c_3 and c_4 defined by equations (6.10), follow immediately from the insertion of the expansion (6.1) into the appropriate equations of the theory and equating successively to zero the coefficients of each power of the density. The prototype for the method is given in detail for the Born–Green–Yvon equation by:
G. S. RUSHBROOKE and H. I. SCOINS, 1951, *Phil. Mag.* **42**, 582.

6.4. The set of expressions (6.6) for c_3, (6.7) for c_4, (6.8) for c_5, and (6.9) for c_6 were first given by:
D. A. MCQARRIE, 1964, *J. Chem. Phys.* **40**, 3455.
The functions a_1, c_3, c_4, and c_5 were independently derived for the Born–Green–Yvon equation by:
G. H. A. COLE, 1966, *J. Chem. Phys.* **44**, 338.

6.5. See, for instance:
J. DE BOER and A. MICHELS, 1939, *Physica*, **6**, 97.

6.6. The function $a_{11}(r)$ was given by:
J. G. KIRKWOOD, 1935, *J. Chem. Phys.* **3**, 300.
The functions associated with the various a_2 for this case were derived by:
G. S. RUSHBROOKE and H. I. SCOINS, 1951, *Phil. Mag.* **42**, 582,
B. R. A. NIJBOER and L. VAN HOVE, 1952, *Phys. Rev.* **85**, 777,
A. E. RODRIGUEZ, 1957, *Proc. Roy. Soc.* (London), A **239**, 373,
G. H. A. COLE, 1961, *J. Chem. Phys.* **34**, 2016.

6.7. B. R. A. NIJBOER and L. VAN HOVE, 1952, *Phys. Rev.* **85**, 777.

6.8. G. H. A. COLE, 1962, *J. Chem. Phys.* **36**, 1680.

6.9. G. H. A. COLE, 1962, *J. Chem. Phys.* **37**, 1631.
For this case we have the variable z defined by:

$$z = 1 - \exp\{-\varepsilon/kT\}, \qquad \text{(A6.1)}$$

where ε is the height of the repulsive core and,

$$a_1(r) = \frac{2}{3}\pi z^2 \left\{ 2 - 2r + \frac{1}{8}r^3 \right\} \quad \text{for} \quad 0 \leqslant r \leqslant 2,$$

$$= 0 \quad \text{for} \quad r \geqslant 2; \tag{A6.2}$$

$$a_2(r) = a_{21}(r) + a_{22}(r) + a_{23}(r), \tag{A6.3}$$

where

$$a_{21}(r) = \pi^2 z^4 \left\{ \frac{8}{9} - \frac{4}{3}r + \frac{1}{2}r^2 + \frac{1}{9}r^3 - \frac{1}{12}r^4 + \frac{1}{288}r^6 \right\},$$

$$= 0 \quad \text{for} \quad r > 1; \quad \text{for} \quad 0 \leqslant r \leqslant 1,$$

$$a_{22}(r) = \pi^2 z^4 \left\{ -\frac{9}{35}\cdot\frac{1}{r} + \frac{29}{9} - \frac{101}{30}r + \frac{3}{4}r^2 + \frac{5}{16}r^3 \right.$$

$$\left. -\frac{2}{15}r^4 + \frac{42}{10080}r^6 \right\} \quad \text{for} \quad 1 \leqslant r \leqslant 2,$$

$$= 0 \quad \text{for} \quad r < 1, \quad \text{and for} \quad r > 2;$$

$$a_{23}(r) = \pi^2 z^3 \left\{ \frac{27}{70}\cdot\frac{1}{r} - \frac{9}{4} + \frac{9}{5}r - \frac{1}{4}r^2 - \frac{1}{6}r^3 + \frac{1}{20}r^4 - \frac{1}{1260}r^6 \right\} \quad \text{for} \quad 2 \leqslant r \leqslant 3,$$

$$= 0 \quad \text{for} \quad r < 2, \quad \text{and for} \quad r > 3. \tag{A6.4}$$

See Figs. 23 – 26.

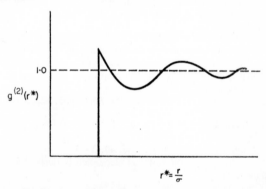

FIG. 23. Pair distribution for hard-sphere gas, plotted as a function of the particle separation distance.

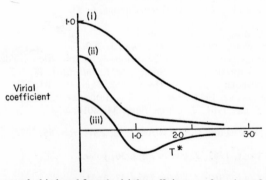

FIG. 24. The second, third and fourth virial coefficients as function of the reduced temperature for a square-mound potential gas. Curve (i) is B/b; curve (ii) is C/b^2; and curve (iii) is D/b^3.

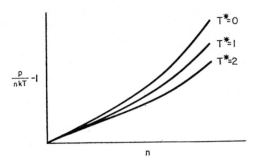

FIG. 25. Plot of pressure as function of number density for square-mound potential gas, for three different temperatures.

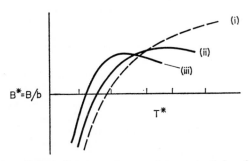

FIG. 26. Virial coefficients for power-law repulsive potential as function of the temperature; and for the square-well potential. Curve (i) is for power law potential; curve (ii) for square-well potential; curve (iii) is C/b^2 for square-well potential to the same scale.

6.10. T. KIHARA, 1943, *Nippon Sagaku. Buturigakaishi*, **17**, 11; 1953, *Rev. Mod. Phys.* **25**, 831.

   S. KATSURA, 1959, *Phys. Rev.* **115**, 1417; 1960, *Phys. Rev.* **118**, 1667.

6.11. J. A. BARKER and J. J. MONOGHAN, 1962, *J. Chem. Phys.* **36**, 2558.

6.12. There is a considerable background literature associated with these values, including calculations in one or two dimensions and for lines, squares, and cubes in distinction to spheres. For discussion and references see:

   J. S. ROWLINSON, 1965, *Rep. Prog. Phys.* **28**, 169.

   R. J. RIDDELL and G. E. UHLENBECK, 1953, *J. Chem. Phys.* **21**, 2056.

   G. STELL, 1963, *Physica*, **29**, 517.

   L. VERLET, 1964, *Physica*, **30**, 95.

   G. STELL, 1962, *J. Chem. Phys.* **36**, 1817.

6.13. The exact values of B, C and D have been known for some time. The deduction of B and C is quite straightforward, but that for D presents more problems. See:

   L. BOLTZMANN, 1899, *Versl. genowe Vergad. wis-en natuurk. Afd. K. Akad. Wet. Amst.* **7**, 484.

   H. HAPPEL, 1906, *Ann. Phys.* **21**, 243.

   R. MAJUMDAR, 1929, *Bull. Calcutta Math. Soc.* **21**, 10.

   B. R. A. NIJBOER and L. VAN HOVE, 1952, *Phys. Rev.* **85**, 777.

6.14   One alternative potential function that has been fairly thoroughly investigated in its application to dilute gases is the so-called Gaussian model defined by the interparticle pair force potential associated with:

$$\alpha(r) = \exp\{-Ar^2\}$$

for all r. The reason for selecting this potential is entirely mathematical: it has no physical interest. With its use, the various formulae of the fluid theories can be evaluated exactly and the value of the various approximations compared with exact values for this potential form. For details see:

G. E. UHLENBECK and G. W. FORD, 1962, *Studies in Statistical Mechanics*, vol. **1**, p. 184 (eds. J. de Boer and G. E. Uhlenbeck).

The value of using physically unrealistic potential functions, as opposed to physically idealised functions, in the various formulae for the fluid structure is open to question. The basis for statistical thermodynamics, and for the equivalence in practice of the canonical and grand canonical ensembles, rests upon a comparison of the calculated data with the single world of our experience. It might be argued that a potential function having, at least qualitatively, the correct features (even if only in certain limiting cases such as when the temperature is indefinitely high), viewed against the real world is essential for a successful comparison with observed data. Calculations using the statistical theory, and involving entirely fictitious interaction potential forms, are outside our present interest.

6.15.   M. N. ROSENBLUTH and A. W. ROSENBLUTH, 1954, *J. Chem. Phys.* **22**, 881.
Other estimates of E are available, but using methods different from those used above. Approximate values of the higher virial coefficients have also been deduced by extrapolating values for squares and cubes. See:

H. REIS, H. L. FRISCH, E. HELFAND, and J. L. LEBOWITZ, 1960, *J. Chem. Phys.* **32**, 119.

E. BYCKLING, 1961, *Physica*, **27**, 1030; 1962, *ibid.* **28**, 959.

W. G. HOOVER and A. D. DE ROCCO, 1962, *J. Chem. Phys.* **36**, 3141.

The virial coefficients for a hard-sphere gas have also been calculated from considerations of the mean force by:

W. G. HOOVER and J. C. POIRIER, 1962, *J. Chem. Phys.* **37**, 1041.

6.16.   B. R. A. NIJBOER and R. FIESCHI, 1953, *Physica*, **19**, 545.

6.17.   G. S. RUSHBROOKE and P. HUTCHINSON, 1961, *Physica*, **27**, 647.
P. HUTCHINSON and G. S. RUSHBROOKE, 1963, *Physica*, **29**, 675.

6.18.   G. S. RUSHBROOKE, 1963, *J. Chem. Phys.* **38**, 1262.

6.19.   G. S. RUSHBROOKE, 1965, *Statistical Mechanics of Equilibrium and Non-Equilibrium*, p. 222 (ed. Meixner), Amsterdam, North-Holland.

6.20.   K. HIROIKE, 1957, *J. Phys. Soc. Japan*, **12**, 327.

6.21.   See, for instance, the book of HIRSCHFELDER, CURTISS, and BIRD quoted in General References. See also:

W. H. KEESOM, 1912, *Comm. Phys. Lab. Leiden*, Supp. **24 B**, 32.

J. E. LENNARD–JONES, 1924, *Proc. Roy. Soc.* (London) A **106**, 463; 1937, *Proc. Phys. Soc.* (London) A **43**, 461.

T. KIHARA, 1948, *J. Phys. Soc. Japan*, **3**, 265; 1951, *ibid.* **6**, 184.

R. B. BIRD, E. L. SPOLTZ, and J. O. HIRSCHFELDER, 1950, *J. Chem. Phys.* **18**, 1395.

E. W. MONTROLL and J. E. MAYER, 1941, *J. Chem. Phys.* **9**, 626.

J. DE BOER and A. MICHELS, 1939, *Physica*, **6**, 97.

A. G. DE ROCCO and W. G. HOOVER, 1962, *J. Chem. Phys.* **36**, 916.

6.22. See the book by HIRSCHFELDER, CURTISS, and BIRD quoted in the general references. Additional references are as follows. Some experimental data for the second virial coefficient for the simpler gases are given by, for argon:
L. HOLBORN and J. OTTO, 1925, *Z. Phys.* **33**, 1.
For krypton:
L. HOLBORN and J. OTTO, 1925, *Z. Phys.* **33**, 1.
J. A. BEATTIE, J. S. BRIERLEY and R. J. BARRIAULT, 1952, *J. Chem. Phys.* **20**, 1615.
For nitrogen:
L. HOLBORN and J. OTTO, 1925, *Z. Phys.* **33**, 1.
A. MICHELS, H. WOUTERS and J. DE BOER, 1934, *Physica*, **1**, 587.
For helium:
L. HOLBORN and J. OTTO, 1925, *Z. Phys.* **33**, 1.
L. J. YUTERNA and W. G. SCHNEIDER, 1950, *J. Chem. Phys.* **18**, 641.
For carbon dioxide:
A. and C. MICHELS, 1936, *Proc. Roy. Soc.* (London) A **153**, 201.
K. E. MACCORMACK and W. G. SCHNEIDER, 1950, *J. Chem. Phys.* **18**, 1269.
For argon, krypton, and argon–krypton mixtures:
B. E. F. FENDER and G. D. HALSEY, JR., 1962, *J. Chem. Phys.* **36**, 1881.
The (m–6) potential has been considered by many authors with m not equal to 12. Thus the (9–6) potential has some interest for helium and mercury – see:
L. F. EPSTEIN and C. J. HIBBERT, 1952, *J. Chem. Phys.* **20**, 752.
T. KIHARA, 1951, *J. Phys. Soc. Japan*, **6**, 184.
J. F. CONOLLY, 1961, *Phys. Fluids*, **4**, 1494.
The second virial coefficient for the Morse potential

$$y(r) = \varepsilon(x^2 - 2x)$$

$$\text{where} \quad x = \exp\left\{-\frac{c}{\sigma}(r - r_0)\right\},$$

is given by:

D. D. KONOWALOW, M. H. TAYLOR, and J. O. HIRSCHFELDER, 1961, *Phys. Fluids*, **4**, 622.
Polyelectrolytes were considered by:
N. ISE, 1962, *J. Chem. Phys.* **36**, 3248.
$B(r)$ for the potential $y(r)$ with exponential repulsion was given by:
R. A. BUCKINGHAM and J. CORNER, 1947, *Proc. Roy. Soc.* (London) A **189**, 118.

6.23. This approach has been considered by COLE. See:
G. H. A. COLE, 1961, *J. Chem. Phys.* **34**, 2016; 1962, *ibid.* **36**, 1680; 1962, *ibid.* **37**, 1631; 1966, *ibid.* **44**, 338.

6.24. J. S. ROWLINSON, 1965, *Rep. Prog. Phys.* **28**, 169.

6.25. An alternative approach to consistency was explored by:
A. E. RODRIGUEZ, 1957, *Proc. Roy. Soc.* London, A **239**, 373.
Here the Kirkwood superposition was entirely modified to obtain consistency for D. The result was:

$$D_v = D_c = 0.2773b^3.$$

The method does not give consistency beyond D.

6.26. But this may need to be specified numerically rather than by any single analytic function over the whole range of separation distance.

6.27. The case of non-spherical potential functions is of great practical interest. Examples are the use of a hard-sphere potential but with impressed dipole (hard-sphere plus Stockmayer potential), and (m–6) potential with Stockmayer potential. In

applying the equations of the theory, it is necessary now to include angular dependencies, and integration is to be made over these angular dependencies as well as over the phase for the particles.
For rigid convex particles, see:
A. ISIHARA, 1950, *J. Chem. Phys.* **18**, 1446.
A. ISIHARA and T. HAYASHIDA, 1951, *J. Phys. Soc. Japan*, **6**, 40.

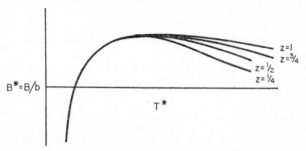

FIG. 27. Second virial coefficient for Sutherland potential function, for different values of the parameter $z = 1 - \exp\{-\varepsilon/kT\}$, where ε is the potential at zero separation.

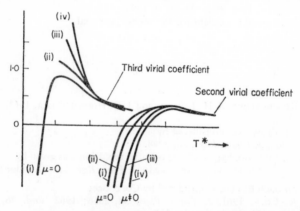

FIG. 28. Second and third virial coefficients for the Stockmayer potential including a dipole. The case of zero dipole strength is curve (i) in each case; curves (ii)–(iv) show the effect of increasing the dipole strength.

For spherocylindrical particles, see:

T. KIHARA, 1951, *J. Phys. Soc. Japan*, **6**, 289.
This author also gives data for general ellipsoidal particles with the regions of interparticle repulsion and attraction having the $(12-6)$ form.
W. H. KEESOM, 1912, *Comm. Phys. Lab. Leiden*, Supp. **24**, 1915. *ibid* Supp. **39**.
S. KIELICH. 1961, *Acta Physica Polonica*, **20**, 433.
W. H. STOCKMAYER, 1941, *J. Chem Phys.* **9**, 398.
S. C. SAXENA and K. M. JOSHI, 1962, *Phys. Fluids*, **5**, 1217.
J. S. ROWLINSON, 1949, *Trans. Faraday Soc.* **45**, 974; 1951, *J. Chem Phys.* **19**, 827.

J. O. Hirschfelder, F. T. McClure and I. F. Weeks, 1942, *J. Chem. Phys.* **10**, 201.

R. J. Lunbeck and C. A. ten Seldam, 1951, *Physica*, **17**, 788.

For discussion of mixtures of gases see the book of Hirschfelder, Curtiss and Bird (General References). For dipole gases, it is necessary to introduce an expression for the effective dipole strength. One possibility for a mixture of two dipole gases is:

$$\mu_E = \sqrt{\mu_1 \mu_2},$$

where μ_1 and μ_2 are the dipole strengths for each gas separately.

6.28. See:
H. S. Green, 1952, *The Molecular Theory of Fluids*, Amsterdam, North-Holland, pp. 75 *et seq.*
A. E. Rodriguez, 1948, *Proc. Roy. Soc.* (London) A **196**, 73.
A. G. McLellan, 1952, *Proc. Roy. Soc.* (London) A **210**, 509.

6.29. See book of H. S. Green (ref. 28), p. 81.

6.30. J. G. Kirkwood and E. M. Boggs, 1942, *J. Chem. Phys.* **10**, 394.

6.31. J. G. Kirkwood, E. K. Maun, and B. J. Alder, 1950, *J. Chem. Phys.* **18**, 1040.
J. G. Kirkwood, V. A. Lewinson, and B. J. Alder, 1952, *J. Chem. Phys.* **20**, 929.
R. W. Zwanzig, J. G. Kirkwood, K. F. Stripp, and J. Oppenheim, 1953, *J. Chem. Phys.* **21**, 1268.

6.32. A. A. Khan, 1964, *Phys. Rev.* **134**, A 367; *ibid.* **136**, A 1260.
Earlier numerical studies of Broyles involved also the BGY equation:
A. A. Broyles, 1960, *J. Chem. Phys.* **33**, 456; 1961, *ibid.* **34**, 359; **35**, 493.
A. A. Broyles, S. U. Chung, and H. L. Sahlin, 1962, *J. Chem. Phys.* **37**, 2462.

6.33. The Buckingham–Corner potential function may be useful here, characterised by an exponential distance dependence at small distances:
R. A. Buckingham, and J. Corner, 1947, *Proc. Roy. Soc.* (London) A **189**, 118.

6.34. M. D. Johnson and N. H. March, 1963, *Phys. Letters* **3**, 313.
M. D. Johnson, P. Hutchinson, and N. H. March, 1964, *Proc. Roy. Soc.* (London) A **282**, 283.

6.35. See, for instance:
E. R. Dobbs and G. O. Jones, 1957, *Rep. Prog. Phys.* **20**, 576.

6.36. N. Metropolis, A. Rosenbluth, M. Rosenbluth, A. Teller, and E. Teller, 1953, *J. Chem. Phys.* **21**, 1087.
B. J. Alder and T. Wainwright, 1957, *J. Chem. Phys.* **27**, 1208.
T. Wainwright and B. J. Alder, 1958, *Supp. Nuovo Cim.* **9**, 116.
W. W. Wood and J. D. Jacobson, 1957, *J. Chem. Phys.* **27**, 1207.
B. J. Alder and T. Wainwright, 1963. *The Many-body Problem*, p. 511 (ed. J. K. Percus) (New York, Wiley & Sons).

6.37. I. Z. Fisher, 1964, *Statistical Theory of Liquids*, Chicago University Press.

6.38. E. Thiele, 1963, *J. Chem. Phys.* **39**, 474; 1963, *Phys. Rev. Letters*, **8**, 321; M. S. Werrheim, 1964, *J. Math. Phys.* **5**, 643.

6.39. H. Reiss, H. L. Frisch, and J. L. Lebowitz, 1959, *J. Chem. Phys.* **31**, 369.
H. L. Frisch, 1964, *Advances in Chemical Physics*, vol. **6**, p. 229 (Ed. Prigogine), Interscience.

6.40. H. N. V. Temperley, 1964, *Proc. Phys. Soc.* (London), **83**, 571, 1013; *ibid.* **84**, 339.

6.41. B. J. ALDER, 1964, *Phys. Rev. Letters*, **12**, 317.

6.42. A. RAHMAN, 1964, *Phys. Rev. Letters*, **12**, 575.

6.43. Approximate equations of state are of great value in practice and for gases at least they can be constructed systematically in principle from the statistical theory. Alternatively, various empirical formulae are available for various circumstances, involving a certain number of variables to be chosen to provide the best fit with experiment.

The van der Waals, Berthelot, and Dieterici equations were early examples: later examples are the five-parameter equation of Beattie and Bridgeman, and the eight-parameter equation of Benedict, Webb, and Rubin. For references see the HIRSCHFELDER, CURTISS, and BIRD book in the General References. Also:

F. H. REE, 1962, *J. Chem. Phys.* **36**, 3373.

J. R. PARTINGTON, 1949, *Advanced Treatise of Physical Chemistry*, vol. **1**, Longmans.

J. D. LAMBERT, G. A. H. ROBERTS, J. S. ROWLINSON, and V. J. WILKINSON, 1949, *Proc. Roy. Soc.* (London) A **196**, 113.

J. A. BEATTIE and O. C. BRIDGEMAN, 1927, *J. Am. Chem. Soc.* **49**, 1665; 1928, *Am. Acad. Arts. Sci.* **63**, 229.

J. O. HIRSCHFELDER and W. E. ROSEVEARE, 1939, *J. Phys. Chem.* **43**, 15.

M. BENEDICT, G. B. WEBB, and L. C. RUBIN, 1940, *J. Chem. Phys.* **8**, 334; 1942, *ibid.* **10**, 747; 1951, *Chem. Eng. Prog.* **47**, 419.

J. O. HIRSCHFELDER, D. P. STEVENSON, and H. EYRING, 1937, *J. Chem. Phys.* **5**, 896.

For gases up to moderately high pressures, a virial expansion stopping at the fourth virial coefficient is often sufficient for the representation of experimental data. Hirschfelder has suggested the use of the equation:

$$\frac{pV}{kT} - 1 = B(T)n + 0 \cdot 625b^2n^2 + 0 \cdot 2896b^3n^3 + 0 \cdot 1928b^4n^4,$$

for simple gases at high temperature. Here, $B(T)$ is the second virial coefficient derived using the appropriate interparticle force potential; C and D are given their hard-sphere values; and the fifth virial coefficient is chosen to satisfy certain compressibility conditions at high fluid density.

An alternative formula for simple fluids at lower temperatures could be:

$$\frac{pV}{kT} - 1 = B(T)n + C(T)n^2 + D_0(T)n^3 + 0 \cdot 110b^4n^4,$$

where $B(T)$ and $C(T)$ are derived using the appropriate interparticle force potential; $D_0(T)$ is the virial coefficient for a square-well potential (presumably the Percus–Yevick expression associated with the compressibility equation). The fifth virial coefficient has the hard-sphere value. This last value might be modified or alternatively the term involving n^5 might also be introduced, possibly through the known hard-sphere value.

6.44. Better agreement between the calculated and experimentally determined thermodynamic data can be obtained by making an appropriate empirical change in the pair distribution. Thus:

R. W. ZWANZIG, J. G. KIRKWOOD, K. F. STRIPP, and J. OPPENHEIM, 1953, *J. Chem. Phys.* **21**, 1268.

have shown that if $g^{(2)}(r)$ is replaced by $g^{(2)}(1 \cdot 026r)$, then the calculated and measured data for the pressure of argon agree very closely. This "stretching" procedure is found in Chapter 9 also to have important consequences in the calculation of transport coefficients. But unfortunately, the best fit for equilibrium theory turns out not to be at the same time that which provides the best fit for the non-equilibrium theory.

6.45. Alternative forms of (6.23) have also been used in calculations. One such is the replacing of (6.23) by

$$c(r) = c_p(r) + \left[y(r) - 1 - \{y(r)\}^m \ln y(r) \right].$$

See:
C. HURST, 1965, *Proc. Phys. Soc.* (London), **86**, 193.
D. HENDERSON, 1966, *Proc. Phys. Soc.* (London), **87**, 592.
With m taken as being a density expansion, the virial coefficients for a hard-sphere gas take the form $D = 0.2824b^3$, $E = 0.1053b^4$, and $F = 0.0351b^5$.

6.46. The solution of the second order equation (4.28) in the form (4.29) involving the superposition approximation (4.14) has been given by COCHRAN and LUND (1964, *J. Chem. Phys.* **41**, 3499) for a hard-sphere gas. The result for the fourth virial coefficient is disappointing. A better superposition expression would presumably be (4.13a) but with $S_{14} = 1$.

ADDITIONS TO APPENDIX 6

Since Chapter 6 and the accompanying Appendix 6 were written further work has been reported which we collect together here. These comments primarily refer to hard-sphere and square-well potential gases.

(a) *Hard-Sphere Potential.*
Refined "exact" fifth and sixth virial coefficients are now confirmed: these are

$$E = (0.1103 \pm 0.0003)b^4 \quad \text{and} \quad F = (0.0386 \pm 0.0004)b^5 \qquad (A6.5)$$

(F. H. REE and W. G. HOOVER, 1964, *J. Chem. Phys.* **40**, 939).
In addition E_v is also available for PY 2 and HNC 2. These are:

$$E_v(\text{PY2}) = 0.124b^4 \quad E_v(\text{HNC2}) = 0.066b^4. \qquad (A6.6)$$

Corresponding values for F are not yet available. It is seen that PY 2 and HNC 2 lead to exact and consistent information for D but not for E. Reference to section 6.2(b) shows that PY 2 using the grand canonical ensemble for the pressure (fluctuation—compressibility formula) gives essentially the same result as HNC 2 using the canonical ensemble for the pressure (virial theorem): and each are too high by about 10 per cent. PY 2 using the virial theorem and HNC 2 using fluctuation are too low, but PY 2 is only about 2 per cent in error. The merit of using the compressibility formula is apparently reversed in moving from PY 1 to PY 2.

Other approaches for calculating the virial coefficients have been attempted and particularly involving arguments of consistency. Of special interest is the suggestion by C. HURST (1965, *Proc. Phys. Soc.* **86**, 193; 1966, *ibid.* **88**, 533) of the introduction of a new direct correlation function for insertion into equation (5.2) of the main text. This amounts to a modification of $c_H(r)$ given by (5.6a) to read

$$c(r) = h(r) - [y(r)]^m \ln y(r)$$
$$= c_H(r) + [1 - y^m(r)] \ln y(r). \qquad (A6.7)$$

This form for $c(r)$ can be related to the hypernetted chain diagram approximation and Hurst suggests that the name generalised hypernetted chain approximation be given to (A6.7). In this expression, m is a simple numeric. Consistency is obtained for D (i.e. $D_c = D_v$) if we set $m = 0.4172$ and the corresponding value for the fourth virial coefficient for a hard-sphere gas is $D = 0.2824\, b^3$. (A6.7) leads, of course, to exact data for the virial coeciffients B and C. This surprisingly is the same as the value (6.24) derived from the use of the Rowlinson expression for consistency (6.23). The function (A6.7) has been used by Hurst to determine E and F. The results that he gives for hard-spheres (see the references quoted above) are

$$E_e = 0.1102\, b^4 \qquad F_e = 0.0386\, b^5$$
$$E_v = 0.0915\, b^4 \qquad F_v = 0.0353\, b^5. \tag{A6.8}$$

Reference to (A6.5) shows that the Hurst values of E_e and F_e are essentially exact, and are better than the values given by PY 2 and HNC 2. The situation is rather curious, particularly when the results of functional differentiation are included in the picture. Apparently a direct correlation function has been devised which is able to provide good data for the first six virial coefficients. The expression (A6.7) retains physical significance at high densities: thermodynamic data for liquid densities derived from solving the equation that results when (A6.7) is inserted into equation (5.2) may well prove highly interesting.

Consistent data for the coefficients E and F simultaneously with D can also be obtained by a slight modification of (A6.7) suggested by D. Henderson (1966, *Proc. Phys. Soc.* **87**, 592). This allows m in (A6.7) to be expanded in a power series in the density. The consistent data given by Henderson are

$$D = 0.2824\, b^3, \qquad E = 0.1053\, b^4, \qquad F = 0.0351\, b^5. \tag{A6.9}$$

These values are comparable with those collected in (6.24) given by Rowlinson. The expansion proposed by Henderson is not capable of immediate application to liquid densities.

It is interesting that we are now working in a region of accuracy of calculation unattainable six or seven years ago. As an example, a consistent value for D obtained by replacing the factor $(1 - y^m)$ in (A6.7) by a simple numeric is $D = 0.2753\, b^4$. This value is hardly interesting now but would have been very welcome not so long ago.

(b) *Square-Well Potential* (see equation (6.2) of the main text)

Calculations for this potential for a gas have still not progressed beyond those for D together with the corresponding coefficients for associated thermodynamic formulae. The formula for D as function of temperature (6.22) derived by consistency arguments from BGY 1 can now be supplemented by data derived using the direct correlation function (6.23) of Rowlinson (J. S. Rowlinson, 1965, *Mol. Phys.* **9**, 217). For consistency we must give β the value

$$[7\,607 - 78\,781\,\alpha + 544\,796\alpha^2 - 1\,568\,560\alpha^3 + 2\,001\,220\alpha^4 + 306\,180\alpha^5]\,\beta$$
$$= [1\,260 - 51\,412\alpha + 360\,640\alpha^2 - 974\,288\alpha^3 + 482\,240\alpha^4 + 1\,224\,720\alpha^5] \tag{A6.10}$$

The corresponding expression for D is:

$$4\,480[7\,607 - 78\,781\alpha + 544\,796\alpha^2 - 1\,568\,560\alpha^3 + 2\,001\,220\alpha^4 + 306\,180\alpha^5]\,D(T)$$
$$= b^3[9\,622\,340 - 50\,109\,728\alpha - 581\,281\,196\alpha^2 + 11\,969\,269\,984\alpha^3$$
$$- 83\,910\,907\,504\alpha^4 + 285\,172\,413\,864\alpha^5 - 363\,663\,447\,840\alpha^6 - 442\,317\,482\,880\alpha^7$$
$$+ 1\,839\,161\,187\,200\alpha^8 - 1\,361\,182\,384\,800\alpha^9 - 374\,984\,769\,600\alpha^{10}]. \tag{A6.11}$$

The various expressions in Chapter 6 for the fourth virial coefficient together with the expression (A6.11) can be compared in their predictions of thermodynamic data. This is performed in the accompanying graphs using unpublished data of A. Moreton.

The most elementary check is that using the consistency criterion (3.56) given first by Hiroike in the form (3.56b). This is made in Fig. 29 for BGY 1, PY 1,

HNC 1, D^M given by (6.22), and D^R given by (A6.11). It is necessary, for this purpose, to have the coefficient U_3 in the expansion (3.54b) for the internal energy, corresponding to B_4 in the expansion (3.54a). The expressions for BGY 1, PY 1, and HNC 1 have been given by D. A. McQuarrie (1964, *J. Chem. Phys.* **41**, 1197). These are as follows. Introduce the function $\omega(T)$ according to $kT\omega(T) = (\alpha + 1)\varepsilon$. Then

$$181\,440\,U_3\,(\text{BGY}) = b^3\omega(T)\,[79\,308 - 2\,287\,053\alpha + 7\,306\,551\alpha^2 + 6\,630\,615\alpha^3$$
$$- 33\,730\,830\alpha^4],$$

$$181\,440\,U_3\,(\text{PY 1}) = b^3\omega(T)\,[68\,292 - 2\,087\,892\alpha + 8\,736\,336\alpha^2 + 5\,403\,960\alpha^3$$
$$- 33\,067\,440\alpha^4], \tag{A6.12}$$

$$181\,440\,U_3\,(\text{HNC 1}) = b^3\omega(T)\,[47\,079 - 1\,726\,200\alpha + 5\,487\,048\alpha^2 + 14\,589\,360\alpha^3$$
$$- 41\,334\,300\alpha^4].$$

The values for U_3 (modified BGY) and U_3 (Rowlinson) can then be deduced from these formulae.

It will be seen from Fig. 29 that the HNC equation provides complete consistency in connection with the thermodynamic expression (3.56) when used in connection with the virial pressure, though not when used with the compressibility arguments. The most consistent general data is that derived using the expres-

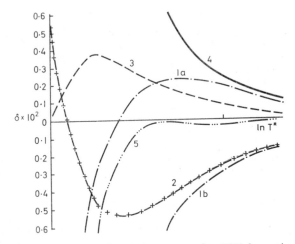

FIG. 29. Plot of thermodynamic consistency test for $D(T)$ for various theories, for the square-well potential equation (6.2). The ordinate is $\delta = \dfrac{U_3}{T} + \dfrac{2}{9}\dfrac{\partial D}{\partial T}$. According to equation (3.55b), $\delta = 0$ for an exact theory. Curve 1b refers to PY 1 with D calculated from fluctuation theory (expression (6.15h)), while 1a is PY 1 using the virial theorem (expression (6.15g)). Curve 2 is for HNC 1 with D given by the fluctuation expression (6.15f). For D given by (6.15e), for all temperatures. Curve 3 involves D calculated from BGY 1 and the virial theorem (expression (6.15a)). Data using (6.15b) lies off the scale of the graph. Curve 4 refers to the consistent D^M using BGY 1, expression (6.22). Curve 5 refers to the consistent D^R of Rowlinson, expression (A6.11). The temperature scale is given by $T_B T^* = T$, where T_B is the Boyle temperature. Curve 5 provides the best general consistent data away from the Boyle temperature (ln $T^* = 0$).

sion (6.23) for $c(r)$ proposed by Rowlinson. The remaining graphs (Figs 30–34) show the temperature dependencies of the coefficient in the density expansion of the various thermodynamic functions for that density term corresponding to Dn^4 in the density expansion for the pressure. It will be seen that no one theory

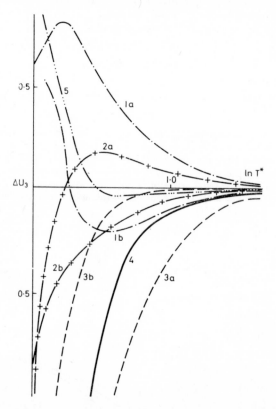

FIG. 30. Plot of difference between U_3 calculated from the various theories for the square-well potential and the highly accurate data given by Barker and Monoghan (see Appendix 6.11) denoted by U_{30}. The ordinate is then $\varDelta U_3 = U_3 - U_{30}$. In each case U_3 is obtained by differentiating the corresponding expression for D using equation (3.56b). Curves 1 refer to PY 1; $1a$ to compressibility and $1b$ to virial forms. Curves 2 refer correspondingly to HNC 1; curves 3 to BGY 1. Curve 4 refers to the consistent modified BGY, and curve 5 to the Rowlinson modified approach. Again $T_B T^* = T$, where T_B is the Boyle temperature.

has any marked superiority over the others for the full temperature range. But the "consistent" data are best away from the Boyle temperature. All the various formulae are poor in the neighbourhood of the Boyle temperature.

Finally, mention must be made of the very recent paper by L. Verlet (1966, *Physica* **32**, 304) reporting certain developments of the procedure of functional differentiation. The remarks on the present application of the technique of functional differentiation to the study of classical fluids made in section 5.4 still, how-

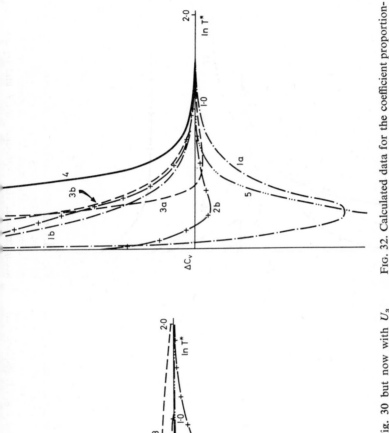

FIG. 32. Calculated data for the coefficient proportional to $n i^3$ in the density expansion of the specific heat at constant volume, relative to exact data. The expressions for U_3 and the graph code are as for Fig. 30. (Square-well potential.)

FIG. 31. The same as for Fig. 30 but now with U_3 calculated directly from equations (A6.12). Curve 1 refers to PY1; curve 2 to HNC1; curve 3 to BGY1; curve 4 to the modified BGY1; and curve 5 to the Rowlinson formula. (Square-well potential.)

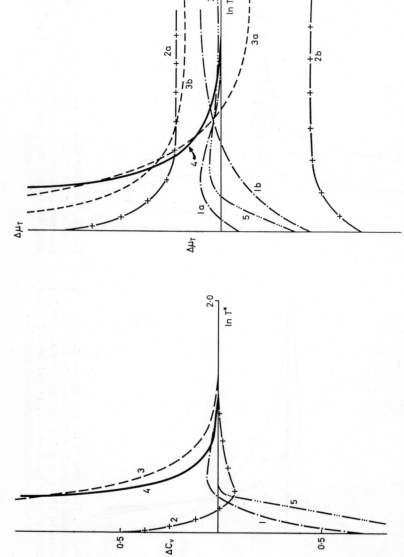

FIG. 34. Calculated data for the coefficient proportional to n^2 in the density expansion of the Joule–Thomson coefficient for the square-well potential, relative to accurate data. The expressions for D and U_3, and the

FIG. 33. Calculated data for the same density coefficient for the specific heat at constant volume as in Fig. 21, relative to exact data. The expressions for U_3 and the graph codes are as for Fig. 31. (Square-well

ever, remain valid. The future of functional differentiation is still problematical. This must particularly be the case when expressions for the direct correlation function such as (A6.7) give such promising results for the lower virial coefficients. Such expressions are associated with mathematical expressions which are at the present time much more tractable than the expressions arising from functional differentiation. Further, the direct correlation function approach can be discussed from the viewpoint of diagram techniques and these have a useful physical interpretation at low densities. The application of these formulae to fluid densities appropriate to liquids, on the other hand, is still very much an open question.

CHAPTER 7

7.1. In practice, it is very unusual to have only one irreversible process evolving in a physical system at a given time. For instance, a temperature gradient, dissipated by the passage of heat energy, also involves a variable particle density due to differential thermal effects. Consequently conductive heat transfer has also an associated irreversible mass transfer (thermal diffusion). In calculating the transport coefficients using statistical arguments, however, it is necessary at the present state of the theory to choose a situation where one transport process predominates over any other so that the system is one where only one dissipative process is active. This is satisfactory for theoretical purposes, and in most cases also experimentally. As an example, there is no difficulty in practice in producing isothermal laminar viscous flow. On the other hand, there is difficulty in producing simple conductive heat flow in fluids whose centre of mass is at rest since free convective heat flow is almost inevitably present; this leads to difficulties in the practical measurement of the conductive flow alone.

The statistical theory of non-equilibrium can, at the present time, only treat simple situations. For practical reasons it is necessary to have information about more complex situations which cannot yet be derived from statistical arguments. In the absence of a statistical theory, where transport effects are related explicitly to molecular data, it is useful to have available certain relations between the transport coefficients defined alternatively. This is the aim of the so-called irreversible thermodynamics based upon certain reciprocal relations described by Onsager. See:

L. ONSAGER, 1931, *Phys. Rev.* **37**, 405; **38**, 2265.

The theory is of wide generality and has been verified experimentally to very high accuracy in a whole range of widely different circumstances. Most progress has been made for steady conditions where external energy sources maintain the irreversible fluxes independent of the time. The fluxes (such as of momentum, energy, or mass) arise in matter because of the presence of external forces (such as pressure differences, temperature or concentration gradients), called generalised forces or sometimes affinities. If X_i denotes an affinity and J_i the associated flux then, for small deviations from equilibrium, a linear proportional relation can be assumed to hold between the X_i and J_i. In general any affinity can give rise to any flux and more than one flux will occur at any given time. Thus for a temperature gradient accompanied by a density (mass) gradient, there are four fluxes viz.: two direct fluxes, i.e. the mass flux of ordinary diffusion and the energy flux of thermal conduction; and two indirect fluxes, i.e. the mass flux due to the temperature gradient (thermal diffusion) and the energy flux due to the mass gradient. This special case can be generalised to include other cases by writing:

$$J_i = \sum \alpha_{ij} X_j.$$

The α_{ij} are called the phenomenological coefficients and are related to the transport coefficients of simple systems taken separately. The diagonal terms α_{ii} are associated with the direct effects (such as viscosity and thermal conductivity) while the non-diagonal terms $\alpha_{ij}(i \neq j)$ are associated with indirect effects. The important theorem, fundamental to the subject, was derived by Onsager (see earlier reference) and states that the α_{ij} are symmetric, i.e.

$$\alpha_{ij} = \alpha_{ji}.$$

These relations are called the reciprocal relations, and apply if the fluxes and affinities are properly chosen. Onsager's proof of the reciprocal relations depends upon arguments of statistical mechanics. It invokes particularly the principal of microscopic reversibility and recognises explicitly the linear character of many dissipative processes. In fact the reciprocal relations are a statement of the mutual effects between linear dissipative processes. Statistical arguments are not invoked for the direct calculation of the transport phenomena and for this reason the theory of irreversible thermodynamics will not be persued here. References in addition to that of Onsager already quoted are as follows:

S. R. DE GROOT, 1951, *Thermodynamics of Irreversible Processes*, Amsterdam, North-Holland.

K. G. DENBEIGH, 1951, *The Thermodynamics of the Steady State*, Methuen Monograph.

R. O. DAVIES, 1956, *Rep. Prog. Phys.* **19**, 326.

L. ONSAGER, 1945, *Ann. N. Y. Acad. Sci.* **46**, 241.

I. PRIGOGINE, 1955, *Introduction to Thermodynamics of Irreversible Processes*, Thomas, Springfield.

H. B. G. CASIMER, 1945, *Rev. mod. Phys.* **17**, 343.

See also:

P. G. BERGMANN and J. L. LEBOWITZ, 1955, *Phys. Rev.* **99**, 578.

J. L. LEBOWITZ and P. G. BERGMANN, 1957, *Ann. Phys.* **1**, 1.

Here the reciprocal relations are deduced without an appeal to detailed balancing. Irreversible thermodynamics is now an extremely important branch of the semi-macroscopic theory of non-equilibria. It is not pursued in the present arguments, however, because it does not attempt to derive the transport coefficients from particle dynamics and so falls outside the scope of our arguments.

7.2.   There is here the problem of the Poincaré period considered in section 7.4.

7.3.   For a detailed discussion see:

J. G. KIRKWOOD, 1946, *J. Chem. Phys.* **14**, 180. Especially pp. 183–5.

R. KUBO, 1959, Contribution to *Lectures in Theoretical Physics*, vol. I, p. 120 (eds. Brittin and Dunham), New York, Interscience.

R. W. ZWANZIG, 1961, Contribution to *Lectures in Theoretical Physics*, vol. III, p. 106 (eds. Brrittin, Downs, and Downs), New York, Interscience.

The inclusion of the imaginary unit i in the definition (7.1) of the Liouville operator assures that L is self-adjoint. Expressions of the same type as (7.3) apply also to relate the momenta and configuration coordinates after some time interval s with the initial values. Thus:

$$\mathbf{r}(s) = \exp\left[-isL\right]\mathbf{r}(0),$$
$$\mathbf{p}(s) = \exp\left[-isL\right]\mathbf{p}(0).$$

The mathematical discussion of $G(s) \equiv \exp\left[-isL\right]$ can be developed rigorously in Hilbert space using the methods of spectral theory: see:

J. VON NEUMANN, 1932, *Proc. Nat. Acad. Sci. (U.S.)* **18**, 70.

B. O. KOOPMAN, 1931, *Proc. Nat. Acad. Sci. (U.S.)* **17**, 315.

B. O. KOOPMAN and J. VON NEUMANN, 1932, *Proc. Nat. Acad. Sci. U.S.* **18**, 255.

The operator $G(s)$ is in fact a contact transformation and is a symbolic representation of the evolution of the phase of the system of particles according to the laws of classical particle mechanics. The function $f^{(N)}$ in (7.3) can, in fact, be replaced by any function of the phase which is not explicitly a function of the time.
In those regions of phase space where there are no singularities of L we can employ the expansion:

$$G(s) \equiv \exp\left[-isL\right] = \sum_{k=0}^{\infty} (-is)^k \frac{L^k}{k!}.$$

In expressions of this type L is chosen so as to satisfy certain boundary conditions such as those defining the total phase at time $t = 0$. See also:
I. PRIGOGINE and F. HENIN, 1960, *J. Math. Phys.* **1**, 349.
R. BALESCU, 1961, *Physica*, **27**, 693.
J. PHILIPPOT, 1961, *Physica*, **27**, 490.
E. G. D. COHEN, 1962, *Physica*, **28**, 1045.

7.4. See in this connection the article of Zwanzig quoted in ref. 3, especially pp. 110 *et seq;* and also:
R. BALESCU, 1961, Contribution to *Lectures in Theoretical Physics*, vol. III, p. 382 (eds. Brittin, Downs, and Downs), New York, Interscience.

7.5. In equilibrium theory the ensemble is isolated, and the constituent systems are only weakly coupled so that energy can be transferred between them, but infinitely slowly. For steady conditions non-equilibrium conditions are different. The ensemble of systems cannot be isolated since external reservoirs are needed to maintain the steady conditions and prevent the non-equilibrium conditions from disappearing. And again, the relaxation time gives a time interval during which significant energy transfer must be accomplished. These points are considered by Bergmann and Lebowitz (see ref. 1 of this chapter) and also by:

J. L. LEBOWITZ and H. L. FRISCH, 1957, *Phys. Rev.* **107**, 917.
E. P. GROSS and J. L. LEBOWITZ, 1956, *Phys. Rev.* **104**, 1528.
J. L. LEBOWITZ, 1959, *Phys. Rev.* **114**, 1192.
G. KLEIN and I. PRIGOGINE, 1953, *Physica*, **19**, 74, 89.
S. A. RICE and H. L. FRISCH, 1960, *Ann. Rev. Phys. Chem.* **11**, 187.

7.6. J. W. GIBBS, 1902, *Elementary Principles of Statistical Mechanics, Collected Works* vol. II.
H. LORENTZ, 1909, *Abh. Theor. Phys.* **11**.

7.7. P. EHRENFEST and T. EHRENFEST, 1911, *Encyclop. der Math. Wissenschaften*, **4**.
P. EHRENFEST and J. R. OPPENHEIMER, 1931, *Phys. Rev.* **37**, 333.

7.8. See also section 7.4 of the text. We can usefully distinguish practical irreversibility (where irreversible behaviour is found in practice but need not *always* apply) and complete irreversibility, where such behaviour must always be found. Complete irreversibility requires the physical system to be composed of an indefinitely large number of particles. Practical irreversibility will be associated with a system containing a finite number of interacting particles. But if the number of particles, though finite, is large, practical irreversibility may be indistinguishable from complete irreversibility for time periods of practical interest.
See also:
H. GRAD, 1958, *Handbuch der Physik*, **12**, 205, Berlin, Springer.

7.9. The important first paper is
J. G. KIRKWOOD, 1946, *J. Chem. Phys.* **14**, 180.

7.10. A study of non-equilibrium based on phase averaging and the H-function of Gibbs has been given by:

M. BORN and H. S. GREEN, 1949, *A General Kinetic Theory of Liquids*, London, Cambridge University Press.

This approach to the problem of fluid transport, while it appears highly interesting, has not yet been developed to the stage of yielding numerical results. It will, in consequence, not be considered in the arguments of the main text. It attempts to deal with liquid non-equilibria in terms of a suitably defined H-function and so implicitly tackles the problem of defining statistically a non-equilibrium entropy function for a liquid. In this way it differs from the Kirkwood approach of the main text according to which the entropy problem is carefully avoided.

See also the book of H. S. GREEN, *Molecular Theory of Fluids*.

7.11. H. POINCARÉ, 1894, *Rev. Gen. des Sciences*, **516**.

S. CHANDRASEKHAR, 1943, *Rev. Mod. Phys.* **15**, 1.

E. MONTROLL, 1961, Contribution to *Lectures in Theoretical Physics*, vol. III, p. 221, (eds. Brittin, Downs, and Downs), New York, Interscience.

7.12. E. ZERMELO, 1896, *Ann. Physik.* **57**, 485; **59**, 793.

Closely related is the statement of J. LOSCHMIDT (1876, *Wien. Ber.* **73**, 139; 1877, *ibid.* **75**, 67) who argued that the inherent reversibility of particle dynamics is in direct contradiction with the standpoint of thermodynamics which maintains that while some processes are reversible others are not.

7.13. L. BOLTZMANN, 1896, *Ann. Physik.* **57**, 773; 1897 *ibid.* **60**, 392.

7.14. The theory of probability after-effects is a most important and highly elegant part of statistical physics, which clarifies many important basic aspects of the arguments. Smoluchowski's work is unfortunately now rather neglected. The central references to this work are:

M. VON SMOLUCHOWSKI, 1916, *Phys. Zeits.* **17**, 557, 585; 1914, *ibid.* **16**, 321; 1914, *Wien. Ber.* **123**, 2381; 1915, *ibid.* **124**, 339; 1916, *Kolloid Zeits.* **18**, 48; 1904, *Boltzmann Festschrift*; 1912, *Physik. Zeits.* **13**, 1069; 1913, **14**, 261.

A very good summary of the theory is given by:

S. CHANDRASEKHAR, 1943, *Rev. Mod. Phys.* **15**, 1, see ch. III.

Full experimental verification of the theory has been given by:

THE SVEDBERG, 1911, *Zeits. f. Physik. Chemie* **77**, 147.

A. WESTGREN, 1916, *Arkiv Math. Astr. och Fysik* **11**; 1918, *ibid.* **13**.

7.15. SIR JAMES JEANS, 1925, *Dynamical Theory of Gases*, London, Cambridge University Press; 1940, *Kinetic Theory of Gases*, London, Cambridge University Press.

S. CHAPMAN and T. G. COWLING, 1939, *The Mathematical Theory of Non-uniform Gases*, London, Cambridge University Press.

7.16. The central references for the Brownian motion studies are as follows. The modern theory was begun by:

A. EINSTEIN, 1905, *Ann. Physik.* **17**, 549; 1906, *ibid.* **19**, 371.

M. VON SMOLUCHOWSKI, 1906, *Ann. Physik.* **21**, 756.

A. EINSTEIN, 1926, *Investigations on the Theory of Brownian Movement*, London, Methuen.

This theory was based on the representation of the Brownian motion as a problem in random flights. In the nomenclature of the equations (7.10) and (7.11) this is true only if we agree to neglect events occurring in time intervals of order β^{-1} or less.

The general treatment is based on the Langevin equation:

P. LANGEVIN, 1908, *Compt. Rend.* **146**, 530.
F. ZERNIKE, 1928, *Handbuch der Physik*, **3**, 456.
The equation of motion for the Brownian particle is written:

$$\frac{dp}{dt} = -\beta p + A(t), \quad \text{and} \quad \beta = \frac{6\pi a \eta}{m},$$

where p is the particle momentum, m the particle mass, and η the fluid viscosity. $-\beta p$ represents a retarding force arising from dynamical friction experienced by the Brownian particle due to its motion in the fluid in which it is suspended; $A(t)$ is a fluctuating force arising from direct encounters with neighbouring particles, and has a form characteristic of the Brownian motion. The separation of the force on the Brownian particle in this way is open to the objection that the two components are treated differently even though they have essentially the same origin.
For a free particle in one dimension:

L. S. ORNSTEIN and W. R. VAN WIJK, 1933, *Physica*, **1**, 235.
W. R. VAN WIJK, 1936, *Physica*, **3**, 111.
G. E. UHLENBECK and L. S. ORNSTEIN, 1930, *Phys. Rev.* **36**, 823.
For three dimensions:
G. E. UHLENBECK and S. GOUDSMIDT, 1929, *Phys. Rev.* **34**, 145.
G. A. VAN LEAR and G. E. UHLENBECK, 1931, *Phys. Rev.* **38**, 1583.
The specification of the Brownian movement in terms of the phase equation (7.10) is due to:
A. D. FOKKER, 1914, *Ann. Physik*, **43**, 812.
M. PLANCK, 1917, *Sitz. der Preuss. Akad.*, p. 324.
The replacement of the phase equation (7.10) by the configuration equation (7.11) is due to:
M. VON SMOLUCHOWSKI, 1915, *Ann. Physik*, **48**, 1103.
R. FURTH, 1917, *Ann. Physik*, **53**, 177.
The theory was greatly clarified by:
H. A. KRAMERS, 1940, *Physica*, **7**, 284.
A discussion of the limits on experimental measurements which is set by the Brownian motion is that of:
R. B. BARNES and S. SILVERMAN, 1934, *Rev. Mod. Phys.* **6**, 162.
The experimental support for the theory is collected in:
J. PERRIN, 1936, *Les Atoms*, Paris, Alcan.
Alternative discussions of Brownian motion are:
J. M. W. MILATZ and L. S. ORNSTEIN, 1940, *Physica*, **7**, 793.
MING CHEN WANG and G. E. UHLENBECK, 1945, *Rev. Mod. Phys.* **17**, 323.
D. K. C. MACDONALD, 1962, *Physica*, **28**, 409.

7.17. R. PEIERLS, 1929, *Ann. Physik*, **3**, 1055.

7.18. A. A. MARKOV, 1912, *Wahrscheinlichkeitsrechnung*, Leipzig.
M. S. GREEN, 1952, *J. Chem. Phys.* **20**, 1281.

7.19. G. S. STOKES, 1845, *Trans. Camb. Phil. Soc.* **8**, 349.
ST. VENANT, 1843, *Compt. Rend.* **17**, 1240.
See also, for the hydrodynamical background:
G. H. A. COLE, 1962, *Fluid Dynamics*, ch. 5, London, Methuen Monograph.

7.20. See also
R. EISENSCHITZ, 1955, *Phys. Rev.* **99**, 1059.
M. BORN and H. S. GREEN, 1947, *Proc. Roy. Soc.* (London) A **190**, 455; A **191**, 168.

J. H. Irving and J. G. Kirkwood, 1950, *J. Chem. Phys.* **18**, 817.
For higher order effects see:
R. G. Storer and H. S. Green, 1962, *Phys. Fluids*, **5**, 1212.
These effects are not included in our discussion.

7.21. See the book by Prigogine:
I. Prigogine, 1962, *Non-equilibrium Statistical Mechanics*, vol. 1 of *Monographs in Statistical Physics and Thermodynamics*, Interscience.
and ch. 7 of the book:
S. A. Rice and P. Gray, 1965, *The Statistical Mechanics of Simple Liquids*, vol. 8 of *Monographs in Statistical Physics and Thermodynamics*, Interscience.

CHAPTER 8

8.1. The best book is still:
S. Chapman and T. G. Cowling, 1952, *The Mathematical Theory of Non-uniform Gases*, London, Cambridge University Press.
Sir James Jeans, 1925, *The Dynamical Theory of Gases*, London, Cambridge University Press; 1940, *An Introduction to the Kinetic Theory of Gases*, London, Cambridge University Press.
J. E. Mayer, 1958, *Handbuch der Physik*, **12**, 73.
H. Grad, 1958, *Handbuch der Physik*, **12**, 205.
R. Eisenschitz, 1958, *Statistical Theory of Irreversible Processes*, London, Oxford University Press.
J. O. Hirschfelder, C. F. Curtiss, and R. B. Bird, 1954, *Molecular Theory of Gases and Liquids*, New York, Wiley.

8.2. J. C. Maxwell, 1860, *Phil. Mag.* **19**, 22; 1879, *Trans. Camb. Phil. Soc.* **12**, 547; 1877, *Nature* **16**, 244; 1890, *Scientific Papers*, London, Cambridge University Press.
L. Boltzmann, 1896/98, *Vorlesungen über Gastheorie*, I.

8.3. J. G. Kirkwood, 1946, *J. Chem. Phys.* **14**, 180; 1947, *ibid.* **15**, 72.
N. N. Bogoliubov, 1946, *J. Phys.* (Moscow), **10**, 265.
See also:
M. Born and H. S. Green, 1946, *Proc. Roy. Soc.* (London) A **188**, 10.

8.4. E. G. D. Cohen, 1962, *Fundamental Problems in Statistical Mechanics*, p. 110, Summer School, Nijenrode Castle, Holland, Amsterdam, North-Holland.
N. N. Bogoliubov, 1946, *Dynamical Theory in Statistical Physics*, Moscow.
H. S. Green, 1961, *J. Math. Phys.* **2**, 344.
The connection between various derivations of MB is considered by:
E. G. D. Cohen, 1961, *Physica*, **27**, 163.
See also:
S. A. Rice, J. G. Kirkwood, and R. A. Harris, 1961, *Physica*, **27**, 717.
J. V. Sengers and E. G. D. Cohen, 1961, *Physica*, **27**, 230.
H. L. Frisch, 1962, *J. Chem. Phys.* **36**, 510.

8.5. It is safer to be more guarded. We can strictly only derive the Maxwell–Boltzmann equation from the Liouville equation when every step is rigorously derived in terms of particle dynamics. This must be associated with a full solution procedure for the Liouville equation in which the various non-equilibrium solutions are systematically isolated from the equilibrium solutions. Such a procedure is not yet available, and in its absence we must be concerned with enumerating the physical and mathematical assumptions necessary to reconcile the Liouville equation with other equations of restricted validity (such as the Maxwell–Boltzmann equation for dilute gases) deduced alternatively. In particular, the discussion in the present chapter must be devoted, at the present time, to showing that the Maxwell–Boltzmann equation is fully compatible physically with the more general Liouville equation, and that solutions of the former equation are not in contradiction with the latter equation.

8.6. This is an essential assumption in the usual kinetic theory of gases, and the consequences of its use agree well with experiment if the density is not too high. The possibility of relaxing this assumption of binary encounters has begun to be explored.

E. G. D. COHEN, 1962, *Physica*, **28**, 1025; 1962, *Fundamental Problems in Statistical Mechanics*, Summer School, Nijenrode Castle, Amsterdam, North-Holland.

H. B. HOLLINGER and C. F. CURTISS, 1960, *J. Chem. Phys.* **33**, 1386.

P. M. LIVINGSTON and C. F. CURTISS, 1961, *Phys. Fluids*, **4**, 816.

8.7. The element of irreversibility is introduced explicitly into the theory at this stage. For a discussion see:

H. B. HOLLINGER, 1962, *J. Chem. Phys.* **36**, 3208.

8.8. In these arguments it is supposed more stringently that any two specific particles which collide during the interval τ are, at long times in the past, so widely separated as to be entirely independent and that after the collision they again pass to remote regions of phase so that they are then again statistically independent. The possibility of these specific particles colliding a second time is firmly rejected.

8.9. If the Kirkwood theory is applied over the time interval $(t-\tau)$ to t rather than over the interval t to $(t+\tau)$ the collision terms have the wrong sign. This is discussed in E. G. D. COHEN and T. H. BERLIN, 1960, *Physica*, **26**, 717.

D. K. C. MACDONALD, 1961, *Phil. Mag.*

8.10. D. ENSKOG, 1922, *Ark. Mat. Ast. och Fys.* **16**, 1.

See also:

R. CHAMBERS, 1952, *Proc. Phys. Soc.* (London) A **65**, 458.

H. BUDD, 1962, *Phys. Rev.* **127**, 4.

H. SUZUKI, 1961, *J. Phys. Soc.* (Japan) **16**, 2347.

V. HEINE, 1957, *Phys. Rev.* **107**, 431.

8.11. Most extensive calculations of this type have been made for particles showing spherical symmetry, and the $(12-6)$ potential is the most practically useful function in this connection. Very little calculated data is available for particles not showing spherical symmetry, although some data are available. See the book of Hirschfelder, Curtiss, and Bird, ch. 8.

Simplifications of the theory are far from superfluous. One simplification which has been considered is where the collision term $J(f_i, f_j)$ of equation (8.34b) of the text is replaced by:

$$\frac{f_0 - f}{\tau}.$$

where f_0 is the equilibrium kinetic distribution function, and τ is a parameter with the dimensions of time. In general, $\tau = \tau(\varrho, \mathbf{p}_0, T, \mathbf{p})$ but $\tau =$ constant is sometimes sufficient. But even this simplified collision term (which can be shown to satisfy the H-theorem) does not reduce calculations into the elementary range but does obscure a great deal of the essential physics of the discussion.

Other equations have also been set up, particularly the so-called Master equations which are particularly useful for quantum systems: see, e.g.

L. VAN HOVE, 1962, *Fundamental Problems in Statistical Mechanics*, p. 157, Summer School, Nijenrode Castle, Amsterdam, North-Holland.

8.12. For details of the derivation see the book of Chapman and Cowling.

8.13. As an example, see:

T. KIHARA, M. H. TAYLOR, and J. O. HIRSCHFELDER, 1960, *Phys. Fluids*, **3**, 715.
L. MONSCHICK and E. A. MASON, 1961, *J. Chem. Phys.* **35**, 1676.
E. A. MASON and L. MONCHICK, 1962, *J. Chem. Phys.* **36**, 1622, 2746.
E. A. MASON, 1957, *J. Chem. Phys.* **27**, 75, 782.
M. J. OFFERHAUS, 1962, *Physica*, **28**, 76.
K. M. JOSHI and S. C. SAXENA, 1961, *Physica*, **27**, 329.

8.14. The problem of the bulk viscosity for a gas is still in doubt.

R. E. NETTLETON, 1958, *J. App. Phys.* **29**, 204.

As a general rule it seems to be that:

$$\frac{\zeta}{\eta} \sim O\left(\frac{pV}{RT} - 1\right).$$

Thus, for a dilute gas, the ratio of the bulk to shear viscosity is of the order of the deviation of the equation of state of the gas from the ideal. This rule does not apply for dense gases or liquids where the ratio ζ/η is likely to be about $\frac{1}{10} - \frac{1}{2}$ if calculations are to be believed.

8.15. These arguments are applied here to gases where the deviation from equilibrium is small, so that the momentum probability distribution shows a sharp peak in the general region of the mean momentum. The argument can, however, be extended to wider gas conditions.

8.16. The identification of the parameter ε appearing in equation (8.35) as an inverse collision frequency is not a necessary mathematical identification. The same development of the theory follows if ε is regarded as no more than a parameter which allows the various orders of deviation from equilibrium to be consistently accounted for.

CHAPTER 9

9.1. The case of hard-spheres is an exception since no attractive potential features are present and the repulsion does not extend beyond the definite particle radius. The particle collisions are impulsive and the arguments of the last chapter involving the singlet distribution are valid for fairly high densities. For liquid type densities the pair distribution must be retained in the collision integral since $g^{(2)}$ is not then unity at small distances of approach as is effectively the case for lower densities. The equation (8.16) of the main text now applies and the integration over the variable r_2 is again to be made subject to the dictates of (8.8) and the conservation laws controlling the encounter. The application of the theory to a system of hard spheres at liquid densities (hard-sphere liquid) has been considered by many authors. The first application of the Maxwell-Boltzmann equation to a hard-sphere fluid at higher densities was made by D. ENSKOG, 1922, *Arc. Mat. Astr. och Fys.* **16**.

More recent and alternative treatments are:

S. A. RICE, J. G. KIRKWOOD, J. ROSS, R. W. ZWANZIG, 1959, *J. Chem. Phys.* **31**, 575.
S. A. RICE, 1959, *J. Chem. Phys.* **31**, 584.
F. COLLINS and H. RAFFEL, 1954, *J. Chem. Phys.* **22**, 1728.
H. C. LONGUET–HIGGINS and J. A. POPLE, 1956, *J. Chem. Phys.* **25**, 884.
R. F. SNIDER and C. F. CURTISS, 1958, *Phys. Fluids*, **1**, 122.
H. B. HOLLINGER and C. F. CURTISS, 1960, *J. Chem. Phys.* **33**, 1386.
P. M. LIVINGSTON and C. F. CURTISS, 1961, *Phys. Fluids*, **4**, 816.
S. A. RICE and A. R. ALLNATT, 1960, *J. Chem. Phys.* **34**, 409.
H. T. DAVIS, S. A. RICE, and J. V. SENGERS, 1961, *J. Chem. Phys.* **35**, 2210.

This last paper includes a square-well attraction. It is, however, dubious as to whether calculations involving hard-spheres can be compared properly with data derived experimentally from real liquid matter. Several points still remain to be clarified. Thus, it is not yet clear whether, or not, a gas of hard-spheres can condense to form a stable liquid of the type observed in practice, although it is sometimes assumed that this can happen. Unstable condensation or crystallisation may be possible.

See:

B. J. ALDER and T. WAINWRIGHT, 1957, *J. Chem. Phys.* **27**, 1208.

It is difficult to visualise a stable interphase region for a hard-sphere system of particles. The formulae of Chapter 5 are not applicable to this case without modification. An additional study along the lines of CHAPMAN and ENSKOG is made by:

J. L. LEBOWITZ, H. L. FRISCH, and E. HELFAND, 1960, *Phys. Fluids*, **3**, 325.

9.2. J. G. KIRKWOOD, 1946, *J. Chem. Phys.* **14**, 180; 1947, *ibid.* **15**, 72.

J. H. IRVING and J. G. KIRKWOOD, 1950, *J. Chem. Phys.* **18**, 817.

In their paper, Irving and Kirkwood explore the microscopic statistical basis of the macroscopic hydrodynamical equations of motion for a fluid.

See also:

D. W. JEPSEN and D. TER HAAR, 1962, *Physica*, **28**, 70.

L. S. HALL, 1962, *Ann. Phys.* **20**, 383.

J. ROSS, 1956, *J. Chem. Phys.* **24**, 375.

J. G. KIRKWOOD and J. ROSS, *Transport Processes in Statistical Mechanics*, New York, Interscience.

S. A. RICE and H. L. FRISCH, 1960, *Ann. Rev. Phys. Chem.* **11**, 187.

J. G. KIRKWOOD and D. D. FITTS, 1960, *J. Chem. Phys.* **33**, 1317.

9.3. R. EISENSCHITZ, 1947, *Proc. Phys. Soc.* (London) **49**, 1030; 1949, *ibid.* A **52**, 41; 1951, *Nature (London)* **167**, 216; 1952, *Proc. Roy. Soc.* (London) A **215**, 29; 1954, *Kolloid-Zeits.* **139**, 38; 1958, *Statistical Theory of Irreversible Processes*, Oxford University Press.

R. EISENSCHITZ and G. H. A. COLE, 1954, *Phil. Mag.* **45**, 394.

R. EISENSCHITZ and A. R. BOOT, 1959, *Proc. Phys. Soc.* (London) **74**, 208.

9.4. The use of the Fokker–Planck and Smoluchowski equations for calculating liquid transport coefficients implies the assumption that the relevant statistical processes are Markovian, i.e. do not depend on the previous history of the liquid. This assumption is obviously wrong in application to non-Newtonian fluids, so that our present concern can only be with Newtonian fluids. The mathematical problems associated with Markovian processes are severe: for non-Markovian processes (where the particle past is relevant) the problems are even more severe. It is, then, natural to solve first the Markovian problems as a basis for simple fluid transport and to appeal to the non-Markovian theory only if the solutions of the Markovian problem are unsatisfactory in comparison with experiment. At the present time the full study of Markovian problems is far from complete. In section 9.6 it will be seen that numerical values of viscosity and thermal conductivity for simple monatomic liquids are of the same order of magnitude as the experimental data and this gives present confidence in the further study of Markovian equations for these purposes. For this reason the present emphasis is on Markovian problems.

See:

R. T. COX, 1950, *Rev. Mod. Phys.* **22**, 238.

9.5. Alternative approaches at the present time can be divided broadly into two parts. First, there are the attempts at developing a general theory of N interacting particles not in equilibrium (i.e. the N-body non-equilibrium problem). These fundamental arguments are of enormous consequence for the construction of a general theory of fluid non-equilibrium but have not yet reached the firm stage where they have crystallised into a form yielding numerical data for direct comparison with experiment. A number of references to this recent work are:

H. S. GREEN, 1961, *J. Math. Phys.* **2**, 344.

H. L. FRISCH, 1962, *J. Chem. Phys.* **36**, 510.

R. KUBO, 1957, *J. Phys. Soc. Japan*, **12**, 570.

R. KUBO, 1959, *Lectures in Theoretical Physics*, vol. I, p. 120, New York, Interscience.

M. S. GREEN, 1961, *Lectures in Theoretical Physics*, vol. III, p. 195, New York, Interscience.

H. MORI, 1958, *Phys. Rev.* **112**, 1829.

E. MONTROLL, 1960, *Termodinamica dei Processi Irreversibili*, p. 217, Bologna, N. Zanichelli; 1961, *Lectures in Theoretical Physics*, vol. III, p. 221, New York, Interscience.

M. S. GREEN, 1954, *J. Chem. Phys.* **22**, 398.

S. TAMOR, 1960, *J. Chem. Phys.* **33**, 1421.

P. L. AUER and S. TAMOR, 1960. *J. Chem. Phys.* **33**, 1426.

D. C. DOUGLASS, 1961, *J. Chem. Phys.* **35**, 81.

D. KISDI, 1962, *Phys. Letters*, **1**, 67.

See also

H. C. LONGUET–HIGGINS, 1963, *Mol. Phys.* **6**, 65.

R. W. ZWANZIG, 1964, *J. Chem. Phys.* **40**, 2527.

The formal development of the theory must encounter, and overcome, formidable mathematical difficulties. It is far from superfluous to have available a simplified, possibly semi-empirical, treatment of liquid non-equilibria as a guide to the development of the more correct theory. This simpler approach is unlikely to be based unambiguously on particle dynamics, and in this way is of limited theoretical, although perhaps wider experimental, use. Self-diffusion of a particle under external constraints (arising from the action of neighbours) is used in a semi-empirical way to derive shear viscosity by:

H. EYRING, 1936, *J. Chem. Phys.* **4**, 283.

R. E. POWELL, W. E. ROSEVEARE, and H. EYRING, 1941, *Ind. and Eng. Chem.* **33**, 430.

J. F. KINCAID, H. EYRING, and A. E. STEARN, 1941, *Chem. Revs.* **28**, 301.

J. O. HIRSCHFELDER, D. STEVENSON, and H. EYRING, 1937, *J. Chem. Phys.* **5**, 896. This approach does not specify the mechanism for momentum flow precisely and so cannot, in its present form, be used as the basis for a self-contained quantitative treatment of viscosity. For thermal conductivity, J. F. KINCAID and H. EYRING (1938, *J. Chem. Phys.* **6**, 620) suppose energy to be transferred by the movement of molecules.

E. N. DA C. ANDRADE (1934, *Phil. Mag.* **17**, 497, 698; 1952, *Nature* **170**, 794) assumes momentum to be transferred between liquid molecules during brief periods where two particles are temporarily bound by the interparticle force. Andrade showed that this assumption leads by dimensional arguments to an expression for the shear viscosity of the form $\eta \sim \exp[C/T]$ where C is a constant. Data calculated in this way agree satisfactorily with many experimental data: see also for details:

E. N. DA C. ANDRADE, 1952, *Proc. Roy. Soc.* (London) A **215**, 36.

The viscosity has been calculated by J. FRENKEL (1926, *Z. Phys.* **35**, 652), using the formula for the diffusion coefficient due to Einstein, viz. $D = kT/6\pi\eta a$, where a is the particle diameter. Other early elementary treatments are:

G. JAGER, 1926, *Handbuch der Physik*, **9**, 456, Berlin, Springer.

R. O. HERZOG and H. C. KUDAR, 1933, *Z. Phys.* **80**, 217.

R. FURTH, 1941, *Proc. Camb. Phil. Soc.* **37**, 281.

F. C. Auluck and D. S. Kothari, 1944, *Proc. Nat. Inst. Sci. India*, **10**, 397.
A preliminary treatment of viscosity and thermal conductivity was made by
M. Born and H. S. Green (1947, *Proc. Roy. Soc.* (London) A **190**, 455) where
in particular an expression for viscosity of the form given by Andrade is inferred.
These initial arguments are essentially dimensional treatments, although they are
made on the basis of the Liouville equation.

9.6. For the use of the transition probability in the Fokker–Planck equation see:
S. Chandrasekhar, 1943, *Rev. Mod. Phys.* **15**, 1.

9.7. It is always possible to choose τ to be sufficiently small for Δp_1 to be very small in
comparison with p_1 taken before or after, or at some time during, the interval τ.
It is possible, however, that the magnitude of τ on this basis will, for a general
system, be of the same order as the time during which force correlations are maintained. For liquids it is assumed here that τ is larger than the time interval for the
persistence of force correlation of a particle, and this assumption will require
further study in any final theory. The assumption that Δr_1 is negligible during the
time interval τ is harmless; see the arguments involving the Smoluchowski equation in section 9.4 of the main text. See also:
P. Gray, 1962, *Proc. Phys. Soc.* (London) **79**, 507.

9.8. See for instance:
S. A. Rice and A. R. Allnatt, 1961, *J. Chem. Phys.* **34**, 2144.
A. R. Allnatt and S. R. Rice, 1961, *J. Chem. Phys.* **34**, 2156.
B. Berne and S. A. Rice, 1964, *J. Chem. Phys.* **40**, 1336.
S. A. Rice, 1965, *Liquids: Structure, Properties, Solid Interactions*, pp. 51–141
(ed. T. J. Hughel), Elsevier.
S. A. Rice and P. Gray, 1965, *The Statistical Mechanics of Simple Liquids*, Inter-
science.
Rice quotes independent supporting evidence for the model as the neutron studies
in liquid argon reported by:
B. A. Dasamacharya and K. R. Rao, 1965, *Phys. Rev.* **137**, A 417.

9.9. For the Brownian motion see equation (322) of the Chandrasekhar paper quoted
in 9.6, but this will not apply to liquid non-equilibria.

9.10. A. Suddaby, 1954, Ph. D. Thesis, University of London.
G. H. A. Cole, 1960, *Nature*, **186**, 301.
E. Helfand, 1961, *Phys. Fluids*, **4**, 681.

9.11. J. G. Kirkwood, 1946, *J. Chem. Phys.* **14**, 180.

9.12. See also:
S. A. Rice and J. G. Kirkwood, 1959, *J. Chem. Phys.* **31**, 901.

9.13. R. Orton, 1954, M. Sc. Thesis, University of London.

9.14. R. E. Turner, 1960, *Physica*, **26**, 274.

9.15. R. Eisenschitz and M. J. Wilford, 1962, *Proc. Phys. Soc.* (London) **80**, 1078.

9.16. A. Suddaby and P. Gray, 1960, *Proc. Phys. Soc.* (London) **75**, 109.

9.17. H. A. Kramers, 1940, *Physica*, **7**, 284.

9.18. A. Suddaby, 1954, Ph. D. Thesis, University of London.
A. Suddaby and J. R. N. Miles, 1961, *Proc. Phys. Soc.* (London) **77**, 1170.

9.19. This procedure is a special case of the general technique of *taking moments* used
extensively in the early kinetic theory arguments of Maxwell, and now generally
employed in many branches of physics.

9.20. See as an example the ref. 18.

9.21. R. EISENSCHITZ and A. SUDDABY, 1954, *Proc. 2nd Int. Congr. Rhed.*, London, Butterworth.

9.22. Simplifications in the theory can be made by replacing the expressions (9.51) for the flow by alternative expressions not based directly on the Fokker–Planck equation. One such approach is P. GRAY (1964, *J. Mol. Phys.* **7**, 235) who applies the small step diffusion model to the problem. In this approach, the centre of gravity term $\partial \mathbf{J}/\partial \mathbf{R}$ in (9.48) is replaced by the phenomenological term $(n^{(2)} - g^{(2)})\gamma$, where $g^{(2)}$ is the equilibrium pair distribution, $n^{(2)}$ is the non-equilibrium pair distribution, and γ is some constant with the dimensions (time)$^{-1}$. The relative flow term $\partial \mathbf{j}/\partial \xi$ is defined in terms of the self-diffusion coefficient, and so involves directly irreversible effects. A form of the Smoluchowski equation follows from this procedure which is similar to that derived by the arguments of the main text. It would seem that the Smoluchowski equation is to be separated from the Fokker–Planck equation in the sense that while the existence of the Fokker–Planck equation is sufficient evidence for the existence of the Smoluchowski equation, it is not necessary for a Fokker–Planck equation to be defined in order that a Smoluchowski equation should result. Consequently, the theory of liquids based on the Smoluchowski equation can be contemplated separately from that based on the Fokker–Planck equation, and the equation (9.52) accepted as a starting point for the statistical treatment of liquids in its own right. If it should ultimately prove necessary to appeal to the high members of the hierarchy of configuration equations (such as the fourth order equation) this, too, can be derived without an appeal to the Fokker–Planck equation.
Attempts to extend the Smoluchowski equation to earlier times have been made by:
H. C. BRINKMAN, 1956, *Physica*, **22**, 29.
R. A. SACK, 1956, *Physica*, **22**, 917.
PER CHR. HEMMER, 1961, *Physica*, **27**, 79.
These arguments will, presumably, apply to smaller values of the friction constants than those associated with the Smoluchowski equation derived in the text.

9.23. R. EISENSCHITZ, 1949, *Proc. Phys. Soc.* (London) A **52**, 41.

9.24. J. G. KIRKWOOD, F. P. BUFF, and M. S. GREEN, 1949, *J. Chem. Phys.* **17**, 988.

9.25. R. EISENSCHITZ and G. H. A. COLE, 1954, *Phil. Mag.* **45**, 394.
Experimental data contained in:
E. N. DA C. ANDRADE and C. DODD, 1951, *Proc. Roy. Soc.* (London) A **204**, 449.

9.26. J. CHAMPION, 1958, *Proc. Phys. Soc.* (London) **72**, 711; 1960, *ibid.* **75**, 421, 799.

9.27. This supposition would be open to question in the light of the comments in ref. 22.

9.28. R. W. ZWANZIG, J. G. KIRKWOOD, K. P. STRIPP, and I. OPPENHEIM, 1953, *J. Chem. Phys.* **21**, 2050.
R. W. ZWANZIG, J. G. KIRKWOOD, I. OPPENHEIM, and B. J. ALDER, 1954, *J. Chem. Phys.* **22**, 783.

9.29. N. S. RUDENKO and L. SCHUBNIKOV, 1934, *Physik Z. Sowj Un.* **6**, 470.
R. SCOTT, 1958, *Prog. Kam. Onnes Conf. Low Temp. Phys. (Leiden)*, p 80.
B. A. LOWRY, S. A. RICE, and P. GRAY, 1964, *J. Chem. Phys.* **40**, 3673.

9.30. A. UHLIR, 1952, *J. Chem. Phys.* **20**, 463.
H. ZIEBLAND and J. T. A. BURTON, 1958, *Brit. J. App. Phys.* **9**, 52.
F. KEYES, 1955, *Trans. ASME*, **77**, 1395.
L. D. IKENBERY and S. A. RICE, 1963, *J. Chem. Phys.* **39**, 1561.

INDEX

Printed in Hungary